1970

This book may be kept

ELEMENTARY FUNCTIONS

Under the Editorship of
Carl B. Allendoerfer

Elementary

Alan J. Heckenbach ■ **J. Colby Kegley**

Iowa State University

An Approach to Precalculus Mathematics

Functions

The Macmillan Company/Collier-Macmillan Limited, London

TO
KAREN KAI
AND
RACHEL ELIZABETH

The Macmillan Company
866 Third Avenue, New York, New York 10022
Collier-Macmillan Canada, Ltd., Toronto, Ontario

Library of Congress catalog card number: 70-84438

First Printing

PREFACE

The purpose of this book is to prepare the student for studying calculus. Such a preparation involves two things: subject matter and attitude.

The subject matter chosen here concentrates on three topics that are indispensable in calculus: inequalities, graphing, and functions. These topics are developed in the first three chapters and then used to discuss the elementary functions in Chapters 4 through 7.

The attitude we are seeking to develop involves in part the realization that there is not something called "theory" and something called "applications" with only some vague connection between the two. Instead, the student should learn that the basic definitions and theorems are the tools he will use in setting up and solving problems, and not just things that an instructor makes him memorize for the "theory" part of an examination.

The building of this attitude starts in Chapter 1 with the algebraic solution of inequalities. Here it is seen that the basic definitions of inequalities are often needed to set up a problem correctly. Then, the basic theorems supply the manipulative techniques needed to carry through to a solution, and finally, to realize that the problem has really been solved. Later, the geometric interpretation of inequalities and absolute value on a coordinate line build confidence in using these concepts. Part of this confidence comes from the realization that the results of the basic theorems become matters of common sense. Section 1.7 can be omitted without interrupting the continuity of the discussion, although the student may use it as a test of his understanding of the earlier material.

Chapter 2 builds on these ideas to discuss the graphing of conditions in a coordinate plane. Special emphasis is placed on graphs of conditions involving inequalities and absolute values. The concepts of symmetry, extent, and translation of coordinate axes are given central roles in handling problems of this type and also are used in the subsequent discussion of real functions. The conic sections are presented in the exercises as applications of these general principles. Rotation of coordinate axes is not discussed.

The function concept is introduced in Chapter 3. Extreme care is taken to avoid confusing a function with its functional values, or with a recipe used to define the function. Also, careful attention is given to the problem of determining the domain of a function. These two topics, which too often are treated lightly, are especially critical for a meaningful discussion of the composition of functions.

These first three chapters lay both the material and psychological groundwork for the remainder of the book. At this point the reader should have a fair amount of confidence in the use of inequalities and absolute values and in the kind of preliminary analysis needed in using functions for solving problems.

Chapter 4 emphasizes the elementary graphical methods for analyzing polynomial and rational functions. The intermediate value property is discussed from an intuitive standpoint and is used to obtain the constant sign properties of rational functions. The qualitative graphing of these functions and graphical methods for solving rational inequalities are then straightforward.

In Chapter 5, the circular functions are defined as real functions in terms of the coordinates of points on the unit circle. Because the circular functions are defined in this manner, the periodicity and symmetry properties of the so-called "winding function" can be used to establish many of the basic identities and reduction formulas.

The first two sections of Chapter 6 treat the inverse of a one-to-one real function from both the algebraic and graphical standpoints. Once again we are in an area where correct use of functional notation and careful attention to determining the domain of a function are crucial. The final section of this chapter deals with the principal circular functions and their inverses.

Chapter 7 takes up the problems involved with defining exponential functions and their inverses, the logarithm functions. In the first section we review the laws of rational exponents and raise the question of how irrational powers of positive numbers are to be defined. A brief discussion of the Dedekind Axiom is presented in Section 7.2 to supply an answer to this question. The exercises in this chapter emphasize the sort of manipulations with exponents and logarithms that are encountered regularly in calculus.

Most of the text is devoted to examples and exercises. For the most part, the examples are designed to give a more than superficial look at a particular concept or set of concepts. It is through these examples that one sees that the so-called theory is indispensable in analyzing and solving problems.

There is a large collection of graded exercises, the most challenging of which are marked with a dagger †. Certain exercises contain results that are referred to later in the book and are marked with an asterisk *. These exercises should be worked individually and then discussed in class.

In planning a course that uses this book, ample time should be allowed for a thorough consideration of the first three chapters. Depending on the previous preparation of the students, the amount of material from Chapters 4 through 7 to be discussed, and the pace and depth at which this material is covered, the book can be used for courses of widely varying duration.

The main body of the text can be covered in a one-semester course for students having a strong high school background.

For students with an average high school background, more time will be required for Chapters 1, 2, and 3. This will entail some selection of topics to be considered from the remaining chapters in order to fit a one-semester course.

For students with a weak preparation, a slower paced course can be designed that incorporates material from Appendixes I and III.

Our opinion on the status of Appendix II, "Mathematical Induction," is that it should not be treated as a separate unit. Rather, the examples and exercises that appear there should be studied periodically as a supplement to the regular course material.

We wish to acknowledge the helpful advice of our colleagues at Iowa State University given during the preparation of this book. Special thanks go to the many instructors and their students who have suffered through several preliminary versions of the manuscript, and also to Professor Wilfred E. Barnes for giving us the time and opportunity to test our ideas.

A. J. H.
J. C. K.

Ames, Iowa

CONTENTS

■ Appendix II Mathematical Induction *291*

■ Appendix III Angle Trigonometry *296*

CHAPTER 1

THE REAL NUMBER SYSTEM

■ 1.1 Sets

One of the central problems in the study of elementary functions and calculus is that of examining the connection between Euclidean geometry and algebra. Specifically, it is desired to formulate statements of geometry in terms of algebra, and conversely, to interpret statements of algebra geometrically.

The language of sets arises in a natural way in dealing with this problem, because the objects of geometry are usually described as sets of points that have certain properties. (Perhaps the reader is more familiar with the word *locus* than the word *set* in this context.) But the set concept is used not only for this reason, nor only as a matter of convenience. The fact is that many of the problems to be dealt with here and in subsequent mathematics can be stated most clearly and precisely by use of the language of sets, and so can the solutions to those problems.

Now, this requires that the reader have an intuitive understanding of what a set is and of what it means for an object to belong to a set of objects. It also requires him to be able to use some notation for sets and set membership, but does not require him to deal with "set theory."

Many of the sets that will be under discussion will be sets of real numbers. In particular, there are some special kinds of real numbers that we will be using rather often:

1

(1) **Natural numbers** are the usual "counting numbers," 1, 2, 3, 4, . . .
(2) **Integers** consist of the natural numbers, 1, 2, 3, 4, . . . , together with the number 0 and the numbers $-1, -2, -3, -4, \ldots$
(3) **Rational numbers** are those numbers that are the quotient p/q of integers p and q where $q \neq 0$.
(4) **Irrational numbers** are the real numbers, such as $\sqrt{2}$ and π, that are not rational numbers.

Also there will be no specific reference made to imaginary or complex numbers, so that no attempt will be made to assign a meaning to symbols such as $\sqrt{-1}$.

To begin our discussion of the notation to be used in dealing with sets, let us agree that if A is a set and x is an object, then the statement "x belongs to A" is abbreviated "$x \in A$," while the statement "x does not belong to A" is written "$x \notin A$." The statements "$x \in A$" and "$x \notin A$" may also be read "x is a member of (or an element of) A" and "x is not a member of (or not an element of) A" respectively.

There are several ways of prescribing just what the members of a set are. The most elementary is to list all the members of the set, and enclose the list in braces. For example, the set whose members are the numbers 1, 2, and 3 is denoted $\{1, 2, 3\}$, and the set whose members are the first four even natural numbers is $\{2, 4, 6, 8\}$. It should be mentioned that when this method is used to describe a set, the order in which the members of the set are listed is immaterial, so that the set whose members are 1, 2, and 3 could be denoted $\{2, 3, 1\}$ or $\{3, 2, 1\}, \ldots$

The set whose members are the first thousand natural numbers could, of course, be written in the same way, but it is more practical to denote this set by $\{1, 2, 3, \ldots, 1{,}000\}$. An extension of this idea allows one to denote the set of all natural numbers by $\{1, 2, 3, \ldots\}$, and the set of all integers by $\{\ldots, -3, -2, -1, 0, 1, 2, 3, \ldots\}$ or by $\{0, \pm 1, \pm 2, \ldots\}$.

Another method of describing a set is to state some property that is shared by the objects in the set and by no other objects. Then, if A is the set whose elements are exactly those objects that have the property P, A is denoted $\{x : x \text{ has the property } P\}$, which is read "the set of all x such that x has the property P." The symbol $\{ : \}$ is called the **classifier symbol**, and Example 1 illustrates how this symbol is used to describe a set.

Example 1

(a) The set of all odd natural numbers can be denoted by $\{x : x \text{ is an odd natural number}\}$, or by $\{y : y \text{ is an odd natural number}\}$. A more complicated description would be $\{x : \text{For some natural number } n, x = 2n - 1\}$. This description has the advantage that it uses a specific algebraic formulation of what an odd natural number is.

(b) The set of all integral multiples of π is

$$\{t: \text{For some integer } m, \ t = m\pi\}.$$

This set could be described by the "listing" method as $\{\ldots, -2\pi, -\pi,$ $0, \pi, 2\pi, \ldots\}$ or as $\{0, \pm\pi, \pm 2\pi, \ldots\}$.

(c) Let A be $\{x: x \text{ is a real number and } x^3 - 6x^2 + 11x - 6 = 0\}$. Although it might be difficult to find out exactly what the members of A are, we can still decide whether or not a given object belongs to A.

For instance:

> $1 \in A$, because 1 is a real number and
> $1^3 - 6 \cdot (1)^2 + 11 \cdot 1 - 6 = 0$;
> $-2 \notin A$, because $(-2)^3 - 6(-2)^2 + 11 \cdot (-2) - 6 \neq 0$;
> King Louis XIV $\notin A$, because King Louis XIV is not a real
> number.

In general, to say that an object b is a member of A is to say that both

$$b \text{ is a real number}$$

and $$b^3 - 6b^2 + 11b - 6 = 0.$$

Similarly, the statement $y \in A$ means that

$$y \text{ is a real number}$$

and $$y^3 - 6y^2 + 11y - 6 = 0.$$

Thus, the set A could just as well be described as $\{b: b \text{ is a real number}$ and $b^3 - 6b^2 + 11b - 6 = 0\}$, or as $\{y: y \text{ is a real number and } y^3 - 6y^2 + 11y - 6 = 0\}$.

(d) In part **(c)**, it was seen that there was no special reason for using the letter x in writing a description of the set A. But one must be consistent in choosing a notation to use in describing a set. Something such as

$$\{b: x \text{ is a real number} \quad \text{and} \quad x^3 - 6x^2 + 11x - 6 = 0\}$$

is nonsense; it is an abuse of the classifier symbol, and doesn't really stand for a set at all.

(e) Another way in which inconsistencies can arise in writing a description of a set is illustrated as follows:

Let x be a positive real number. Then the set of all real numbers whose square is x can be denoted

$$\{y: y \text{ is a real number and } y^2 = x\},$$

or $$\{b: b \text{ is a real number and } b^2 = x\},$$

but can *not* be denoted

$$\{x: x \text{ is a real number and } x^2 = x\},$$

since the symbol x has already been used to stand for a particular object.

Example 2 Let A denote $\{t: t \text{ is a real number and } t^2 = 4\}$, and let B denote $\{2, -2\}$.

Evidently, A and B have exactly the same members. A laborious proof of this "obvious" fact is as follows:

If $t \in A$, then t is a real number and $t^2 = 4$. Hence, $0 = t^2 - 4 = (t - 2)(t + 2)$. From known properties of real numbers, it follows that either $t - 2 = 0$ or $t + 2 = 0$, that is, either $t = 2$ or $t = -2$. Thus, every member of A is a member of B. Conversely, if $t \in B$, then either $t = 2$ or $t = -2$. In either case, t is a real number and $t^2 = 4$, so every member of B is a member of A.

The demonstration in Example 2 gives a clue to a practical way of defining what it means for a set A to be equal to a set B.

DEFINITION If A is a set and B is a set, then the statement $\boldsymbol{A = B}$ means that every member of A is a member of B, and that every member of B is a member of A.

The point to be remembered about this definition is that to actually show that a set A is equal to a set B, there are *two* statements that must be verified, and not just one. Each of the two statements, however, involves the same type of relationship between sets, and it is convenient to have some terminology and notation for this relationship.

DEFINITION If A is a set and B is a set, then the statement $\boldsymbol{A}$ **is a subset of** $\boldsymbol{B}$ means that every member of A is a member of B. The statement "A is a subset of B" is written "$A \subset B$," and the statement "A is not a subset of B" is written "$A \not\subset B$."

Thus, if each of A and B is a set, then to say that $A = B$ is to say that both $A \subset B$ and $B \subset A$. To emphasize the matter another way, the set A is *not* equal to the set B (which is written "$A \neq B$") when either $A \not\subset B$ or $B \not\subset A$ or both.

Example 3   Let $A = \{x: (x-1)(x-2)(x) = 0\}$, and let $B = \{0, 1, 2\}$.
   We can see that $A = B$ as follows:

Suppose $x \in A$.

Then $(x-1)(x-2)(x) = 0$.

Hence, $x-1 = 0$,   or $x-2 = 0$,   or $x = 0$.

Therefore, $x = 1$,   or $x = 2$,   or $x = 0$,

so $x \in B$.

   Thus, we have verified the statement

(#)   *If $x \in A$,   then $x \in B$.*

That is, we have shown that $A \subset B$.
   Conversely, suppose

                                   $x \in B$.

Then $x = 1$,   or $x = 2$,   or $x = 0$,

so $x-1 = 0$,   or $x-2 = 0$,   or $x = 0$.

Hence, $(x-1)(x-2)(x) = 0$,

so $x \in A$.

   This means that we have verified the statement

(##)   *If $x \in B$,   then $x \in A$,*

which is the converse of statement (#). That is, we have shown that $B \subset A$.
   Since we have shown that both $A \subset B$ and $B \subset A$, it follows that $A = B$.

Example 4   Let $A = \{-2, 3\}$ and let $B = \{1, -2, -1, 3\}$.
   First, $A \subset B$, because we can verify the statement

(#)   *If $x \in A$,   then $x \in B$.*

   For, suppose

                                   $x \in A$.

Then $x = -2$ or $x = 3$,

and in either case, $x \in B$.

Therefore, $A \subset B$.

However, $B \not\subset A$, because we can show that the statement

(##)   If $x \in B$,   then $x \in A$

is false.

In fact, $1 \in B$, but $1 \notin A$. Or, we could point out that $-1 \in B$, but $-1 \notin A$.

Notice that we didn't show that statement (##) is false by simply naming something that doesn't belong to A, nor by naming something that doesn't belong to B. Rather, we named an object that *does* belong to B, but *does not* belong to A.

Given sets A and B, an investigation of the relationship between A and B often begins with these questions:

Is $A \subset B$ or not?
Is $B \subset A$ or not?
Is $A = B$ or not?

Example 5 Let A be the set of all integers, and let B be the set of all rational numbers.

There are many interesting connections between these two sets, but we will settle for answering the three questions raised above.

First, suppose

$x \in A.$

Then x is an integer.

But   1 is a nonzero integer,

and $x = x/1.$

Therefore, x is the quotient of integers p/q, where $p = x$ and $q = 1 \neq 0$. Hence, x is a rational number, so $x \in B$.

Thus, we know that the statement

If $x \in A$,   then $x \in B$

is true, that is, we know that

$A \subset B.$

But $B \not\subset A,$

because there is at least one member of B that isn't a member of A. For example,

$$\frac{1}{2} \in B, \quad \text{but} \quad \frac{1}{2} \notin A,$$

so the statement   If $x \in B$,   then $x \in A$

is false.

Also, $A \neq B$ because we have seen that $B \not\subset A$.

In many cases, the question of how two sets are related arises in this way: suppose we are given a set A that has a fairly complicated description; can we find a set B that has a relatively simple description and has the property that $A = B$?

Example 6   Let $A = \{x : x$ is a real number and $4x^2 - 7x + 3 = 0\}$, and let $B = \{1, \frac{3}{4}\}$. Find the relationship between A and B.

First, suppose

$$x \in A.$$

Then
$$x = \frac{7 \pm \sqrt{(-7)^2 - 4 \cdot 4 \cdot 3}}{2 \cdot 4}$$

by the quadratic formula.

Therefore, $x = 1 \quad \text{or} \quad x = \frac{3}{4},$

so $x \in B.$

Thus, we know that $A \subset B.$

Conversely, every member of B can be shown to be a member of A by replacing x in the expression $4x^2 - 7x + 3$ by the real numbers 1 and $\frac{3}{4}$ in turn, with the result that in each case the expression is equal to zero.

This shows that $B \subset A$.

Since both $A \subset B$ and $B \subset A$, it follows that $A = B$.

A comment is in order about the radical symbol $\sqrt{\ }$. Let x be a nonnegative real number, that is, x is either a positive number or 0. Then $\sqrt{x}$ denotes the unique nonnegative number whose square is x, and is called the **nonnegative square root of** x. Also, if x is nonnegative, then $x^{1/2}$ means the same thing as $\sqrt{x}$, and is not used to mean "$\pm\sqrt{x}$". Finally, notice that if x is a positive number, then both $\sqrt{x}$ and $-\sqrt{x}$ are square roots of x, $\sqrt{x}$ being the positive square root of x and $-\sqrt{x}$ being the negative square root of x, so there is no such thing as *the* square root of a positive number.

Example 7   If $A = \{x : x$ is a real number and $2x + x^{1/2} - 6 = 0\}$, find explicitly the members of A.

This means that we must find a set B that can be described by the "listing" method such that $A = B$.

First, suppose

$$x \in A.$$

Then
$$2x - 6 = -x^{1/2},$$

so
$$(2x - 6)^2 = (-x^{1/2})^2 = x.$$

Hence,
$$4x^2 - 25x + 36 = 0.$$

By the quadratic formula,

$$x = 4 \quad \text{or} \quad x = \frac{9}{4}.$$

Thus,
$$A \subset \left\{4, \frac{9}{4}\right\}.$$

We cannot conclude from this that $A = \{4, \frac{9}{4}\}$. All we know at this stage is that the only *possible* members of A are the numbers 4 and $\frac{9}{4}$. In fact,

if
$$x = 4,$$

then
$$2x + x^{1/2} - 6 = 4 \neq 0,$$

so
$$4 \notin A;$$

if
$$x = \frac{9}{4},$$

then
$$2x + x^{1/2} - 6 = 0,$$

so
$$\frac{9}{4} \in A.$$

Therefore,
$$A = \left\{\frac{9}{4}\right\},$$

that is, A is the set whose only member is $\frac{9}{4}$.

Notice that the method used in solving Example 7 introduced a so-called "extraneous solution" of the equation $2x + x^{1/2} - 6 = 0$, namely, the number $x = 4$. This, however, does not mean that there is something wrong with the way the problem was solved. It only emphasizes that, after we have correctly concluded that the set A is a *subset* of $\{4, \frac{9}{4}\}$, we cannot conclude immediately that A is *equal* to $\{4, \frac{9}{4}\}$, but must determine just which subset of $\{4, \frac{9}{4}\}$ A actually is.

Example 8 Find all integers n such that $2n^3 + 3n^2 - 8n - 12 = 0$. This means that if

$$A = \{n : n \text{ is an integer and} \quad 2n^3 + 3n^2 - 8n - 12 = 0\},$$

then the members of A are to be listed explicitly.

If $n \in A$, then n is an integer, and

$$0 = 2n^3 + 3n^2 - 8n - 12$$
$$= n^2(2n + 3) - 4(2n + 3)$$
$$= (n^2 - 4)(2n + 3),$$

so either $n = 2$ or $n = -2$, because $2n + 3 \neq 0$ if n is an integer. Hence, $A \subset \{2, -2\}$. Conversely, if $n = 2$ or $n = -2$, then n is an integer and direct substitution shows that $2n^3 + 3n^2 - 8n - 12 = 0$, so $\{2, -2\} \subset A$. Therefore, $A = \{2, -2\}$, i.e., 2 and -2 are the integer solutions of $2n^3 + 3n^2 - 8n - 12 = 0$.

Example 9   It happens that there arise in a natural way such expressions as $\{r : r$ is a real number and $r^2 = -1\}$. We have two choices: either this expression doesn't stand for a set at all, or if it is to stand for a set, then that set has no members because there is no real number whose square is -1. It is more convenient to make the second of the two choices, that is, to permit the existence of a set that has no members.

Now, suppose $A = \{r : r$ is a real number and $r^2 = -1\}$, and $B = \{x : x$ is a real number and $0 \cdot x = 1\}$. We certainly want it to be the case that either $A = B$ or $A \neq B$. Suppose in fact that $A \neq B$. By our definition of equality of sets, at least one of the following statements must be true:

(1)   There is a member of A that is not a member of B.
(2)   There is a member of B that is not a member of A.

But the first statement is impossible, because there is no member of A at all, let alone a member of A that fails to belong to B. Similarly, the second statement is impossible by the same type of argument, because B has no members either. Thus, we are forced to conclude that $A \neq B$ can't be true, so that $A = B$ must hold.

The same reasoning can be used to show that if each of C and D is a set and neither C nor D has any members, then $C = D$. The result is that there is only one set that has no members. It is called the **empty set,** or the **null set,** and is denoted by $\varnothing$. As is shown by the examples A and B given above, $\varnothing$ can be described in many ways, and the student should be alert for the possibility that a very ordinary problem may have $\varnothing$ for its set of solutions.

EXERCISES

1. Without referring to the text, write a careful statement of what each of the following means.
   (a) Natural number.
   (b) Integer.
   (c) Rational number.
   (d) Irrational number.
   (e) The set A is equal to the set B.
   (f) The set A is a subset of the set B.

2. In each of the following, use the classifier symbol to describe the given set in at least two ways.
   (a) The set of all real numbers whose cube is -3.
   (b) $\{2, 4, 6, 8, \ldots\}$
   (c) $\{\ldots, -6, -3, 0, 3, 6, \ldots\}$
   (d) $\left\{\dfrac{1}{2}\right\}$
   (e) $\{-1, 1\}$

(f) $\{2, 4, 8, 16, \ldots\}$

(g) $\left\{1, 3, -\dfrac{5}{2}\right\}$

3. Let $A = \{x : x \text{ is an integer}\}$,
   let $B = \{y : y \text{ is a real number}\}$,
   let $C = \{t : t \text{ is a real number and } t^2 = 1\}$.

   (a) Which of the following belong to A? Which belong to B? Which belong to C?

   (i) -2

   (ii) 1

   (iii) $\dfrac{3}{2}$

   (iv) $-\dfrac{4}{3}$

   (v) $\dfrac{24}{12}$

   (vi) -1

   (vii) $\dfrac{2\pi}{\pi}$

   (viii) $\sqrt{2}$

   (ix) $\dfrac{1/2}{1/2}$

   (b) What does the statement $y \in A$ mean?

   (c) What does the statement $r \in B$ mean?

   (d) What does the statement $t \in C$ mean?

4. For each pair of sets A and B, decide whether $A \subset B$, or $B \subset A$, or $A = B$. In each case, give an argument that supports your conclusion.

   (a) $A = \{0, -1, 3\}$,
       $B = \{3, -2, 4, 0, -1\}$

   (b) $A = \{2, 4, 6\}$,
       $B = \{1, 4, 6, 7\}$

   (c) $A = \{x : x \text{ is a real number and } 2x + 1 = 0\}$
       $B = \{0, -1/2\}$.

   (d) $A = \{x : x \text{ is a real number and } x^2 = x\}$
       $B = \{1\}$.

   (e) $A = \{y : y \text{ is a real number and } 2y^2 - 4y = 2\}$
       $B = \{y : y \text{ is a real number and } (y - 1)^2 = 0\}$

(f) $A = \left\{t : t \text{ is a real number and } \dfrac{t + 1}{t} = 2\right\}$
    $B = \left\{z : z \text{ is a real number and } \dfrac{z + 1}{z} = 2\right\}$

(g) $A = \{x : \text{For some integer } n, x = 2n - 1\}$
    $B = \{y : \text{For some integer } m, y = 2m + 1\}$

(h) $A = \{a : \text{For some integer } j, a = 4j - 1\}$
    $B = \{b : \text{For some integer } k, b = 4k + 3\}$

5. In each of the following, a set is described by means of the classifier symbol. Describe each set by the "listing" method, that is, find explicitly what its members are.

   (a) $\{t : t \text{ is a real number and } 2t - 3 = -4(t + 1)\}$

   (b) $\{n : n \text{ is an integer and } 3(4n - 1) = 15n + 2\}$

   (c) $\left\{x : x \text{ is a real number and } \dfrac{3x}{2} - \dfrac{1}{4} = -\dfrac{4}{3}\right\}$

   (d) $\left\{y : y \text{ is a real number and } \dfrac{1}{y} + 5 = \dfrac{6}{y}\right\}$

   (e) $\{t : t \text{ is a real number and } (2t - 1)(5t + 4) = 0\}$

   (f) $\{x : x \text{ is a real number and } x^2 - 2x - 8 = 0\}$

   (g) $\{b : b \text{ is a real number and } -3b^2 + 5b + 2 = 0\}$

   (h) $\{a : a \text{ is a real number and } 2a^2 - 2a - 3 = 1\}$

   (i) $\{m : m \text{ is an integer and } 2m^2 + 5m - 3 = 0\}$

   (j) $\{x : x \text{ is a real number and } x^2 - x - 1 = 0\}$

   (k) $\{c : c \text{ is a real number and } 4c^2 - 6c + 1 = 0\}$

6. In each of the following, decide what the relation is between the set A and the set B.

   (a) $A = \left\{u : u \text{ is a real number and } \dfrac{2}{u^2} - \dfrac{1}{u} = \dfrac{(2 - u^2)}{u^2}\right\}$,
       $B = \{0, 1\}$.

(b) $A = \{x : x \text{ is real and}$
$\qquad x + 4\sqrt{x} - 12 = 0\},$
$\quad B = \{4, 36\}.$

(c) $A = \{v : v \text{ is real and}$
$\qquad \dfrac{(v-2)^2(v+1)}{v-2} = 0\},$
$\quad B = \{2, -1\}.$

(d) $A = \{t : t \text{ is real and } t^4 = t^2\},$
$\quad B = \{1\}.$

7. Find the real solutions to each of the following equations. State both the problem and your solution in terms of sets.

(a) $\dfrac{x^4 - 1}{x - 1} = 0$

(b) $6y^2 - 5y - 4 = 0$

(c) $\dfrac{5}{p-3} + \dfrac{4}{(p-3)^2} = 6$

(d) $2t^4 - 3t^2 - 2 = 0$

(e) $\dfrac{1}{1 + 1/a} = \dfrac{a}{a+1}$

(f) $x + \dfrac{1}{1 + 1/x} = 2$

(g) $\dfrac{3}{t} - \dfrac{4}{t^2} = -1$

(h) $\dfrac{t}{t-1} - \dfrac{t}{t+1} = 2$

(i) $1 - c + 2(1-c)^2 = 3$

(j) $r^6 - 64 = 0.$

(k) $\dfrac{y-1}{y-2} \div \left(1 - \dfrac{1}{y^2}\right) = 1$

(l) $t^2 + 2t + 2 = 0$

8. Do all real numbers belong to $\{s : s \text{ is a real number and } \sqrt{s^2} = s\}$?

9. Are there any numbers in $\{t : t \text{ is a real number and } \sqrt{t^2} = -t\}$?

10. Are there any numbers in $\{z : z \text{ is a real number and } \dfrac{2}{z} + \dfrac{3}{4} = \dfrac{5}{z+4}\}$?

11. Which numbers belong to $\{x : x \text{ is a real number and } (x+1)^3 = x^3 + 1\}$?

12. Which numbers belong to $\{t : t \text{ is a real number and } \sqrt{t^2 + 4} = t + 2\}$?

13. Explain why the definition of what it means for two sets to be equal justifies the statement that when a set is described by the "listing" method, it makes no difference in which order the elements of the set are listed.

14. In each of the following, find all real values of x and y that make the statement true.

(a) $\{2x, y\} = \{0, 1\}.$

(b) $\{x^2, y\} = \{4\}.$

(c) $\{x + y, y\} = \{2, -2\}.$

(d) $\{\sqrt{x^4 y^4}\} = \{x^2 y^2\}.$

15. Without reading Example 9 again, prove that if each of C and D is a set, and neither C nor D has any members, then $C = D$.

16. Prove that if A is any set, then $\varnothing \subset A$. (*Hint:* What would happen if for some set A, $\varnothing \not\subset A$?

17. Give examples of two nonempty sets A and B such that $A \subset B$ but $B \not\subset A$. Then decide whether or not each of the following statements is true, and explain your decision.

(a) If $x \in A$, then $x \in B$.

(b) If $x \in B$, then $x \in A$.

(c) If $x \in B$, then $x \notin A$.

(d) If $x \notin B$, then $x \notin A$.

(e) If $x \in A$, then $x \notin B$.

(f) If $x \notin A$, then $x \notin B$.

(g) Some member of A belongs to B.

(h) Some member of B belongs to A.

(i) Some member of A does not belong to B.

(j) Some member of B does not belong to A.

Note: In parts (g)–(j), the word *some* is used to mean *at least one*. This word will always be used this way in mathematical statements.

18. Prove that if each of A, B, and C is a set such that $A \subset B$ and $B \subset C$, then $A \subset C$.

†19. Explain the difference between these two problems:

(a) Let x be a real number. Find $\{y : 3y + 4x = 1\}$.

(b) Find $\{y : \text{For some real number } x, 3y + 4x = 1\}$.

■ 1.2 Order

In order to develop the relation between geometry and algebra, it will be assumed that the reader has already attained some degree of competence in these areas. In geometry this includes the usual results concerning congruence and similarity of geometric figures, parallel lines, and mensuration formulas. In algebra, we assume an elementary understanding of the algebraic properties of the set R of real numbers and some skill in using the manipulative techniques derived from these—factoring, operations involving fractions, solving of equations, and so on. The algebraic manipulations involved in working the exercises in Section 1.1 give a fair indication of what is assumed in this respect. If the reader had considerable difficulty with the algebra in those exercises, he should review this material in Appendix I.

The real number system begins with a set R, each element of which is called a **real number.** Given any real numbers a and b, there is associated a unique real number, written $a + b$, and called the **sum** of a and b. Also, given any real numbers a and b, there corresponds a unique real number, written ab, or $a \cdot b$, and called the **product** of a and b. The operations of taking the sum and product of real numbers are called **addition** and **multiplication,** respectively. The set R with addition and multiplication has the following properties:

A1 Associative Law for Addition. If a, b, and c are any real numbers, then

$$(a + b) + c = a + (b + c).$$

A2 Commutative Law for Addition. If a and b are any real numbers, then

$$a + b = b + a.$$

A3 Existence of an Additive Identity. There is a unique real number, denoted by 0, such that

$$a + 0 = a$$

for every real number a.

A4 Existence of Additive Inverses. For each real number a, there is a unique real number, denoted $-a$, such that

$$a + (-a) = 0.$$

M1 Associative Law for Multiplication. If a, b, and c are any real numbers, then

$$(ab)c = a(bc).$$

M2 Commutative Law for Multiplication. If a and b are any real numbers, then

$$ab = ba.$$

M3 Existence of a Multiplicative Identity. There is a unique nonzero real number, denoted by 1, such that

$$1 \cdot a = a$$

for every real number a.

M4 Existence of Multiplicative Inverses. For each real number a different from 0, there is a unique real number, denoted a^{-1}, such that

$$a \cdot a^{-1} = 1.$$

D   Distributive Law. If a, b, and c are any real numbers, then

$$a(b + c) = ab + ac.$$

We give the usual definitions of subtraction and division. Given any real numbers a and b, the **difference** of a and b, written $a - b$, is the number $a + (-b)$. It will be useful to note also that the sum of any two numbers c and d can be written as a difference. Thus, $c + d = c - (-d)$. For any real numbers a and b with $b \neq 0$, the **quotient** of a and b, written a/b, is the number $a \cdot b^{-1}$. Notice that for any number $b \neq 0$, $1/b = 1 \cdot b^{-1} = b^{-1}$, and for any numbers c and d with $d \neq 0$, $c \cdot d = c/d^{-1}$. The point is that problems involving differences can be handled by converting them into sums, and vice versa. A similar relation holds between products and quotients.

The nine properties of the real numbers listed as A1–A4, M1–M4, and D are sufficient to derive the computational rules involved in factoring, working with fractions and exponents, and solving simple algebraic equations, all of which should be familiar. They are, however, inadequate to handle some very important problems. Notice that the results derived from these properties all deal with equality or identity of two expressions. However, there is no machinery for comparing numbers if they are not equal. Our lives are full of such comparisons—cost of the same item in different stores, number of votes received by candidates for a public office, the number of points scored by the home and visiting teams in an athletic contest.

Whenever we try to apply mathematics to the solution of a physical problem, we encounter comparisons of numbers. A scientist usually deals with numbers as representations of measurements of physical quantities. Because of human limitations and limitations of the instruments used, any such measurements are, in fact, approximations. Thus, if we measure the length of an object as 3.4 inches, we can say only that the actual length L in inches is approximately 3.4 inches or that 3.4 is in some sense "close" to L. The idea that two numbers are "close" clearly involves a comparison of the numbers. In order to make precise the notions of comparison and closeness of numbers, we will state several more basic properties of the real numbers from which a definition of inequality will be given and methods for working with inequalities will be derived.

There is a unique subset P of R, called the set of **positive** real numbers, such that the following two conditions are satisfied:

O1 Trichotomy Law. For each real number a, exactly one of the following statements holds:

(i) a is an element of P
(ii) $a = 0$
(iii) $-a$ is an element of P

O2 Closure Laws. If a and b are any positive real numbers, then

$$a + b \text{ is a positive real number, and}$$
$$ab \text{ is a positive real number.}[1]$$

Properties O1 and O2 are the basic order properties of the real number system. We will not assume that the reader is familiar with the consequences of these properties. We begin with the definition of the basic inequalities.

DEFINITION Let a and b be real numbers.

(i) a is less than b, written $a < b$, means $b - a$ is a member of P.
(ii) b is greater than a, written $b > a$, means $a < b$.
(iii) $a \leq b$ means $a < b$ or $a = b$.
(iv) $b \geq a$ means $b > a$ or $a = b$.

By way of illustration, $3 < 7$ because $7 - 3 = 4$ is positive, while $-2 > -4$ because $-2 - (-4) = -2 + 4 = 2$ is positive. To see that $-1 \leq 1$, notice that $1 - (-1) = 1 + 1 = 2$ is positive, so $-1 < 1$; since one of the statements $-1 = 1$ and $-1 < 1$ is true, it follows that $-1 \leq 1$. Similary, $5 \leq 5$ because $5 = 5$.

In these examples, we assumed some prior knowledge of the set P of positive numbers, in particular that 2 and 4 are positive. The following

---

[1] It should be noted that these eleven properties, if taken as axioms, are not sufficient to char-acterize completely the system of real numbers, because there are number systems other than the reals that possess all these properties. That this is the case may be seen by observing that the system of rational numbers, $i.e.$, numbers expressible in the form p/q, where p and q are integers and $q \neq 0$, has all the properties ascribed to real numbers. (See Exercise 22.) Hence, the real number system must have some additional properties that distinguish it from all other number systems. What these are will be discussed later when we have a genuine need for them.

examples indicate how we might prove from our basic assumptions that our prior "knowledge" is indeed correct, and at the same time illustrate the type of reasoning to be used repeatedly in subsequent material.

Example 1   For each real number a, exactly one of the following is true:

(i) $a > 0$
(ii) $a = 0$
(iii) $a < 0$

From the definition, $a > 0$ means that $a - 0 = a \in P$, and $a < 0$ means that $0 - a = 0 + (-a) = -a \in P$. By the Trichotomy Law O1, exactly one of the statements, $a \in P$, $a = 0$, $-a \in P$ is true. Hence, exactly one of the statements $a > 0$, $a = 0$, $a < 0$ is true. Notice that this is just a restatement of the Trichotomy Law in terms of inequalities.

As a consequence of this and the definition of inequalities, it is seen that given any real numbers a and b, exactly one of the following is true: $a > b$, $a = b$, $a < b$. A number a is said to be **negative** provided $a < 0$.

Example 2   The product of two negative real numbers is positive.

If a and b are negative, then by O1 and Example 1, $-a$ and $-b$ are positive. Since $ab = (-a)(-b)$ (see Appendix I), O2 implies that ab is positive.

From this and O2 it is seen that the product of any nonzero number with itself is positive. Consequently, $1 = 1 \cdot 1$ is positive. Also, $2 = 1 + 1$, is the sum of two positive numbers that, by O2, is positive. Proceeding in the same way, we can show that the rest of the natural numbers $3, 4, 5, \ldots$ are positive.

Example 3   The multiplicative inverse of a positive number is positive.

If b is any positive number then $b^{-1} = 1/b$ is not 0. (Why?) So $1/b$ is either positive or negative. Suppose $1/b$ is negative. Then, by the Trichotomy Law, $-1/b$ is positive and $b(-1/b) = -(b \cdot 1/b) = -1$ must be positive by O2. But this is false. Thus, the assumption that $1/b$ is negative must be false. Therefore, $1/b$ is positive.

Example 4   The quotient of two positive numbers is positive. If each of a and b is positive, then $1/b$ is also positive. Hence, an application of O2 tells us that $a/b = a(1/b)$ is positive.

It is important to realize that the definition works two ways: (**1**) If we have two real numbers x and y and we know that x is less than y, then we can conclude that the number $y - x$ is positive. (**2**) If we know that the difference $c - d$ of the real numbers c and d is positive, then we can conclude that the number d is less than the number c.

Example 5   If $x > 1$ then we know that $x - 1$ is positive. In order to conclude that $x + 2 > 3$ we must show that $(x + 2) - 3$ is positive. But $(x + 2) - 3 = x - 1$. Hence, if $x > 1$ then $(x + 2) - 3$ is positive, so $x + 2 > 3$.

Example 6   For any real numbers p and q, $p^2 + q^2 \geq 2pq$. We want to con-
clude that $(p^2 + q^2) - 2pq$ is positive or zero. Notice that $(p^2 + q^2) - 2pq = p^2 - 2pq + q^2 = (p - q)^2$. But, $(p - q)^2$ is the square of a real number, which, as was seen earlier, is positive or zero. Hence, we have $p^2 + q^2 \geq 2pq$.

The next example further illustrates the use of the definition of inequalities and has some interesting and useful corollaries. We use the usual convention that the statement "$a < b < c$" means "$a < b$ and $b < c$," and we say that b is **between** a and c.

Example 7   If $a < b$, then the average, or arithmetic mean, of a and b is between a and b. That is, if $a < b$, then

$$a < \frac{a + b}{2} < b.$$

To prove this, it must be shown that $a < (a + b)/2$ *and* $(a + b)/2 < b$. To prove the first of these inequalities, observe that $(a + b)/2 - a = (1/2)(b - a)$, which is the product of the positive number $1/2$ and the number $b - a$, which is also positive, since $a < b$. Hence, by O2, $(a + b)/2 - a$ is positive, so by the definition, $a < (a + b)/2$. The proof of the second inequality is similar.

This result implies that between any two distinct real numbers there is another real number. Indeed, between any two distinct real numbers there are infinitely many real numbers. (Proof?) Other consequences of this example appear in the exercises.

EXERCISES

1. Without referring to the text, give a careful statement of the basic order properties of the real number system, and the definitions of the basic inequalities.

2. State precisely what each of the following means in terms of the difference of two numbers. All letters denote real numbers.
   (a) $x < y$
   (b) $t > 2$
   (c) $c + d \geq a - p$
   (d) $x^2 - 2 < e$
   (e) $x^2 - 2 > -e$
   (f) $-e < x^2 - 2 < e$
   (g) $-d < x + \sqrt{2} < d$
   (h) $\sqrt{ab} \leq \dfrac{a + b}{2}$
   (i) $\dfrac{1}{y} < 1$

   (j) $\dfrac{2cd}{c + d} \leq \sqrt{cd}$

3. For each of the following, find a statement about inequalities that has the same meaning.
   (a) $x - y$ is positive.
   (b) $(a + c) - (b + c)$ is positive or zero.
   (c) $p + q$ is positive.
   (d) $r + (-s)$ is positive or zero.
   (e) $a - b$ is negative.
   (f) If $b - a$ is positive, then $\dfrac{a + 2b}{3} - \dfrac{2a + b}{3}$ is positive.

4. Justify each of the following statements.
   (a) $4 < 7$ (d) $3.14 < 22/7$
   (b) $-6 \leq 1$ (e) $5 \geq -3$
   (c) $2 \geq 2$ (f) $-7/3 \leq 7/3$

5. Prove or disprove each of the following statements.
   (a) $10/3 > 3$
   (b) $4 > 5$
   (c) $3 < 3$
   (d) $1/3 \geq .333$
   (e) $-.1 < .1$
   (f) $\dfrac{1709}{183} < \dfrac{28}{3}$

6. Prove: If $a \in R, b \in R$, and $b > 0$, then $a < a + b$.

7. Prove: If $a \in R, b \in R$, and $b < 0$, then $a + b < a$.

8. Let z be a real number. Show that if $z + 1 > 0$, then $z > -1$. Is the converse of this statement true or false?

9. If c is a real number, show that $c + 4 < c + 5$. Does the result hold if $<$ is replaced by $\leq$?

10. Prove that there is no largest real number. (*Hint:* Assume to the contrary, that there is a largest real number.)

°11. Show that if $a > 0$ and $b < 0$, then $ab < 0$.

°12. Property O2 and Example 2 show that if two numbers a and b are both positive or both negative, then their product ab is positive. Exercise 11 shows that the product of a positive number and a negative number is negative. Prove the converses of these statements. That is, for any real numbers c and d, prove
   (a) If cd is positive, then either c and d are both positive or they are both negative.
   (b) If cd is negative, then either c is positive and d is negative, or c is negative and d is positive.

°13. State and prove results similar to those in Exercise 12 for the quotient of two numbers.

14. Find results similar to those in Exercise 12 for the product of three real numbers.

15. Prove or disprove: If $a < b$, then $a < 2b$.

16. Disprove this statement: If $a < b$, then $a^2 < b^2$. *Hint:* It suffices to give an example of two particular numbers a and b for which $a < b$ but $a^2 \not< b^2$.

17. One frequently hears people talk about the "smallest positive real number." Show that there is no smallest positive real number. (Recall Example 7.) Is there a largest negative real number?

18. Is there a smallest real number that is greater than 2? Explain.

19. Show that if $a \leq b$, then
$$a \leq \frac{a + b}{2} \leq b.$$

20. Prove that if $a < b$, then
$$a < \frac{2a + b}{3} < \frac{a + 2b}{3} < b.$$

21. Use mathematical induction to verify the assertion made in the text that every natural number is positive.

†22. Verify the assertion made in the footnote in Section 1.2 that the system of rational numbers has all the properties listed for the real numbers. Recall that if a/b and c/d are rational numbers, their sum and product are defined by
$$\frac{a}{b} + \frac{c}{d} = \frac{ad + bc}{bd}$$
$$\frac{a}{b} \cdot \frac{c}{d} = \frac{ac}{bd}.$$

(a) Show first that the sum and product of two rational numbers are rational numbers. You may assume the necessary properties of the integers.
(b) Show that the first nine properties hold.
(c) Now decide how to define the set P such that properties O1 and O2 hold.

■ 1.3 Inequalities

In dealing with inequalities it is always possible to use the definition in order to gain information, and certainly at the present stage of development we must do this. There are, however, several results involving inequalities that are used sufficiently often to warrant formal derivations and designations as theorems. Some of these are stated in the following theorem, some will appear in the exercises, and others will appear in later sections.

THEOREM 1.3.1   Let a, b, and c be real numbers. Then
(i)   If $a < b$ and $b < c$, then $a < c$. .
(ii) $a < b$ if, and only if, $a + c < b + c$.
(iii) For $c > 0$, $a < b$ if, and only if, $ac < bc$.
(iv)   For $c < 0$, $a < b$ if, and only if, $ac > bc$.

Before proving this theorem, a few comments are in order. If A and B denote statements, then to say the statement "A if, and only if, B" is true is to say that the statements A and B are equivalent, so that if A is true then B must be true, *and* if B is true then A must be true. The implication "if B, then A" is called the "if" part of the statement and the implication "if A, then B" is called the "only if" part. Assertion (ii) of the theorem is of this type, where A is the statement "$a < b$" and B is the statement "$a + c < b + c$." Thus, in order to prove assertion (ii), it is necessary to prove each of the following:

(1) If $a < b$, then $a + c < b + c$.
(2) If $a + c < b + c$, then $a < b$.

To get a better intuitive feeling for what the various parts of the theorem say and for how they will be used, we restate them in less formal language. Assertion (ii) consists of statements (1) and (2). (1) says that an inequality is preserved when the same number is added to each side of the inequality; (2) states that an inequality is preserved if the same number is subtracted from each side. Similarly, (iii) states that an inequality is preserved if each side is multiplied or divided by the same *positive* number, whereas (iv) states that the "sense" or "direction" of an inequality is reversed if each side is multiplied or divided by the same *negative* number.

   PROOF   **(i)** It is given that $a < b$ and $b < c$, which, by the definition, means that $b - a$ and $c - b$ are positive. Using these facts, it is required to show that $a < c$; that is, $c - a$ is positive. Now, $c - a = (c - b) + (b - a)$, which is positive by O1. Hence, $a < c$.

(iv) "Only if" part: It is given that $c < 0$ and $a < b$. Therefore, $-c$ is positive and $b - a$ is positive, so by O2, $ac - bc = (b - a)(-c)$ is positive, which means that $ac > bc$.

"If" part: It is given that $c < 0$ and $ac > bc$. Since c is negative, so is $1/c$. We have already shown in the "only if" part that when we multiply each side of an inequality by the same negative number, the "sense" or "direction" of the inequality is reversed. Hence, if we multiply each side of the given inequality $ac > bc$ by the negative number $1/c$, we obtain $(ac)(1/c) < (bc)(1/c)$, which clearly implies that $a < b$.

The proofs of assertions (ii) and (iii) of the theorem are left to the reader.

COROLLARY Let a, b, c, and d be real numbers. Then
(i)   If $a < b$ and $c < d$, then $a + c < b + d$.
(ii) If $0 < a < b$ and $0 < c < d$, then $ac < bd$.

PROOF   (i) Applying part (ii) of the theorem to each statement in the hypotheses gives

$$a + c < b + c \quad \text{and} \quad b + c < b + d.$$

By part (i) of the theorem, then, $a + c < b + d$.

(ii) From the hypotheses we note that each of the numbers b and c is positive. Using part (iii) of the theorem when we multiply each side of the inequality $a < b$ by the positive number c and each side of $c < d$ by the positive number b, we have

$$ac < bc \quad \text{and} \quad bc < bd.$$

An application of part (i) of the theorem now gives the desired conclusion that $ac < bd$.

Example 1   It is frequently necessary to find all numbers that satisfy some condition. Suppose it is required to determine all numbers z that satisfy the condition

$$7z + 5 < 1.$$

Let us begin by working backwards. If z is a number that satisfies this condition, then by part (ii) of the theorem,

$$7z < -4,$$

which by part (iii) implies

$$z < -\frac{4}{7}.$$

The problem, however, is not yet solved! All that has been shown is that *if* z satisfies the original condition, *then* it must be less than $-4/7$. It remains to show that every number z that is less than $-4/7$ does indeed satisfy the original condition. In this instance we can show this by simply reversing the steps already taken. If $z < -4/7$, then (iii) of the theorem implies $7z < -4$ and by (ii), $7z + 5 < 1$.

Thus, the solution to the problem is the set of all numbers less than $-4/7$. In the notation of Section 1.1, we have shown that

(#) $\{z : 7z + 5 < 1\} = \{z : z < -4/7\}$

by showing that each of these sets is a subset of the other.

This set, no matter how it is described, is called the **solution set** of the inequality

$$7z + 5 < 1.$$

By solving an inequality is meant describing its solution set in as simple a manner as possible; that is, so that it is immediately obvious what the elements of the set are. Thus, the second description in (#) meets this requirement for Example 1.

Example 2 Solve the inequality $2s + 5 > s - 7$.

By part (ii) of the theorem, $2s + 5 > s - 7$ if, and only if, $2s + 5 + (-s - 5) > s - 7 + (-s - 5)$, that is, $s > -12$. Hence, the solution is $\{s : s > -12\}$.

Example 3 Solve the inequality $(x - 3)(x + 2) > 0$.

The solution of this inequality cannot be found by an automatic application of the theorem. Here, we must ask ourselves when the product of two real numbers is positive. From Exercise 12 of Section 1.2, the product of the numbers $(x - 3)$ and $(x + 2)$ is positive if and only if either $x - 3$ and $x + 2$ are both positive or both negative.

Thus,

$$(x - 3)(x + 2) > 0 \quad \text{if and only if}$$
$$x - 3 > 0 \quad \text{and} \quad x + 2 > 0$$

or $$x - 3 < 0 \quad \text{and} \quad x + 2 < 0.$$

By the theorem, this is equivalent to

$$x > 3 \quad \text{and} \quad x > -2, \quad \text{or} \quad x < 3 \quad \text{and} \quad x < -2.$$

Now, $x > 3$ and $x > -2$ if, and only if, $x > 3$.
Also, $x < 3$ and $x < -2$ if, and only if, $x < -2$.
Hence, the solution set is $\{x : x > 3 \text{ or } x < -2\}$.

Example 4   Solve the inequality $\dfrac{1}{x-1} < 2$.

   It would be tempting to try to solve this by first multiplying each side by $x-1$ to eliminate the fractions. This impulse is dangerous! For, without knowing whether $x-1$ is positive or negative, we have no way of knowing whether the sense of the inequality would be preserved or reversed. This could be done if we break the problem into cases depending on whether $x-1$ is positive or negative and apply parts (iii) and (iv) respectively of the theorem. A much safer approach is to either use the definition of inequality or part (ii) of the theorem. Thus, from the definition, $1/(x-1) < 2$ if and only if $2 - 1/(x-1) = (2x-3)/(x-1)$ is positive. Now, the quotient of two numbers is positive if and only if the numerator and denominator are both positive or both negative. Hence, a number x is a solution if and only if

$$2x - 3 > 0 \quad \text{and} \quad x - 1 > 0$$

or

$$2x - 3 < 0 \quad \text{and} \quad x - 1 < 0,$$

that is,

$$x > \frac{3}{2} \quad \text{and} \quad x > 1, \quad \text{or} \quad x < \frac{3}{2} \quad \text{and} \quad x < 1.$$

This is equivalent to

$$x > \frac{3}{2} \quad \text{or} \quad x < 1.$$

Therefore, the solution set is

$$\left\{ x : x > \frac{3}{2} \quad \text{or} \quad x < 1 \right\}.$$

Example 5   Solve the inequality $x^2 - 2 > x$.
$\quad\quad x^2 - 2 > x$ if, and only if, $x^2 - x - 2 > 0$;
$\quad\quad x^2 - x - 2 > 0$ if, and only if, $(x-2)(x+1) > 0$;
$\quad\quad (x-2)(x+1) > 0$ if, and only if, $x-2$ and $x+1$
have the same sign; *i.e.*, either $x - 2 > 0$ and $x + 1 > 0$, or $x - 2 < 0$ and $x + 1 < 0$.
This holds if, and only if,

$$x > 2 \quad \text{and} \quad x > -1$$

or

$$x < 2 \quad \text{and} \quad x < -1,$$

which is equivalent to

$$x > 2 \quad \text{or} \quad x < -1.$$

Hence, the solution set is $\{x: x > 2 \text{ or } x < -1\}$.

Examples 6 and 7 illustrate another type of problem.

Example 6 If $1 < x < 11/10$, what can be said about $x^2 - 1$?
  If $1 < x < 11/10$, then by part (ii) of the corollary, $1 < x^2 < 121/100$. Hence, by part (ii) of the theorem

$$0 < x^2 - 1 < \frac{21}{100}.$$

Example 7 If $-0.1 < x - 2 < 0.1$, what can be inferred about $x^2 + 3x - 5$?
  If $-0.1 < x - 2 < 0.1$, then adding 2 to each term of the inequality, we get $1.9 < x < 2.1$ and if we multiply each term of this inequality by the positive number 3, we obtain $5.7 < 3x < 6.3$. Bounds on x^2 are obtained by applying part (ii) of the corollary to $1.9 < x < 2.1$, which gives $3.61 < x^2 < 4.41$. By the use of part (i) of the corollary and part (ii) of the theorem, we have

$$4.31 < x^2 + 3x - 5 < 5.71.$$

Example 8 Examples 6 and 7 typify problems of error analysis encountered in making computations with approximate measurements. Suppose we have a ruler with which we can measure the length of an object correct to the nearest tenth of an inch. Thus, if we measure the length L of a side of a square in inches as $L = 3.2$, what we actually know is that

$$3.15 \leq L \leq 3.25.$$

If we then use this value of L to compute the area L^2 of the square, we know that

$$(3.15)^2 \leq L^2 \leq (3.25)^2.$$

That is, we know that the actual area in square inches is between 9.9225 in.² and 10.5625 in.². Hence, the largest possible error incurred in computing the area by taking the length to be 3.2 inches is the larger of the quantities $[(3.2)^2 - (3.15)^2]$ in.² and $[(3.25)^2 - (3.2)^2]$ in.², which is 0.3225 in.².

We conclude this section with a theorem that will be used repeatedly in the material to follow.

THEOREM 1.3.2 Let a and b be real numbers, and let n be a positive integer. If $0 < a < b$, then $a^n < b^n$.

PROOF   Here we want to prove that infinitely many statements are true —one corresponding to each positive integer. As often in such situations, we use the principle of mathematical induction. The reader is referred to Appendix II for a discussion of this principle.

We verify the result first in the case where $n = 1$. Since it is given that $0 < a < b$, we have trivially that $a^1 < b^1$.

It remains to show that *if* k is a positive integer for which the statement is true, *then* the statement is also true for the positive integer $k + 1$. That is, under the assumption that $0 < a < b$, we want to prove that *if* k is any positive integer for which $a^k < b^k$, *then* $a^{k+1} < b^{k+1}$.

Since each of a and b is positive, each of a^k and b^k is a product of positive numbers and hence is positive. From the hypotheses, then, we have

$$0 < a < b$$

and

$$0 < a^k < b^k.$$

Therefore, from part (ii) of the corollary to Theorem 1.3.1,

$$a \cdot a^k < b \cdot b^k$$

whence,

$$a^{k+1} < b^{k+1}.$$

Under the assumption that $0 < a < b$, we have shown

(1) The statement $a^n < b^n$ is true in the case where $n = 1$;

(2) *If* the statement $a^n < b^n$ is true in the case where n is replaced by a positive integer k, *then* it is also true in the case where n is replaced by the positive integer $k + 1$.

Therefore, by the principle of mathematical induction, if a and b are real numbers for which $0 < a < b$ and n is any positive integer, then $a^n < b^n$.

EXERCISES

1. State each of the results contained in Theorem 1.3.1, the corollary, and Theorem 1.3.2 in your own words without using any symbols.

2. Solve each of the following in-equalities. Recall that this means you are to describe the solution set so it is immediately obvious what its elements are.

(a) $2x - 3 < 5$

(b) $-x > x + 6$
(c) $3s + 4 < 4s - 6$
(d) $1 - t < 3 - 2t$
(e) $x^2 - 2x + 5 > 1 + 2x + x^2$
(f) $y + 1 < y + 2$
(g) $1/x > 1/2$

3. Solve each of the following inequalities
   (a) $x^2 + 5x + 6 > 0$
   (b) $(2x + 5)(x - 2) < 0$
   (c) $(7 - 2x)/(x - 5) < 0$
   (d) $(x + 5)/(x - 2) < 1$
   (e) $x^2 + 2x \geq -1$
   (f) $(x - 6)^2 > (3x + 2)^2$
   (g) $x^2 + 1 \leq 2x$
   (h) $x/2 + 2/x - 1 < 7x$
   (i) $x^3 - 3x^2 \leq 1 - 3x$
   (j) $(x - 1)(x - 2)(x - 3) > 0$

4. Show each of the following.
   (a) If $1 < x - 2 < 2$, then $-12 > 3 - 5x > -17$.
   (b) If $-3 < x + 5 < -1$, then $-9 < 3x/2 + 17 < 9$.
   (c) If $-.1 < x + 1 < .1$, then $-.63 < 3x^2 - 3 < .63$.
   (d) If $-1 < x < 1$, then $0 \leq x^2 < 1$.
   (e) If $0 < d < 1$, then $d^2 < d$.
   (f) If $c > 1$, then $c^2 > c$.
   (g) If $0 < e < 3$, then $-e < -2e/3 + e^2/9$ and $2e/3 + e^2/9 < e$.
   (h) If $0 < e < 3$ and $-e/3 < x - 1 < e/3$, then $-e < x^2 - 1 < e$.

*5. Show that if $0 < c < d$, then $\sqrt{c} < \sqrt{d}$. *Hint:* Use Theorem 1.3.2 with $n = 2$ and trichotomy. Remember that $\sqrt{c}$ denotes the nonnegative square root of c.

   Combining Theorem 1.3.2 in case $n = 2$ and this exercise gives the result that if x and y are positive numbers, then $x < y$ if, and only if, $x^2 < y^2$.

*6. Let a and b be positive real numbers such that $a < b$.
   (a) For each positive integer n, show that $\sqrt[n]{a} < \sqrt[n]{b}$. (Recall the proof of Exercise 5 and the fact that for $x \geq 0$, $\sqrt[n]{x}$ denotes the nonnegative nth root of x.)
   (b) For each pair p, q of positive

integers, show that $a^{p/q} < b^{p/q}$. (Recall that for $x \geq 0$, $x^{p/q} = \sqrt[q]{x^p}$.)
   (c) Restate the results in parts (a) and (b) in your own words without using symbols.

7. If $-1 < x - 2 < 1$, state what can be inferred about each number.
   (a) $7x - 6$
   (b) $-5x - 2$
   (c) $3x - 6$
   (d) $x^2 - 4$
   (e) $3x^2 + 2x - 16$

8. If $-.1 < x - 1 < .1$, state what can be inferred about each number.
   (a) $4x^2 - 3x + 2$
   (b) $-6x^2 + 2x + 4$
   (c) $1/x - 1$
   (d) $1/x^2 - 1$
   (e) $x^3 - 1$

*9. (a) Prove: If $ab > 0$ and $a < b$, then $1/a > 1/b$.
   (b) Practically speaking, what does the condition $ab > 0$ mean?
   (c) State the result of part (a) without using any symbols.

10. Show each of the following.
    (a) If $0 < t < 1$, then $1/t > 1$.
    (b) If $x > 10$, then $1/x^2 < 1/100$.
    (c) If $7 < x < 9$, then
    $$\frac{1}{62} < \frac{1}{x^2 - 3x + 2} < \frac{1}{24}.$$

11. State under what conditions on x each of these is true.
    (a) $1/x < 100$
    (b) $1/x < 1$
    (c) $1/x < 10^{-2}$
    (d) $1/x < 10^{-20}$
    (e) $\dfrac{1}{x^2 - 1} < 10^{-3}$

*12. The properties of inequalities listed in Theorem 1.3.1, its corollary, Theorem 1.3.2, and Exercises 5, 6, and 9 are all stated using strict inequality ($<$ or $>$). Which of these remain true if $<$ is replaced by $\leq$, and $>$ is replaced by $\geq$?

13. Given a ruler with which you can measure to the nearest hundredth of an inch, and you measure the

length L and width W in inches of a rectangle as 4.00 and 2.55 respectively, what do you actually know about L and W? What can be said about the area A of the rectangle?

14. Suppose $p > -1$. Use mathematical induction to show that

$$(1 + p)^n \geq 1 + np$$

for every positive integer n.

15. Let a and b be positive real numbers. Show that

$$\frac{2ab}{a + b} \leq \sqrt{ab} \leq \frac{a + b}{2}.$$

16. Give examples of numbers $a, b, c,$ and d for which $a < b$ and $c < d$ but $ac \nless bd$. How do you reconcile this with part (ii) of the corollary to Theorem 1.3.1?

17. (a) Show that if $a < b < 0$, then $a^2 > b^2$. Compare this with Theorem 1.3.2 for $n = 2$.

   (b) Show that if $a < b < 0$ and n is a positive even integer, then $a^n > b^n$. Compare this with Theorem 1.3.2.

18. In Theorem 1.3.2, show that if n is a positive odd integer, the hypothesis that a and b are positive can be omitted.

†19. For each positive integer n, show that

$$\left(1 + \frac{1}{n + 1}\right)^{n+1} \geq \left(1 + \frac{1}{n}\right)^n.$$

Hint: Show first that

$$\left(1 + \frac{1}{n + 1}\right)^{n+1} \bigg/ \left(1 + \frac{1}{n}\right)^n$$
$$= \left(\frac{n + 1}{n}\right)\left(1 - \frac{1}{(n + 1)^2}\right)^{n+1}.$$

Then use Exercise 14 to show that this is greater than or equal to 1.

†20. Use an argument similar to that in Exercise 19 to prove that for each positive integer n,

$$\left(1 + \frac{1}{n + 1}\right)^{n+2} \leq \left(1 + \frac{1}{n}\right)^{n+1}.$$

†21. (a) Use Exercise 19 and mathematical induction to show that if n is a positive integer, then for every positive integer k,

$$\left(1 + \frac{1}{n}\right)^n \leq \left(1 + \frac{1}{n + k}\right)^{n+k}.$$

   (b) Use Exercise 20 and mathematical induction to show that if m is a positive integer, then for every positive integer k,

$$\left(1 + \frac{1}{m}\right)^{m+1} \geq \left(1 + \frac{1}{m + k}\right)^{m+k+1}.$$

   (c) Conclude from parts (a) and (b) that for any two positive integers m and n,

$$\left(1 + \frac{1}{m}\right)^{m+1} \geq \left(1 + \frac{1}{n}\right)^n.$$

■ 1.4 Coordinate Systems for a Line

The basic idea behind the notion of a coordinate system for a line is the idea of matching real numbers with points of the line in a certain way. This idea of matching numbers with members of other sets is at least as old as man's concept of counting, and it extends to the modern practice of keeping track of people by assigning social security numbers to them. As one becomes more versed in mathematics, he finds examples of quite sophisticated coordinate systems, but those systems will be found to share the properties that the following definition insists upon for a coordinate system for a line.

DEFINITION If L is a line, then a **coordinate system for L** is a correspondence between the real numbers and the points of L that satisfies the two conditions:
(**i**)   To each real number, there corresponds exactly one point of L.
(**ii**) Each point of L is made to correspond to one and only one real number, which is called the **coordinate** of the point. Once a coordinate system for L has been established, L is called a **coordinate line**.

The definition appears to allow lots of correspondences to be coordinate systems for a line, because the definition does not give a definite recipe for constructing a coordinate system. It only says that however a correspondence between numbers and points of a line is defined, it must satisfy (i) and (ii) to be a coordinate system, and conversely, *any* correspondence that satisfies (i) and (ii) will be a coordinate system.

But our object in introducing coordinates on a line is to be able to translate geometric statements about the line into the language of real numbers, and vice versa. For this reason, those coordinate systems in which one is ordinarily interested are related to one that is constructed as follows.

Let L be a horizontal line, and choose two points P_0 and P_1 on L with P_1 to the right of P_0. These are the points assigned to the numbers 0 and 1, respectively, and the segment $P_0 P_1$ is called a **unit segment**. By marking off unit segments to the left and right of P_0, each integer n can be assigned to exactly one point P_n of L:

The next step is to assign points of L to the rational numbers, *i.e.*, those numbers of the form n/m where n and m are integers and $m \neq 0$. For a fixed integer $m > 1$, divide the unit segment $P_0 P_1$ into m equal parts. The numbers $1/m, 2/m, \ldots, (m-1)/m$ are then assigned to the points of division:

The rest of the rational numbers that have denominator m are assigned to points obtained by starting with one of the points of division obtained above and marking off unit segments to the left and right of that point. For example, the number $\frac{8}{3} = 2 + \frac{2}{3}$ is assigned to the point $P_{8/3}$ found by dividing $P_0 P_1$ into three equal parts and marking off two unit segments to the right of the point $P_{2/3}$, while the number $-\frac{11}{3} = -4 + \frac{1}{3}$ is assigned to the opint $P_{-11/3}$

obtained by marking off four unit segments to the left of the point $P_{1/3}$.

The numbers that have not been assigned to points of L by the above method are the irrational numbers. Some of these numbers can be assigned to points of L by means of geometric constructions, but for many this is not the case. We will avoid this problem by making the basic assumption that the irrational numbers *can* be assigned to the points of L that remain after the above construction, and that to each such remaining point of L a unique irrational number can be assigned. We will also assume that this can be carried out in such a way that whenever a and b are real numbers and P_a, P_b are the corresponding points of L, then the point P_b is to the right of point P_a if, and only if, $b > a$.

A coordinate system for a line L arrived at in this way is called a **natural coordinate system** for L. As long as we stick to a system of this kind for a given line, we will not distinguish between a point on the line and the coordinate of that point. That is, if x is a real number, then the point of the line whose coordinate is x will also be denoted by x. This is done not only for the sake of convenience, but also to stress that certain statements about real numbers are to be interpreted as statements about points on a line, and vice versa. For example, to say that the number x is greater than the number y is to say that x is to the right of y, while the statement that the number y is between the numbers x and z means that either $x < y < z$ or $z < y < x$.

With this idea in mind, there is a natural way to define the distance between numbers.

DEFINITION If each of x and y is a number, then the **distance** between x and y is $x - y$ in case $x \geq y$, and is $y - x$ in case $x < y$.

Notice that the distance from a number x to the number 0 is x in case $x \geq 0$, and is $-x$ in case $x < 0$. This quantity is so important that it requires a special name.

DEFINITION If x is a number, then the **absolute value** of x is the number, denoted $|x|$, which is found as follows:

$$|x| = x, \quad \text{if} \quad x \geq 0$$
$$|x| = -x, \quad \text{if} \quad x < 0$$

The properties of absolute value will be examined closely in later sections. At the present time, we note the fact that the notion of absolute value can be used to give a concise expression for the distance between any two numbers.

THEOREM 1.4.1   If each of x and y is a number, then the distance between x and y is $|x - y|$.

PROOF   If $x \geq y$, then the distance between x and y is $x - y$, by definition of distance. But $x - y \geq 0$, since $x \geq y$, so $x - y = |x - y|$.

If $x < y$, then the distance between x and y is $y - x$. But $y - x = -(x - y) = |x - y|$, since $x - y < 0$ when $x < y$.

Example 1   Solve the equation $|x - 3| = 4$.

This can be solved algebraically, that is, by using the definition of absolute value. Thus, a number x is a solution, if, and only if, one of the following is true:

CASE 1 $x - 3 \geq 0$ and $x - 3 = 4$;
CASE 2 $x - 3 < 0$ and $-(x - 3) = 4$.

In case 1, we find $x \geq 3$ and $x = 7$, *i.e.*, $x = 7$; in case 2, $x < 3$ and $x = -1$, *i.e.*, $x = -1$. Hence, the solution set is $\{-1, 7\}$.

Now, if the problem is looked at geometrically, its solution is much easier. For, the solutions are just those numbers whose distance from the number 3 is 4. A sketch of a coordinate line shows that the solutions are the numbers -1 and 7.

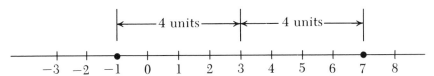

Example 2   Solve the equation $|x + 2| = 2$.

Again, a geometric solution is simple, provided that we realize that $|x + 2| = |x - (-2)|$, the distance between x and -2, so the solution set is $\{-4, 0\}$.

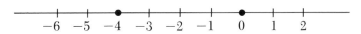

EXERCISES

1. Without referring to the text, give a careful statement of what is meant by

   (a) The absolute value of a real number.
   (b) The distance between two real numbers.

2. Find the distance between the

given numbers. Simplify your answer as much as possible.
(a) 2 and -3
(b) 0 and 10
(c) -6 and 6
(d) $3a$ and a, where $a \leq 0$
(e) $\dfrac{x}{x+1}$ and $\dfrac{x-1}{x}$
(f) $\sqrt{2}$ and 1.414
(g) $\dfrac{3}{13}$ and $\dfrac{4}{17}$
(h) $\dfrac{4}{21}$ and $\dfrac{3}{16}$

3. Solve each equation both algebraically and geometrically.
(a) $|x+1| = 3$
(b) $|x-4| = 2$
(c) $|x-6| = 1$
(d) $|x+4| = \dfrac{1}{2}$
(e) $\left|x - \dfrac{4}{3}\right| = 4$
(f) $|x+2| = 0$

4. Solve each equation.
(a) $|x-1| = 4$
(b) $\left|x + \dfrac{1}{2}\right| = \dfrac{1}{2}$
(c) $\left|x + \dfrac{5}{6}\right| = \dfrac{1}{6}$
(d) $|x-3| = -1$

(e) $|3-x| = 1$
(f) $|3-x| = -1$

5. Solve each equation.
(a) $|x-3| = x-3$
(b) $|y+4| = y+4$
(c) $|a-2| = 2-a$
(d) $|2x+1| = 2x+1$
(e) $|4b+3| = -4b-3$
(f) $|x^2-4| = x^2-4$
(g) $|3x^2+2| = 3x^2+2$
(h) $|2+5x-3x^2| = 3x^2-5x-2$

°6. Prove that if $a \in R$ and $d > 0$, then
$$\{x: |x-a| = d\} = \{a-d, \ a+d\}$$

°7. Prove that $|x| \geq 0$ for every number x.

°8. Prove that $|-x| = |x|$ for every number x.

°9. Prove that $x \leq |x|$ and $-x \leq |x|$ for every number x.

10. What can you say about $|x^2|$? About $|(-x)^2|$? About $|-x^2|$?

11. Use the definition of absolute value to answer the following questions.
(a) Is it true that if $x < y$, then $|x| < |y|$?
(b) Is the converse of the statement in (a) true?

■ 1.5 Intervals and Rays

There are several basic subsets of the set R of all real numbers that are used so frequently that they demand a special terminology and notation.

DEFINITION   If a and b are real numbers with $a < b$, then
(i) $\{x: x \in R \text{ and } a < x < b\}$ is the **open interval** from a to b, and is denoted (a, b);
(ii) $\{x: x \in R \text{ and } a \leq x \leq b\}$ is the **closed interval** from a to b, and is denoted $[a, b]$;
(iii) $\{x: x \in R \text{ and } a \leq x < b\}$ and $\{x: x \in R \text{ and } a < x \leq b\}$ are called **semiopen intervals**, and are respectively denoted $[a, b)$ and $(a, b]$.
    For any of these intervals, a and b are called the **endpoints** of the interval.

DEFINITION If c is a real number, then
(i) $\{x: x \in R \text{ and } x > c\}$ and $\{x: x \in R \text{ and } x < c\}$ are called **open rays**, and are respectively denoted (c, ∞) and $(-\infty, c)$.
(ii) $\{x: x \in R \text{ and } x \geq c\}$ and $\{x: x \in R \text{ and } x \leq c\}$ are called **closed rays**, and are respectively denoted $[c, \infty)$ and $(-\infty, c]$.
For any of these rays, c is called the **endpoint**.

Remark: The symbols ∞ and $-\infty$ are used only as notational devices, and no attempt is to be made to regard these symbols as standing for numbers. In particular, no meaning is to be assigned to the symbols $[c, \infty]$ and $[-\infty, c]$.

DEFINITION If S is a set of real numbers, then the **graph** of S on a coordinate line L is

$\{P: P \text{ is a point of } L \text{ whose coordinate belongs to } S\}.$

The following illustrations indicate how the graphs of intervals and rays are to be draw on a line with a natural coordinate system. Notice that an endpoint of either an interval or a ray that actually belongs to the set is designated by •, while an endpoint that does not belong to the set is designated by ∘.

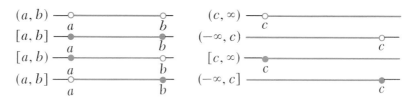

Keeping these graphs in mind makes it easier to avoid mistakes in solving conditions on real numbers, as the following examples show.

Example 1 Find all real numbers x such that $1 \leq x < 6$ and $x \leq 4$.

If
$$A = \{x: 1 \leq x < 6\} = [1, 6), \quad \text{and}$$
$$B = \{x: x \leq 4\} = (-\infty, 4],$$

then the solution set S that we are after is

$$\{x: x \in A \quad \text{and} \quad x \in B\}.$$

The graphs of A and B indicate that the set $S = [1, 4]$.

Example 2   Find all real numbers x such that $1 \le x < 6$ or $x \le 4$.
   Again, if $A = [1, 6)$ and $B = (-\infty, 4]$, then the solution set T is $\{x: x \in A$ or $x \in B\}$, and the graphs of A and B show that $T = (-\infty, 6)$.

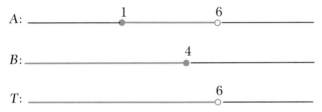

   Although Examples 1 and 2 may not seem to be very difficult, mistakes are often made in problems like these because of confusion as to how the words *and* and *or* are used. In Example 1, we see that the members of S are exactly those numbers that are common to both of the sets A and B, while in Example 2, the members of T are those numbers that belong to *at least one* of the sets A and B, so the numbers belonging to *both* A and B are to be included in T.

   A final example indicates how a graphical solution can allow one to avoid a lot of case-by-case analysis of a problem.

Example 3   Find a simple description of the following set.

$$S = \{x: -1 \le x < 3 \quad \text{or} \quad 5 < x, \quad \text{and} \quad x \le 1 \quad \text{or} \quad 4 < x \le 6\}.$$

$\{x: -1 \le x < 3 \quad \text{or} \quad 5 < x\}$:

$\{x: x \le 1 \quad \text{or} \quad 4 < x \le 6\}$:

S:

$$S = \{x: -1 \le x \le 1 \quad \text{or} \quad 5 < x \le 6\}.$$

   If we were determined to find S by considering cases, there would be four of them:

(1) $-1 \leq x < 3$ and $x \leq 1$
(2) $-1 \leq x < 3$ and $4 < x \leq 6$
(3) $5 < x$ and $x \leq 1$
(4) $5 < x$ and $4 < x \leq 6$

Then, S consists of those numbers that satisfy at least one of (1), (2), (3), and (4). This method is simply too time-consuming, and there is a much greater chance of making errors than in using a graphical solution.

The concept of absolute value is often useful in describing intervals and rays. Keeping Theorem 1.4.1 in mind makes it easier to remember the results of the following theorem.

THEOREM 1.5.1 If a is a real number, and d is a positive number, then
(i) $\{x: x \in R \text{ and } |x - a| < d\} = (a - d, a + d);$
(ii) $\{x: x \in R \text{ and } |x - a| \leq d\} = [a - d, a + d];$
(iii) $\{x: x \in R \text{ and } |x - a| \geq d\} = \{x: x \in (-\infty, a - d] \text{ or } x \in [a + d, \infty)\};$
(iv) $\{x: x \in R \text{ and } |x - a| > d\} = \{x: x \in (-\infty, a - d) \text{ or } x \in (a + d, \infty)\}.$

PROOF   Notice that to prove part (i) of the theorem is to show that $|x - a| < d$ if, and only if, $a - d < x < a + d$.
"Only if" part: Assume $|x - a| < d$. There are two cases.
CASE 1 $x - a \geq 0$. Then $|x - a| = x - a$, so $x - a < d$. Hence, $x < a + d$. But $x \geq a > a - d$, since d is positive. Therefore, $a - d < x < a + d$.
CASE 2 $x - a < 0$. Then $|x - a| = -(x - a) = a - x$, so $a - x < d$. Hence, $a - d < x$; but $x < a < a + d$, so $a - d < x < a + d$.
"If" part: If $a - d < x < a + d$, then $-d < x - a < d$, and by again considering the cases $x - a \geq 0$ and $x - a < 0$, we find that $|x - a| < d$.

Part (ii) of the theorem follows by observing that $\{x: x \in R \text{ and } |x - a| \leq d\}$ equals $\{x: x \in R \text{ and either } |x - a| < d \text{ or } |x - a| = d\}$, which, by part (i), is $(a - d, a + d)$ together with the two numbers $a - d$ and $a + d$.

Part (iii) is seen by noticing that each of the descriptions in (iii) is of the set of numbers that do *not* belong to the set in (i); part (iv) follows from (ii) in similar fashion.

The graph of each of the sets in (i)–(iv) of Theorem 1.5.1 is sketched in Figure 1.

The graphs sketched in Figure 1 emphasize how Theorem 1.4.1 fits with Theorem 1.5.1. For example, to say that a real number x satisfies the condition $|x - a| < d$ is to say that the distance between x and a is less than d, while the statement $|x - a| \geq d$ means that the distance from x to a is greater than or equal to d. The reader should supply similar statements for the sets (ii) and (iv) of Theorem 1.5.1.

(i): $|x - a| < d$ (ii): $|x - a| \le d$

(iii): $|x - a| \ge d$ (iv): $|x - a| > d$

Figure 1

The reason that it is important to understand the connection between the algebraic statements of Theorem 1.5.1 and the geometric interpretation as depicted in Figure 1 is this: once it is realized what Theorem 1.5.1 says in terms of the distance between numbers, then the results of that theorem should be matters of common sense. Having this point of view makes inequalities involving absolute values much less frightening, and makes it easier to analyze more complicated sets of numbers.

Example 4 Let $S = \{x: |x - 2| > 1 \text{ and } |x - 4| \le 2\}$.

Thus, for a number x to belong to S, x must satisfy both the condition $|x - 2| > 1$ and the condition $|x - 4| \le 2$. In the language of sets, if $A = \{x: |x - 2| > 1\}$ and $B = \{x: |x - 4| \le 2\}$, then $S = \{x: x \in A \text{ and } x \in B\}$.

We know that $A = \{x: x > 3 \text{ or } x < 1\}$ (which numbers are at a distance greater than 1 from the number 2?), and we know that $B = \{x: 2 \le x \le 6\}$ (which numbers are at a distance not greater than 2 from the number 4?). Then, the graphs of A and B indicate clearly what the graph of S is.

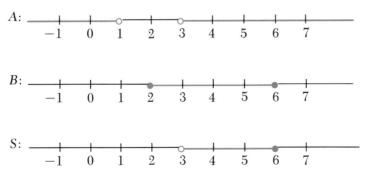

That is, $S = \{x: 3 < x \le 6\} = (3, 6]$.

Example 5   Let $T = \{x: |x - 2| > 1 \text{ or } |x - 4| \leq 2\}$.

In the notation of Example 4, $T = \{x: x \in A \text{ or } x \in B\}$. Remember that this means that $x \in T$ if, and only if, x belongs to *at least one* of the sets A and B. The graphs of A and B indicate that $T = \{x: x < 1 \text{ or } x \geq 2\}$.

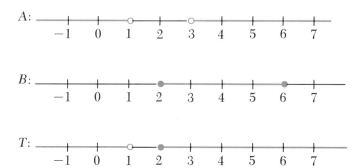

One word of warning: T cannot be described as $\{x: 1 > x \geq 2\}$, because there is in fact *no* number x that satisfies both the condition $1 > x$ and the condition $x \geq 2$.

EXERCISES

1. Graph each of the solution sets found in Exercise 3 of Section 1.3.
2. Obtain a graphical solution of each of the following conditions. State both the problem and your solution in terms of sets.
   (a) $x \geq 1$ and $x > 2$.
   (b) $x \geq 1$ or $x > 2$.
   (c) $-3 < x < 0$ and $-4 \leq x \leq -2$.
   (d) $-3 < x < 0$ or $-4 \leq x \leq -2$.
   (e) $-1 < x \leq 1$ and $-2 < x \leq 3$.
   (f) $-1 < x \leq 1$ or $-2 < x \leq 3$.
   (g) $x < 1$ or $x \geq 3$, and $-2 \leq x < 0$ or $2 < x < 5$.
   (h) $0 \leq x \leq 2$ and $x < 1$, or $x \geq 3$ and $x > 4$.
   (i) $x \leq 2$, or $x > -1$, or $-4 \leq x < 3$.
3. Graph each of the following sets.
   (a) $\{x: -1 < x \leq 2\}$
   (b) $\{z: |z + 2| > 1\}$
   (c) $\{y: |y - 3| < 4\}$
   (d) $\{t: |t - 2| \leq 1 \text{ or } |t + 1| < 2\}$
   (e) $\{x: |x + 2| > 2 \text{ and } |x - 1| < 1\}$

   (f) $\{x: |x| < 3 \text{ and } |x - 4| \leq 2\}$
   (g) $\{a: |a - 2| \geq 4 \text{ or } |a + 1| \leq 1\}$
   (h) $\{b: |2b - 3| < 3b\}$
4. If $a \in R$ and $d \leq 0$, what is $\{x: |x - a| \geq d\}$?
5. Is there any difference between $\{x: |x - 1| < 2\}$ and $\{x: 0 < |x - 1| < 2\}$?
6. Suppose $a < b$, and c is any point of (a, b). Find a positive number d so that $\{x: |x - c| < d\}$ is a subset of (a, b). Does the same result hold for an arbitrary point c of $[a, b]$?
7. Show that any closed interval $[a, b]$ can be written in the form $[c - d, c + d]$ for a suitable choice of numbers c and d.
8. Graph $\{x: \text{if } 0 < x < 2, \text{ then } |x + 3| < 4\}$.
   Hint: Which numbers do *not* belong to this set?

■ 1.6 Properties of Absolute Value

In this section appear some of the results that are indispensable in working with absolute values. They should be learned thoroughly, as should the results of Exercises 7, 8, and 9 of Section 1.4.

The first theorem states the fundamental relationships between absolute value and the operation of multiplication.

THEOREM 1.6.1
(i) If $x \in R$, then $|x| = \sqrt{x^2}$.
(ii) If $x \in R$ and $y \in R$, then $|xy| = |x||y|$.

REMEMBER If $t \geq 0$, then $\sqrt{t}$ denotes the *nonnegative* square root of t, *i.e.*, the unique number r such that $r \geq 0$ and $r^2 = t$.

PROOF **(i)** If $x \in R$, then $|x|$ is a square root of x^2, because $|x|^2 = x^2$ if $x \geq 0$, and $|x|^2 = (-x)^2 = x^2$ if $x < 0$. But also $|x| \geq 0$ (Exercise 7 of Section 1.4). Hence, $|x| = \sqrt{x^2}$.

(ii) $|xy| = \sqrt{(xy)^2} = \sqrt{x^2 y^2} = \sqrt{x^2}\sqrt{y^2} = |\underline{x}||y|$.

The next result states the basic connection between absolute value and the operation of addition. Its technical importance will be seen in Section 1.7.

THEOREM 1.6.2 If $x \in R$ and $y \in R$, then $|x + y| \leq |x| + |y|$.

PROOF Since both $|x + y| \geq 0$ and $|x| + |y| \geq 0$, it follows by Exercises 5 and 12 of Section 1.3 that

$$|x + y| \leq |x| + |y| \quad \text{if, and only if,} \quad |x + y|^2 \leq (|x| + |y|)^2.$$

Now, Theorem 1.6.1 implies that

$$(|x| + |y|)^2 - |x + y|^2 = |x|^2 + 2|x||y| + |y|^2 - (x + y)^2$$

$$= x^2 + 2|xy| + y^2 - (x^2 + 2xy + y^2)$$

$$= 2\,(|xy| - xy).$$

But $xy \leq |xy|$, by Exercise 9 of Section 1.4.

Hence, $$(|x| + |y|)^2 - |x + y|^2 \leq 0,$$

so, $$|x + y|^2 \leq (|x| + |y|)^2,$$

and $|x + y| \leq |x| + |y|$ follows.

This theorem in combination with some of the results of Section 1.4 yield some properties of distance on a coordinate line.

THEOREM 1.6.3

(i)   If $x \in R$ and $y \in R$, then $|x - y| \geq 0$, and $|x - y| = 0$ if, and only if, $x = y$.

(ii) If $x \in R$ and $y \in R$, then $|x - y| = |y - x|$

(iii) If $x \in R$, $y \in R$, and $z \in R$, then $|x - z| \leq |x - y| + |y - z|$.

PROOF **(i)** That $|x - y| \geq 0$ follows from Exercise 7 of Section 1.4, and since the statement $|x - y| = 0$ is clearly equivalent to $x - y = 0$, it is also equivalent to $x = y$.

(ii) Since $x - y = -(y - x)$, the result is a direct consequence of Exercise 8 of Section 1.4.

(iii) This follows from Theorem 1.6.2 by replacing x by $x - y$ and y by $y - z$ in the statement of that theorem.

It is important to learn what these theorems say about absolute value. But learning does not consist of memorizing alone.

For example, suppose you have memorized the statement of Theorem 1.6.1 (i):

$$\text{If } x \in R, \text{ then } |x| = \sqrt{x^2}.$$

Now, suppose you encounter the expression

$$\sqrt{(1 - 3t)^2}, \text{ where } t \in R.$$

If you conclude that

$$\sqrt{(1 - 3t)^2} = 1 - 3t.$$

then you have *not* learned what Theorem 1.6.1 (i) says. You *can* reason that

$$\text{If } t \in R, \text{ then also } 1 - 3t \in R,$$

so Theorem 1.6.1 (i) implies that

$$\sqrt{(1 - 3t)^2} = |1 - 3t|.$$

Similarly, one cannot expect that the only time Theorem 1.6.2 applies is in connection with the expression $|x + y|$. Indeed, in the proof of Theorem 1.6.3 (iii), we applied Theorem 1.6.2 to the expression $|(x - y) + (y - z)|$, realizing that if x, y, and z are real numbers, then so are $x - y$ and $y - z$, so Theorem 1.6.2 applies.

The point is that these theorems say things about *all* real numbers, and until this is realized, the theorems are going to be fairly useless to you. It may help you to rephrase these results in your own words without using any symbols at all, e.g.,

"The absolute value of the product of any two real numbers is the product of the absolute values of the numbers" is such a restatement of Theorem 1.6.1 (ii).

Finding solution sets of equations and inequalities that involve absolute values can be facilitated by using these theorems, and also by the device of squaring expressions in order to eliminate absolute value signs. The latter technique must be used with extreme care, however, as the following example shows.

Example 1   Solve $|x + 1| = x$ for x.

If $|x + 1| = x$, then $(x + 1)^2 = |x + 1|^2 = x^2$, so $2x + 1 = 0$ and $x = -1/2$. This shows that the only *possible* solution is $x = -1/2$. But if $x = -1/2$, then $|x + 1| = |-1/2 + 1| = |1/2| = 1/2 \neq x$. Hence, the only possible solution has been eliminated, so the equation has *no* solutions.

Example 2   Solve $|2t - 5| \leq |3t + 1|$ for t.

In this case, since $|2t - 5| \geq 0$ and $|3t + 1| \geq 0$ no matter what t is, the inequality may be solved by squaring each of its members. That is, by Exercises 5 and 12 of Section 1.3, t is a solution if, and only if,

$$|2t - 5|^2 \leq |3t + 1|^2.$$

But this is equivalent to

$$(2t - 5)^2 \leq (3t + 1)^2.$$

This inequality can be solved by performing the indicated squaring operations, combining like terms, and factoring the result. It is easier, however, to notice that the difference $(3t + 1)^2 - (2t - 5)^2$ is the difference of squares, so it can be factored immediately. Thus, one may proceed as follows:

$$(3t + 1)^2 - (2t - 5)^2 \geq 0,$$
$$[(3t + 1) - (2t - 5)][(3t + 1) + (2t - 5)] \geq 0,$$
$$(t + 6)(5t - 4) \geq 0.$$

Hence, t is a solution if, and only if, $t \geq 4/5$ or $t \leq -6$.

Example 3   Solve $|2b - 3| < 3b$. This is Exercise 3(h) of Section 1.5, and it is likely that there were some differences of opinion as to what the answer was.

Here is an erroneous "solution":

CASE 1 $2b - 3 < 3b$.

Then $b > -3$.

CASE 2 $-(2b - 3) < 3b$.

Then $b > \frac{3}{5}$.

Thus, b is a solution if, and only if, $b > -3$ or $b > 3/5$, which is the same as saying $b > -3$. But this is absurd, since for example, $b = -2$ is clearly not a solution.

The trouble with the "solution" is that in Case 1, it should also be asserted that $2b - 3 \geq 0$, and in Case 2 that $2b - 3 < 0$. Thus, a proper solution is as follows:

CASE 1 $2b - 3 \geq 0$ and $2b - 3 < 3b$.

This means $b \geq \frac{3}{2}$ and $b > -3$, i.e., $b \geq \frac{3}{2}$.

CASE 2 $2b - 3 < 0$ and $-(2b - 3) < 3b$.

This means $b < \frac{3}{2}$ and $b > \frac{3}{5}$, i.e., $\frac{3}{5} < b < \frac{3}{2}$.

Hence, the solution set is $\{b : b \geq \frac{3}{2}$ or $\frac{3}{5} < b < \frac{3}{2}\}$, which is just $\{b : \frac{3}{5} < b\} = (\frac{3}{5}, \infty)$.

The "squaring" device can also be used to obtain a solution, but once again care must be taken. For b is a solution if and only if

$$(2b - 3)^2 < (3b)^2 \quad and \quad b \geq 0. \qquad \text{(Why?)}$$

Simplification gives

$$b \geq 0, \quad \text{and either} \quad b > 3/5 \quad \text{or} \quad b < -3,$$

which boils down to $b > 3/5$.

It is hoped that the examples of Section 1.5 and this section have made the following clear:

(I)   Being able to use results such as Theorem 1.5.1 that relate algebraic statements to the geometry of the line can simplify the solving of an algebra problem.

(II)   In more complicated problems such as those in this section, finding a solution is hopeless unless one knows the definitions of the basic concepts and has a working knowledge of what the theorems say about those concepts.

These two principles apply not only to the ideas met in this chapter, but to those that follow in the reader's future encounter with mathematics.

EXERCISES

1. Restate each of Theorems 1.6.1, 1.6.2, and 1.6.3 in your own words without using symbols.
2. Solve each equation.
   (a) $|x - 1| = 2x$
   (b) $|x - 3| = -2x$
   (c) $|t + 4| = t$
   (d) $|4y - 1| = |2y + 5|$
   (e) $|3x + 2| - |x + 1| = 0$
   (f) $|a| + a^2 = 0$
   (g) $||b| - 2| = b$
   (h) $|3x - 1| = |x| + |2x - 1|$
   (i) $|2t - 3| = |5t - 1| + |3t + 2|$
3. Solve each inequality, and graph the solution set.
   (a) $|1 - x| > |x|$
   (b) $|5t - 3| \le 2|t|$
   (c) $|1 - 4x| \le x$
   (d) $|7u - 6| > u$
   (e) $|2 - 3c| \le 4c + 2$
   (f) $|x| \le -x$
   (g) $|t + 3| > t + 3$
   (h) $t - \sqrt{t^2} \ge 0$

4. What is $\{x : x \in R,$ and if $|x + 1| > 2,$ then $x > 2\}$?
5. Prove or disprove: If $x \in R$ and $y \in R$, then $|x - y| \le |x + y|$.
°6. Show that if x and y are real, then the following statements are true.
   (a) $|x - y| \le |x| + |y|$
   (b) $|x - y| \ge |x| - |y|$
   (c) $|x - y| \ge ||x| - |y||$
   (d) If $y \ne 0$, then $|x/y| = |x|/|y|$
7. Exactly which numbers satisfy $|x + y| = |x| + |y|$?
   Hint: Look at the proof of Theorem 1.6.2.
8. Use mathematical induction to prove that if n is a positive integer, and $x_0, x_1, \ldots, x_n$ are real numbers, then
   (a) $|x_0 + x_1 + \cdots + x_n| \le |x_0| + |x_1| + \cdots + |x_n|$;
   (b) $|x_0 x_1 \cdots x_n| = |x_0||x_1| \cdots |x_n|$.

■ 1.7 Estimation (optional)

We conclude our formal discussion of absolute values and inequalities with some examples of the problem of estimating the size of one quantity in terms of the size of a given quantity.

Example 1   Suppose x is a number such that $|x - 1| < 3$. What can be inferred about $|x + 1|$?

There are two ways of arriving at an answer.

METHOD 1   If $|x - 1| < 3$, then $-2 < x < 4$, by (i) of Theorem 1.5.1. Therefore, $-1 < x + 1 < 5$, so $-5 < x + 1 < 5$ as well. Hence, $|x + 1| < 5$.

METHOD 2   For *any* real number x, $|x + 1| = |(x - 1) + 2| \le |x - 1| + |2|$, by Theorem 1.6.2. Thus, if $|x - 1| < 3$, then $|x + 1| < 3 + 2 = 5$.

Each method requires a tricky observation. In the first one, we have to notice that $-1 < x + 1 < 5$ implies $-5 < x + 1 < 5$ in order to conclude something about $|x + 1|$; in the second, we have to express $x + 1$ in terms of $x - 1$ before proceeding. The advantage of Method 2 is that it gives more information than Method 1, for it is seen that $|x + 1| \le |x - 1| + 2$ for *any* real number x. The expression $|x - 1| + 2$ is called an upper estimate of $|x + 1|$ in terms of $|x - 1|$. (In general, a quantity b is an **upper estimate** of a quantity a in case $a \le b$.)

A more complicated example shows that Method 2 can save some detail work.

Example 2   If $|x + 2| < 0.1$, what can be said about $|x^2 - 4|$?

METHOD 1   If $|x + 2| < 0.1$, then $-2.1 < x < -1.9$. Since $-1.9 < 0$, we have $3.61 < x^2 < 4.41$. Hence, $-.39 < x^2 - 4 < .41$, so $-.41 < x^2 - 4 < .41$ as well. Therefore, $|x^2 - 4| < .41$.

METHOD 2   For *any* real number x,

$$
\begin{aligned}
|x^2 - 4| &= |(x + 2)(x - 2)| \\
&= |x + 2||x - 2| \\
&= |x + 2||(x + 2) - 4| \\
&\le |x + 2|(|x + 2| + |-4|), \quad \text{by Theorem 1.6.2.}
\end{aligned}
$$

In particular, if $|x + 2| < 0.1$, then

$$
|x^2 - 4| < (.1)(.1 + 4) = .41.
$$

In Method 2, the first crucial step is writing $x - 2$ in terms of $x + 2$. In the step following, one must be careful to apply Theorem 1.6.2 correctly, remembering that $|(x + 2) - 4| \le |x + 2| - |4|$ is not true, in general.

Here is an example of the use of this technique in estimating the error in a physical measurement.

Example 3   In Example 8 of Section 1.3, it was shown that if we have a ruler that measures lengths to the nearest tenth of an inch, and a side L of a square is measured as 3.2 inches, then the area L^2 of the square is $(3.2)^2$ square inches, with an error of at most 0.3225 square inches.

Suppose we turn the problem around, and ask how accurately we must be able to measure lengths in order that taking the length L of a side of a square as 3.2 inches guarantees that the area of the square is $(3.2)^2$ square inches, with an error of at most 0.01 square inches. The algebraic problem, then, is that of finding a positive number d such that

$$
|L - 3.2| \le d \quad \text{implies} \quad |L^2 - (3.2)^2| \le 0.01.
$$

Thus, d is a "solution" to the problem if measuring $L = 3.2$ inches with an error of at most d inches implies the error in taking L^2 as $(3.2)^2$ square inches is at most 0.01 square inches.

Now, no matter what L actually is,

$$|L^2 - (3.2)^2| = |(L + 3.2)(L - 3.2)|$$
$$= |L + 3.2| \, |L - 3.2|$$
$$= |(L - 3.2) + 6.4| \, |L - 3.2|$$
$$\leq (|L - 3.2| + 6.4)(|L - 3.2|).$$

Then, no matter what $d > 0$ is, if $|L - 3.2| \leq d$, then

$$|L^2 - (3.2)^2| \leq (d + 6.4)(d).$$

At this stage, we could find a positive number d such that

$$(d + 6.4)d = 0.01,$$

and d would be a solution to the problem. We certainly want to be able to measure length with an error of at most one inch, however, so we may assume that $0 < d \leq 1$.

In this case, we have

$$(d + 6.4)d \leq (1 + 6.4)d = 7.4d,$$

and $7.4d \leq 0.01$ if, for example, $d = .001$.

Hence, if we can measure length with an error of at most .001 of an inch, and the side L of a square is measured as 3.2 inches, so that $|L - 3.2| \leq .001$, then $|L^2 - (3.2)^2| \leq .01$, that is, the actual area L^2 differs from $(3.2)^2$ by at most .01 square inches.

Example 4   Find an upper estimate of $|1/(x - 3)|$ under the condition $|x - 1| < 1/2$.

If we attempt to use Method 2, we find that

$$|x - 3| = |(x - 1) - 2| \leq |x - 1| + |-2| < \frac{5}{2}$$

if

$$|x - 1| < \frac{1}{2}.$$

Hence,

$$\left| \frac{1}{x - 3} \right| = \frac{1}{|x - 3|} > \frac{1}{5/2},$$

which is no help at all.

However, Exercise 6(c) of Section 1.6 is useful here.

$$|x - 3| = |(x - 1) - 2| \geq ||x - 1| - |2||$$
$$\geq 2 - |x - 1|$$
$$\geq 2 - 1/2 = 3/2,$$

if

$$|x - 1| < 1/2.$$

Therefore,

$$\left|\frac{1}{x-3}\right| = \frac{1}{|x-3|} < \frac{1}{3/2} = \frac{2}{3} \quad \text{if} \quad |x-1| < \frac{1}{2}.$$

EXERCISES

1. Use Method 2 to show each of the following.
   (a) $|x-4| \le |x-3| + 1$
   (b) $|x+5| \le |x+2| + 3$
   (c) $|4x-1| \le 4|x+1| + 5$
   (d) $|3x+5| \le 3|x-1| + 8$

2. Find an upper estimate of each of the following in terms of $|x-1|$.
   (a) $|2x+3|$ (c) $|3x+4|$
   (b) $|x|$ (d) $|3x^2 + x - 4|$

3. Use Method 2 to show that
   (a) If $|x-3| < 1/2$, then $|x^2 - 9| < 13/4$.
   (b) If $|x-3| < d$, then $|x^2 - 9| < d(d+6)$.
   (c) If $|x-1| < d$, then $|3x^2 + x - 4| < d(3d + 7)$.
   (d) If $|x-1| < d$, and $0 < d \le 1$, then $|3x^2 + x - 4| < 10d$.
   (e) If $|x+2| < d$, then $|5x^2 + 9x - 2| < d(5d + 11)$.
   (f) If $|x+2| < d$, and $0 < d \le 1$, then $|5x^2 + 9x - 2| < 16d$.

4. (a) Find an upper estimate of $|3x^2 + x - 10|$ in terms of $|x+2|$.
   (b) Use the result of (a) to show that if $|x+2| < d$ and $0 < d \le 1$, then $|3x^2 + x - 10| < 14d$.
   (c) Find a positive number d so that if $|x+2| < d$, then $|3x^2 + x - 10| < .07$.

5. (a) Find an upper estimate of $|2x^2 + 5x - 3|$ in terms of $|x - 1/2|$.
   (b) Use the result of (a) to show that if $|x - 1/2| < d$ and $0 < d \le 1$, then $|2x^2 + 5x - 3| < 9d$.
   (c) Find a positive number d such that if $|x - 1/2| < d$, then $|2x^2 + 5x - 3| < .027$.

6. Use the pattern of Exercises 4 and 5 to find a positive number d so that if $|x+1| < d$, then $|4x^2 - x - 5| < .0039$.

7. Use Exercise 6(c) of Section 1.6 to show that if $|x| < 2/3$, then
   (a) $|2/(x+1)| < 6$
   (b) $|1/(x-2)| < 3/4$.

8. Can Method 2 be used to find an upper estimate of $|x^2 - x + 1|$ in terms of $|x+1|$?

9. Show that it is impossible to find a number $d > 0$ such that if $|x| < d$, then $|x^2 - 4| < 1$.

10. Can you find an upper estimate of $|1/(x-1)|$ under the condition than $|x| < 1$?

CHAPTER 2

PLANE COORDINATE SYSTEMS

■ 2.1 Coordinates in the Plane

In Section 1.4 the notion of a coordinate system on a line was introduced, and by use of a natural coordinate system it was seen that algebraic relationships could be characterized geometrically and geometric properties described algebraically. The benefits of this type of interplay between algebra and geometry will come into much sharper focus when a coordinate system is introduced in the plane.

The most common way to coordinatize a plane is to select a horizontal line and endow it with a natural coordinate system. This line, to be denoted by H, is called the **horizontal axis** (or **first coordinate axis**, or **axis of abscissas**). On the point of H having coordinate 0 construct a line V perpendicular to H and give it a natural coordinate system with 0 corresponding to the point of intersection of H and V, the points with positive coordinates lying above H, and with V having its unit segment congruent to the unit segment of H. The line V is called the **vertical axis** (or **second coordinate axis**, or **axis of ordinates**), and the point of intersection of H and V is called the **origin**. For any point P in the plane, construct the line through P perpendicular to H. Its point of intersection with H is called the **projection of P on H,** and the coordinate of this point, say a, is called the **horizontal coordinate** (or **first coordinate**, or **abscissa**) of P. Similarly, the coordinate of the **projection of P on V,** say b, is called the **vertical coordinate** (or **second coordinate** or **ordinate**) of P. Thus, to each point P in the plane there corresponds a unique

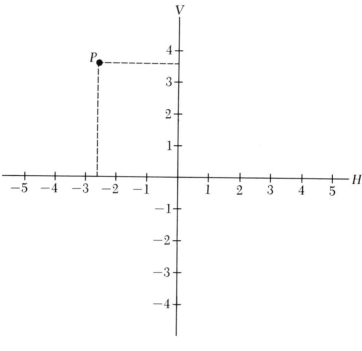

Figure 1

ordered pair (a, b) of real numbers, called the **coordinates** of P. Conversely, given any ordered pair (c, d) of real numbers, there corresponds a unique point Q in the plane having (c, d) as its coordinates, namely, the point of intersection of the vertical and horizontal lines through the points of H and V with coordinates c, d, respectively. Several examples are given in Figure 2. This type of correspondence between points and ordered pairs of numbers is called a **natural coordinate system** for the plane.

A coordinate system for the plane identifies each point, a geometric object, with an ordered pair of numbers, an algebraic object. Consistent with our attempt to combine algebra and geometry and with the agreement made for coordinate systems on a line, no distinction will be made between a point and its coordinates. Thus, if (a, b) are coordinates of a point, we write $P = (a, b)$ and think of (a, b) either as a point or an ordered pair of numbers, depending on whether we want to emphasize geometric or algebraic aspects of the situation.

Points on the coordinate axes have the distinction of possessing coordinates, both as points of the plane and points of the line. If P is a point of H with coordinate a, then as a point of the plane it has coordinates $(a, 0)$.

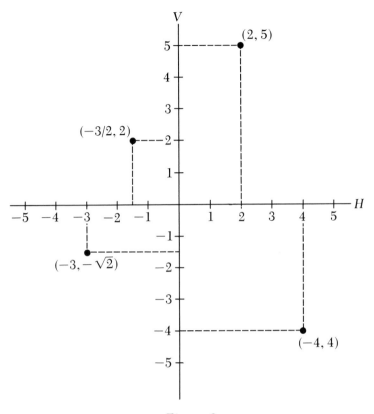

Figure 2

If a point Q has coordinate b considered as a point of V, then it has coordinates $(0, b)$ when considered as a point in the plane. This property, besides being necessary in coordinatizing the plane, will prove to be very useful.

   Two points are on the same vertical line if and only if they have the same projection on H and consequently the same horizontal coordinate. Hence, the vertical line L through the point $P = (c, d)$ can be described algebraically by

$$L = \{(x, y) : x = c\}.$$

Similarly, the horizontal line L' through $P = (c, d)$ is

$$L' = \{(x, y) : y = d\}.$$

In the case of the coordinate axes this means

$$H = \{(x, y) : y = 0\}$$

and $$V = \{(x, y) : x = 0\}.$$

(See Figure 3.)

It is now possible to compute the distance between any two points of the plane, or equivalently, the length of the line segment joining them. If P and Q are points, the juxtaposition of P and Q, PQ, will denote the line segment

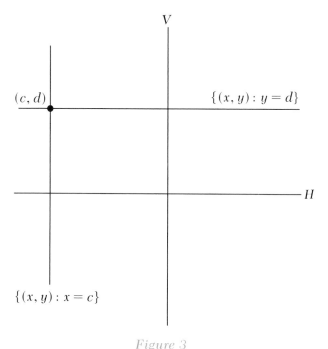

Figure 3

connecting them and $|PQ|$ will denote the length of the segment or distance between the points. Beginning with a special case, suppose P and Q lie on the same horizontal line, say $P = (x_1, y_1)$ and $Q = (x_2, y_1)$. The projections of P and Q on H are $P' = (x_1, 0)$ and $Q' = (x_2, 0)$ respectively. As points on the coordinate line H, P' and Q' have coordinates x_1 and x_2 respectively, and from Theorem 1.4.1,

$$|P'Q'| = |x_2 - x_1|.$$

Since PQ and $P'Q'$ are opposite sides of a rectangle,

$$|PQ| = |P'Q'| = |x_2 - x_1|.$$

See Figure 4. Similarly, if S and T are points on the same vertical line, say $S = (a_1, b_1)$, $T = (a_1, b_2)$, then

$$|ST| = |b_2 - b_1|.$$

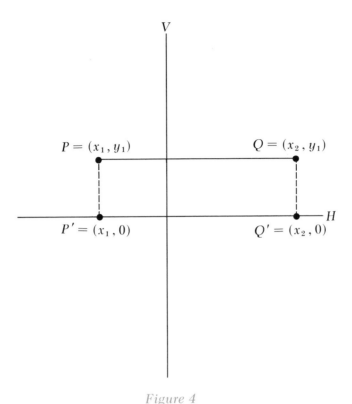

Figure 4

Now, if $P = (x_1, y_1)$ and $Q = (x_2, y_2)$ are not both on the same line parallel to a coordinate axis, then the horizontal line through P and the vertical line through Q will meet in the point $T = (x_2, y_1)$ and P, Q, T are vertices of a right triangle. (See Figure 5.) Then $|PT| = |x_2 - x_1|$ and $|TQ| = |y_2 - y_1|$. Hence, from the Pythagorean Theorem,

$$|PQ| = \sqrt{|PT|^2 + |TQ|^2} = \sqrt{|x_2 - x_1|^2 + |y_2 - y_1|^2}$$

or equivalently,

$$|PQ| = \sqrt{(x_2 - x_1)^2 + (y_2 - y_1)^2}.$$

Notice that this formula gives correct results even if P and Q lie on the same line parallel to a coordinate axis. To emphasize the importance of this result, we state it as a theorem.

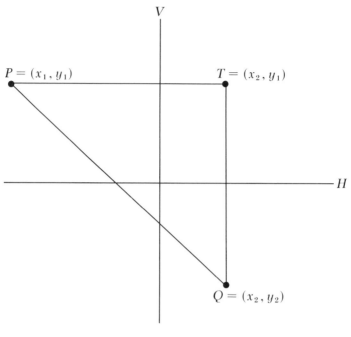

Figure 5

THEOREM 2.1.1   If $P = (x_1, y_1)$ and $Q = (x_2, y_2)$ are any points in a natural coordinate plane, then

$$|PQ| = \sqrt{(x_2 - x_1)^2 + (y_2 - y_1)^2}.$$

Example 1   Find the distance between the points $P = (-5, 2)$ and $Q = (1, 7)$.

$$|PQ| = \sqrt{(1 - (-5))^2 + (7 - 2)^2} = \sqrt{6^2 + 5^2} = \sqrt{61}.$$

Example 2   Find the distance d between $(4, -8)$ and $(0, -8)$.

$$d = \sqrt{(4 - 0)^2 + (-8 + 8)^2} = 4.$$

Example 3   Find all points on the horizontal axis that are equidistant from $S = (1, -2)$ and $T = (3, 5)$.

If P is such a point then $P = (x, 0)$ for some number x and $|PT| = |PS|$.

$$|PT| = \sqrt{(x - 3)^2 + (0 - 5)^2} = \sqrt{(x - 1)^2 + (0 + 2)^2} = |PS|.$$

If we square both sides and solve for x we find that $x = \frac{29}{4}$. Thus, *if* there is a solution it must be the point $P = (\frac{29}{4}, 0)$. That this is in fact a solution (and hence the only solution) is verified by substitution.

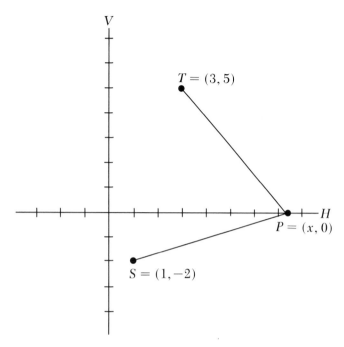

Figure 6

Example 4 Give an algebraic description of the perpendicular bisector of the line segment with endpoints $A = (0, 1)$ and $B = (2. 3)$.

From our knowledge of geometry we know that the perpendicular bisector of the line segment AB is the set of all points that are equidistant from A and B. If L denotes the perpendicular bisector, then $L = \{P\colon P$ is a point of the plane and $|PA| = |PB|\}$.

Now, for $P = (x, y)$ in L,

$$\sqrt{(x - 0)^2 + (y - 1)^2} = \sqrt{(x - 2)^2 + (y - 3)^2}.$$

We square and simplify to obtain $x + y = 3$ or $y = -x + 3$.

Hence, $L \subset \{(x, y)\colon x + y = 3\} = \{(x, y)\colon y = -x + 3\}$.

Hopefully, we can replace set inclusion by equality. To determine this let

$$Q = (x, y)$$

be any point for which $y = -x + 3$,

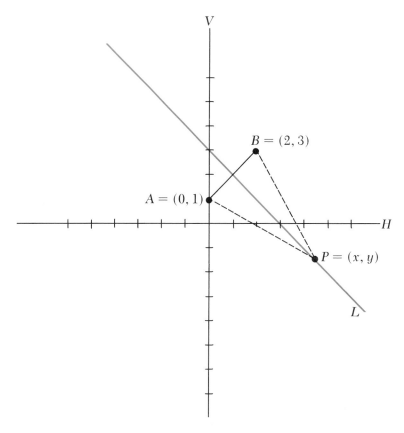

Figure 7

so that $\qquad\qquad\qquad Q = (x, -x + 3)$.

Then $\qquad\qquad |QA| = \sqrt{(x - 0)^2 + (-x + 3 - 1)^2} = \sqrt{2x^2 - 4x + 4}$

and $\qquad\qquad |QB| = \sqrt{(x - 2)^2 + (-x + 3 - 3)^2} = \sqrt{2x^2 - 4x + 4}$

so $|QA| = |QB|$ and $Q \in L$. That is $\{(x, y) : x + y = 3\} \subset L$ and consequently

$$\{(x, y) : x + y = 3\} = L.$$

This description of L affords an easy test to decide whether or not any given point $C = (a, b)$ is a point of the line L.

For example, $\qquad (7, -4) \in L \quad$ because $\quad 7 + (-4) = 3$,

whereas $\qquad\qquad (-6, 5) \notin L \quad$ because $\quad (-6) + 5 = -1 \neq 3$.

EXERCISES

1. Compute the distances between each of the following pairs of points.
   (a) $(1, -1)$ and $(4, 2)$
   (b) $(6, 11)$ and $(3/2, 0)$
   (c) $(\pi, 1)$ and $(4, 3)$
   (d) $(8/7, 1/4)$ and $(4/3, 1/4)$

°2. Describe geometrically each of the following sets.
   (a) $\mathrm{I} = \{(a, b) : a > 0 \text{ and } b > 0\}$
   (b) $\mathrm{II} = \{(c, d) : c < 0 \text{ and } d > 0\}$
   (c) $\mathrm{III} = \{(p, q) : p < 0 \text{ and } q < 0\}$
   (d) $\mathrm{IV} = \{(h, k) : k < 0 \text{ and } h > 0\}$

   By what names are these sets commonly known?

3. Plot the points $A = (1, 1)$, $B = (-1, -1)$ and $C = (-4, 2)$ in a coordinate plane.
   (a) Show that they are vertices of a right triangle. (*Hint:* Use the converse of the Pythagorean Theorem).
   (b) Find a point $D = (x, y)$ such that $ABCD$ is a rectangle.

4. (a) Find the distance between the point $(4, -3)$ and
      (i)   the horizontal axis.
      (ii) the vertical axis.
   (b) Find the distance between the point $(-7, 1)$ and
      (i)   the horizontal axis.
      (ii) the vertical axis.
   (c) Find the distance between the point (a, b) and
      (i)   the horizontal axis.
      (ii) the vertical axis.
   (d) Find the distance between the point $(2, 3)$ and
      (i)   the line
            $L_1 = \{(x, y) : x = 5\}$
      (ii) the line
            $L_2 = \{(x, y) : y = -3\}$.
   (e) Find the distance between the

   point (a, b) and
   (i)   the line
         $L_1 = \{(x, y) : x = c\}$
   (ii) the line
         $L_2 = \{(x, y) : y = d\}$.

5. Give an algebraic description of the (i) horizontal (ii) vertical line through these points.
   (a) $(2, -5)$ (c) $(7, 0)$
   (b) $(-6, 3)$ (d) $(0, -2)$

6. What points, if any, on the vertical axis are equidistant from the points $(1, 7)$ and $(2, 3)$?

7. Find a point on the line L of Example 4 that is equidistant from the points $(0, 0)$ and $(-1, -2)$.

8. If $A = (2, 3)$ and $B = (-2, 1)$, find the coordinates of the midpoint of the line segment AB.

°9. If $A = (x_1, y_1)$ and $B = (x_2, y_2)$, show that the midpoint of the line segment AB is

$$\left(\frac{x_1 + x_2}{2}, \frac{y_1 + y_2}{2} \right).$$

Use this formula to check your answer in Exercise 8. Try the formula with several other line segments. In each case plot the points to see if your answer is plausible.

10. Let $A = (-2, -1)$, $B = (1, -3)$, $C = (2, 7)$ and $D = (0, 1)$, and consider the quadrilateral $ABCD$.
   (a) Find the midpoint of each side.
   (b) Show that the midpoints of the sides are vertices of a parallelogram. (Recall that a quadrilateral in a plane is a parallelogram if and only if opposite sides have equal length).
   (c) Show that the midpoints of the sides of any quadrilateral in the plane are vertices of a parallelogram.

11. Let $A = (1, 7)$, $B = (4, -2)$, $C = (-1, 2 - \sqrt{21})$, and $D = (3, 2 + \sqrt{21})$.

(a) Show that each of these points is on a circle with center $(1, 2)$.

(b) What is the radius of the circle?

(c) Show that CD is a diameter of the circle.

(d) Find points $U = (u, v)$ and $S = (s, t)$ such that AU and BS are diameters of the circle.

(e) At what points does the line $L' = \{(x, y) : x = 4\}$ intersect the circle?

(f) For each point P found in (e) determine the point Q so that PQ is a diameter of the circle.

(g) Work parts (e) and (f) for the line $L = \{(x, y) : x + y = 3\}$.

12. Find an algebraic description of the perpendicular bisector of the line segment AB, if

(a) $A = (-1, 2)$ and $B = (1, -2)$.

(b) $A = (-1, 3)$ and $B = (2, 2)$.

13. In Exercise 12, you should have obtained the set $L_1 = \{(x, y) : x - 2y = 0\}$ for the answer to part (a), and the set $L_2 = \{(x, y) : 3x - y + 1 = 0\}$ as the answer to part (b).

(a) Which of the following points are in L_1? Which are in L_2? $(14, -2)$, $(0, 0)$, $(7, -5)$, $(1/4, -1/2)$.

(b) Find the points at which L_1 and L_2 intersect the coordinate axes.

(c) Find the point of intersection of L_1 and L_2.

14. Give an algebraic description of the circle with center at the origin and radius 1.

15. Let F be the point $(1, 0)$ and L be the vertical line through the point $(-1, 0)$.

(a) If $P = (x, y)$ is any point in the plane, find $|PF|$.

(b) If $P = (x, y)$, what is the distance between P and L?

(c) What condition must the numbers x and y satisfy in order that the point $P = (x, y)$ is equidistant from the point F and the line L?

(d) Give an algebraic description of the set S of all points which are equidistant from F and L.

16. Let $F_1 = (1, 0)$ and $F_2 = (-1, 0)$ and let $\mathscr{E} = \{P : |PF_1| + |PF_2| = 6\}$. Show that

$$\mathscr{E} = \left\{ (x, y) : \frac{x^2}{9} + \frac{y^2}{8} = 1 \right\}.$$

17. Let $F_1 = (2, 0)$ and $F_2 = (-2, 0)$. Find an algebraic description of the set $\mathscr{H} = \{P : ||PF_1| - |PF_2|| = 2\}$.

■ 2.2 Graphs of Conditions

In Section 1.5 the graph of a set S of numbers was defined to be the set of points on a coordinate line whose coordinates are elements of S. This provided a geometric "picture" of the algebraic object S. The extension of this idea to the plane is supplied by the following definition.

DEFINITION Let S be a set of ordered pairs of real numbers. The **graph** of S is the set of all points in a coordinate plane whose coordinates (ordered pairs of real numbers) are elements of S.

In light of our agreement to identify a point of a natural coordinate plane with its coordinates, it is seen that a set of ordered pairs and its graph are identical except for emphasis—algebraic or geometric. By the graph of a set, then, is meant a geometric description, or "picture," of its elements. Thus, in Example 4 of the previous section it was seen that the graph of the set $\{(x, y): x + y = 3\}$ is the line that is the perpendicular bisector of the line segment connecting the points $(0, 1)$ and $(2, 3)$.

Example 1   What is the graph of the set $C_1 = \{(x, y): x^2 + y^2 = 1\}$?

The point $(x, y) \in C_1$ if and only if $\sqrt{x^2 + y^2} = 1$, or equivalently $\sqrt{(x - 0)^2 + (y - 0)^2} = 1$. This means that (x, y) is a point whose distance from the origin is 1. Hence, the graph of C_1 is the set of all points lying one unit from $(0, 0)$, that is, the circle with center at the point $(0, 0)$ and radius 1. Similarly, the graph of the set

$$C_r = \{(x, y): x^2 + y^2 = r^2\}, \quad \text{where} \quad r > 0,$$

is the circle with center at the origin and radius r. Reversing the above procedure we can ask: The circle C with center at the point $P_0 = (h, k)$ and radius r is the graph of what set? We are asking, then, for an algebraic description of the geometric object C. Using the definition of a circle,

$$C = \{P: |PP_0| = r\} = \{(x, y): \sqrt{(x - h)^2 + (y - k)^2} = r\}$$
$$= \{(x, y): (x - h)^2 + (y - k)^2 = r^2\},$$

since the radius r of a circle is positive.

With this it is seen that the graph of

$$\{(x, y): (x + 1)^2 + (y - 3)^2 = 2\}$$

is the circle with center at $(-1, 3)$ and radius $\sqrt{2}$. The graph of $\{(s, t): s^2 + (t + 5)^2 = 17\}$ is the circle with center $(0, -5)$ and radius $\sqrt{17}$.

To find the graph of $D = \{(x, y): x^2 - 2x + y^2 + y - 3 = 0\}$ we note that this can be put in the form of set C above by completing the squares in x and y. Thus,

$$D = \{(x, y): (x^2 - 2x + 1) + (y^2 + y + \tfrac{1}{4}) = 3 + 1 + \tfrac{1}{4}\}$$
$$= \{(x, y): (x - 1)^2 + (y + \tfrac{1}{2})^2 = \tfrac{17}{4}\}$$

represents the circle with center $(1, -\tfrac{1}{2})$ and radius $\sqrt{17}/2$. The reader should convince himself that the graph of the set $\{(x, y): x^2 + y^2 = 0\}$ is a single point—the origin, and the graph of the set $\{(x, y): (x - 1)^2 + y^2 = -4\}$ is the empty set.

Example 2   Sketch the graph of the set $Z = \{(x, y) : y = \sqrt{1 - x^2}$ if $x \in [0, 1]$ and $x + y = 3$ if $x \notin [0, 1]\}$.

Let $(x, y) \in Z$. If $x \in [0, 1]$ then $x^2 + y^2 = 1$ and $y \geq 0$ so (x, y) is a point on the quarter circle as shown in Figure 1. If $x \notin [0, 1]$ then (x, y) is a point

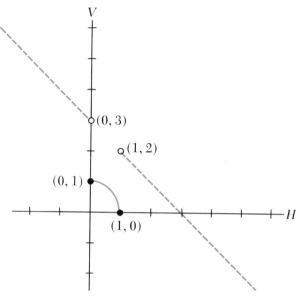

Figure 1

on the line L of Example 4, Section 2.1. Recall the convention introduced for graphs on a line; a solid dot indicates that the point is included, whereas a small circle indicates that the point is not included in the graph. Thus, in Figure 1, the points $(0, 1)$ and $(1, 0)$ are in the graph, the points $(0, 3)$ and $(1, 2)$ are not.

Example 3   Sketch the graph of the set $W = \{(x, y) : x + y \geq 3\}$.

If (x_1, y_1) is in W then $y_1 \geq 3 - x_1$. Since $(x_1, 3 - x_1)$ is a point on the line $L = \{(x, y) : x + y = 3\}$ it is clear that (x_1, y_1) must be a point that is above or on the line L. Conversely, if (x_1, y_1) is above or on L, then its vertical coordinate y_1 is greater than or equal to the vertical coordinate of the point $(x_1, 3 - x_1)$ on L. Therefore, the graph is the set of all points above or on the line L, as is indicated in Figure 2.

Example 4   The graph of $U = \{(x, y) : x + y > 3$ or $x^2 + y^2 < 1\}$ is clearly the set of points above the line L of Example 3 plus the set of points inside

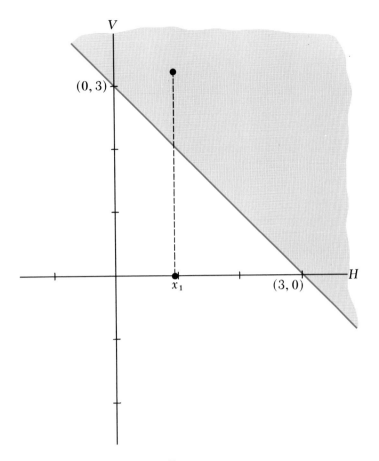

Figure 2

the circle C_1 of Example 1. The set of all points not in U is $W = \{(x, y):$ $x + y \leq 3$ *and* $x^2 + y^2 \geq 1\}$. It is important here to distinguish between *and* and *or*. The point $(x, y) \in U$ provided either $x + y > 3$ or $x^2 + y^2 < 1$ or both. The point $(x, y) \in W$ provided both $x + y \leq 3$ and $x^2 + y^2 \geq 1$. In Figure 3, U is the shaded portion and W is the unshaded portion together with the dashed portion.

In graphing a set S in the plane, if the points on the boundary of S are included in S, the boundary is drawn as a solid curve, whereas if the points on the boundary are not included in S, the boundary is drawn as a dashed curve. (See Figures 2 and 3.)

So far, we have talked about graphs of sets, and in each case the set was determined by some condition. It is often more convenient, or at least

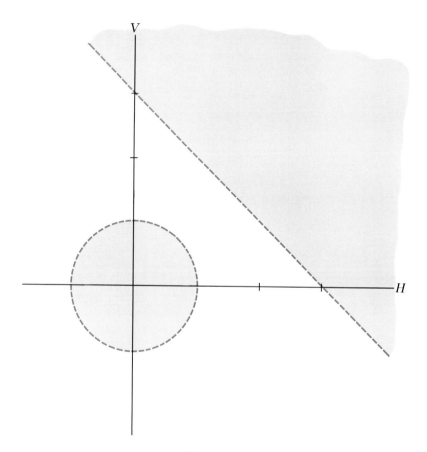

Figure 3

economical, to speak of the graph of the condition and thus avoid the rather "bulky" set notation. Hence, instead of saying that the circle with center $(0, 0)$, radius 4 is the graph of the set $\{(x, y) : x^2 + y^2 = 16\}$, it is simpler to call it the graph of the equation $x^2 + y^2 = 16$. Similarly, the graph of the set W in the previous example is the graph of the simultaneous inequalities $x + y \leq 3$ and $x^2 + y^2 \geq 1$.

There is, however, a potential source of ambiguity in doing this. For example, the graph of the equation

$$(\#) \qquad\qquad (s - 1)^2 + t^2 = 2$$

could mean either the graph of the set $M = \{(s, t) : (s - 1)^2 + t^2 = 2\}$, a circle with center $(1, 0)$ and radius $\sqrt{2}$, or the graph of the set $N = \{(t, s) : t^2 + (s - 1)^2 = 2\}$, a circle with center $(0, 1)$ and radius $\sqrt{2}$. (See Figure 4.)

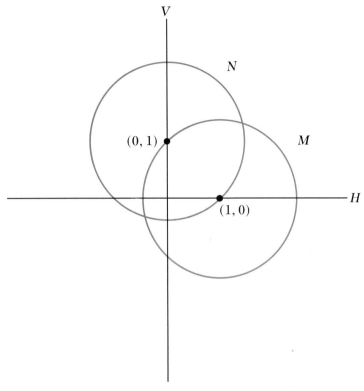

Figure 4

In order to avoid this confusion it is necessary to specify which of the symbols s or t is to represent the horizontal coordinate of points on the graph and which is to represent the vertical coordinate.

There are several prevalent ways of circumventing the problem. One is to write all conditions using the symbols x and y with x always representing the horizontal coordinate. This approach tends to be unduly restrictive and causes at least a minor embarrassment in situations when it is actually more convenient and natural to have x represent the vertical coordinate. A second way, and the one to be used in this book, is to tack on the phrase "in the XY plane" if x is the horizontal and y the vertical coordinate, respectively, or "in the TS plane" if t and s denote the horizontal and vertical coordinates, respectively. For example, the graph of the set M above is the graph of (#) in the ST plane, whereas the graph of N is the graph of (#) in the TS plane. This is often emphasized by labeling the horizontal and vertical axes with the upper case of the letters used to denote the horizontal and vertical coordinates, instead of with H and V respectively (Figure 5).

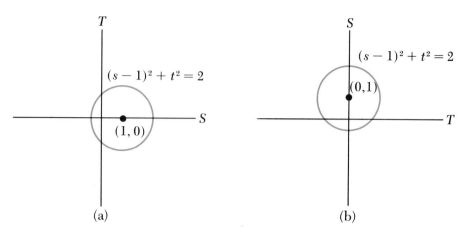

Figure 5

Persisting in our identification of algebraic and geometric objects, we will frequently make such statements as, "the circle $x^2 + y^2 = 1$ in the XY plane" and "the line $s + t = 3$ in the ST plane," meaning, of course, the circle that is the graph in the XY plane of the equation $x^2 + y^2 = 1$ and the line that is the graph in the ST plane of the equation $s + t = 3$.

Example 5   Sketch the graph of the inequality $x > 2$ in the XY plane and in the YX plane.

The graph of the inequality $x > 2$ in the XY plane is the set of points to the right of the line $x = 2$. The graph of this inequality in the YX plane is the set of points above the line $x = 2$. (See Figure 6.)

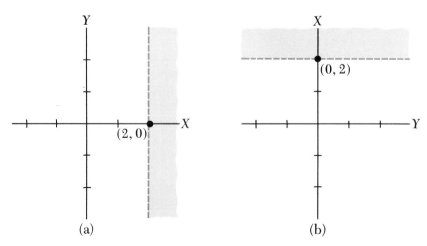

Figure 6

Example 6 Sketch the graph of $u^2 - v - 1 = 0$ in the UV plane.

The method of graphing this equation with which the reader is probably most familiar is to plot points and connect them with a smooth curve, as in Figure 7.

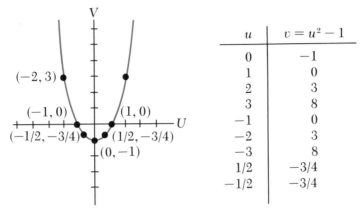

u	$v = u^2 - 1$
0	-1
1	0
2	3
3	8
-1	0
-2	3
-3	8
$1/2$	$-3/4$
$-1/2$	$-3/4$

Figure 7

In sketching the graph in Figure 7 many assumptions were made. Many different graphs could be sketched using only those points that were plotted, those in Figure 8, for example.

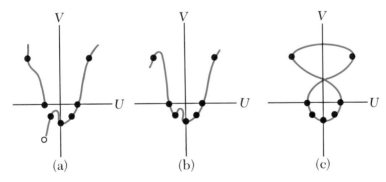

(a)   (b)   (c)

Figure 8

That the sketches in Figure 8 do not represent the graph of the equation could be checked by plotting more points. This would also strengthen our belief that Figure 7 is correct, but could not prove it to be since there are infinitely many points on the graph and we could not possibly list them all.

There are several properties of the graph that could only be guessed at by point plotting. For example, we note that if the point (u, v) is on the graph, then $v = u^2 - 1 \geq -1$, since $u^2 \geq 0$. Hence, no point on the graph lies below the horizontal line $v = -1$. Also, if $0 < u_1 < u_2$ then $u_1^2 - 1 < u_2^2 - 1$. That is, if (u_1, v_1) and (u_2, v_2) are any two points on the graph to the right of the vertical axis, with (u_2, v_2) to the right of (u_1, v_1), then $v_1 < v_2$, which means that (u_2, v_2) is also above (u_1, v_1). Hence, to the right of the vertical axis the graph is "rising." Similarly, the graph is "falling" to the left of the vertical axis. Consequently, the point $(0, -1)$ must be the lowest point on the graph. Finally, if (u_1, v_1) is on the graph, then $v_1 = u_1^2 - 1 = (-u_1)^2 - 1$, so that $(-u_1, v_1)$ is also on the graph. This implies that if we know the portion of the graph to the right of the vertical axis, then we also know the portion of the graph to the left. (Why?)

Example 7 Sketch the graph of $\{(x, y): \text{If } 0 < x < 1, \text{ then } y = 3\}$.

This problem is a bit more tricky than the preceding ones. The reader should refer back to Exercise 8 of Section 1.5. Notice that the condition imposes no restriction on pairs (x, y) unless x is between 0 and 1, in which case y must equal 3. Hence, the only points not on the graph are those whose horizontal coordinate is between 0 and 1 and whose vertical coordinate is different from 3. The graph appears in Figure 9.

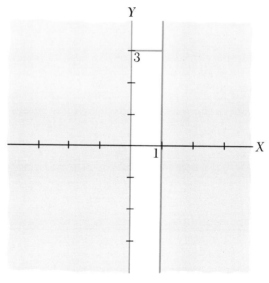

Figure 9

EXERCISES

1. Sketch the graph of each of the following sets.

(a) $\{(f, g) : f^2 + g^2 = 8\}$

(b) $\{(z, w) : (z - 1)^2 + (w + 5)^2 = 4\}$

(c) $\{(x, y) : (x + 1/2)^2 + (y - 3/2)^2 \geq 1/4\}$

(d) $\{(p, q) : pq > 0\}$

(e) $\{(x, y) : x^2 - 3x + y^2 + 4y + 5 = 0\}$

(f) $\{(y, x) : y^2 - 2y + x^2 - 4x \leq 5\}$

(g) $\{(a, b) : 3b^2 + 7b - 2 = 3 + 5a - 3a^2\}$

(h) $\{(x, y) : |y - 2| \leq 1 \quad \text{and}$

$|x + 3| \leq 2\}$

2. Find the sets whose graphs are sketched in Figure 10.

3. Describe each of the graphs in Exercises 1 and 2 as graphs of conditions.

4. Find an equation of each of the following sets in (i) the XY plane, (ii) the ST plane, (iii) the ZW plane.
   (a) The circle with center at the origin, radius 3.
   (b) The circle with center $(-1/2, 1/4)$, radius 2.
   (c) The circle with center $(\pi, \sqrt{2})$, radius $\sqrt[3]{3}$.
   (d) The horizontal axis.
   (e) The vertical axis.
   (f) The line bisecting the first and third quadrants.

*5. Show that the line that bisects the first and third quadrants in the XY plane is the graph of the equation $y = x$. Find an equation of the line that bisects the second and fourth quadrants in the XY plane.

6. Sketch the graph in the XY plane of
   (a) $x^2 = y^2$
   (b) $x^2 > y^2$
   (c) $x^2 < y^2$.

7. Sketch the graph of the equation $y = x^3$ in the XY plane.

8. Sketch the graph of the inequality $u(u^2 + v^2 - 1) > 0$
   (a) in the UV plane.
   (b) in the VU plane.

9. Sketch the graph of the set $\{(c, d) : c^2 + d^2 = 16$ and $c + d = 3\}$.

10. Sketch the graph of the condition:

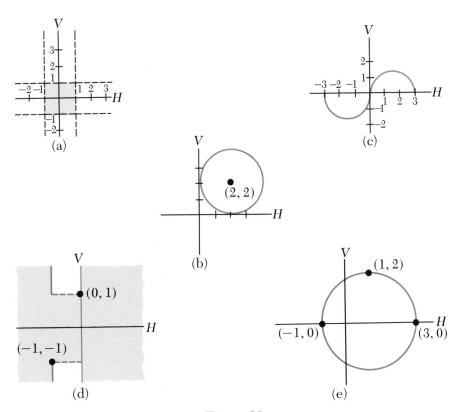

Figure 10

$x > 0$ or $y > 0$,

(a) in the XY plane.

(b) in the YX plane.

11. Sketch the graph of each of the following sets.

    (a) $\{(x, y): x \geq 1$ or $|y - 1| < 1/2\}$

    (b) $\{(x, y): $ If $|x| < 1$ then

$|y - 1| < 1/2\}$

(c) $\{(x, y): |x - 1| \geq 2$ or $|y + 1| < 1\}$

(d) $\{(x, y): $ If $|x - 1| < 2$ then $|y + 1| \leq 1\}$

(e) $\{(e, a): $ If $-2 < e < 1$ then $a = 2\}$

■ 2.3 Lines

One of the simplest geometric objects in a plane is a line. It is the purpose of this section to develop methods for finding an equation of any given line, and conversely, recognizing an equation of a line and determining its graph by inspection. In Section 2.1, equations were found for a rather limited class of lines. It was found that the equation of a vertical line in the XY plane passing through the point (c, d) could be written in the form $x = c$. Similarly, an equation of the horizontal line in the XY plane passing through the point (c, d) is $y = d$.

In Example 4 of that section a method was given for finding an equation of the perpendicular bisector of a line segment and an opportunity to practice using the method was afforded by the exercises. Every line L is the perpendicular bisector of some line segment. For example, if T is a point that is not on L, it is a straightforward construction problem to find the point S such that L is the perpendicular bisector of the line segment TS. Hence, we can, at least theoretically, find an equation of any line. The reason for the word *theoretically* will become obvious as this discussion progresses.

Let L be a line in the XY plane and let $T = (a_1, b_1)$ and $S = (a_2, b_2)$ be two points in the plane such that L is the perpendicular bisector of the segment TS, as shown in Figure 1.

Then $P = (x, y)$ is a point of L if, and only if, $|PT| = |PS|$. That is,

$$(x - a_1)^2 + (y - b_1)^2 = (x - a_2)^2 + (y - b_2)^2.$$

Simplifying, $-2a_1 x + a_1^2 - 2b_1 y + b_1^2 = -2a_2 x + a_2^2 - 2b_2 y + b_2^2$

or $2(a_2 - a_1)x + 2(b_2 - b_1)y + (a_1^2 + b_1^2 - a_2^2 - b_2^2) = 0.$

This is an equation of the form

(1) $$Ax + By + C = 0,$$

where $A = 2(a_2 - a_1)$, $B = 2(b_2 - b_1)$ and $C = a_1^2 + b_1^2 - a_2^2 - b_2^2$. Observe that A and B are not both 0, else $T = S$ and there would be no line segment

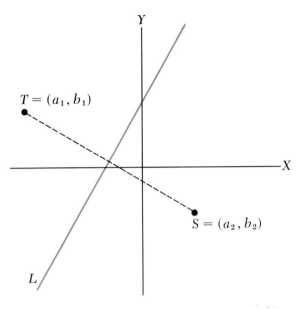

Figure 1

connecting T and S. Hence, $Ax + By + C = 0$ is a **linear equation** in x and y. Since all of the above equations are equivalent, any point $P = (x, y)$ that satisfies $Ax + By + C = 0$, with A, B, and C as above must also satisfy $|PT| = |PS|$; *i.e.*, P is a point of L. Hence, $Ax + By + C = 0$ is an equation of L. This result is formalized by stating it as a theorem.

THEOREM 2.3.1   Every line in the XY plane has an equation of the form (1),

$$Ax + By + C = 0,$$

where A and B are not both zero.

There are two questions that come immediately to mind. First, given a line L, what practical way is available for finding an equation of L? The method used in obtaining equation (1) supposes the knowledge of a line segment having L as its perpendicular bisector. Given L, however, there seems to be no simple way of finding such a line segment. This is indeed the case, and the techniques to be developed to answer the question are much less involved. The second question: Is the converse of Theorem 2.3.1 true? That is, given an equation as in (1), is its graph a line, and if so, what line? Each of these questions is answered by Theorem 2.3.3.

Let L be a nonvertical line in the XY plane. It has an equation that can be written in the form $Ax + By + C = 0$ with $B \neq 0$. (Why?) Hence, we can divide by B to obtain an equation of the form

(2)
$$y = mx + b$$

where
$$m = -A/B \quad \text{and} \quad b = -C/B.$$

If $P_1 = (x_1, y_1)$ and $P_2 = (x_2, y_2)$ are any two distinct points of L, they must satisfy equation (2) so that

$$y_2 = mx_2 + b \quad \text{and} \quad y_1 = mx_1 + b.$$

Therefore,
$$y_2 - y_1 = m(x_2 - x_1) \quad \text{and}$$

(3)
$$m = \frac{y_2 - y_1}{x_2 - x_1}. \quad (x_2 - x_1 \neq 0. \quad \text{Why?})$$

DEFINITION   Given points $P_1 = (x_1, y_1)$ and $P_2 = (x_2, y_2)$ with $x_1 \neq x_2$, the ratio $(y_2 - y_1)/(x_2 - x_1)$ is called the **slope** of the line segment P_1P_2.

This discussion has shown that the slopes of all line segments contained in a nonvertical line L are the same. Hence, it is possible to define the slope of a nonvertical line.

DEFINITION   The **slope** of a nonvertical line L is the slope of any line segment contained in L.

A nonvertical line L will intersect the vertical axis in exactly one point, say $(0, b)$. The vertical coordinate b of this point is called the **vertical intercept of L**. A nonhorizontal line L' intersects the horizontal axis in exactly one point, say $(a, 0)$. The horizontal coordinate a of this point is called the **horizontal intercept of L'**.

THEOREM 2.3.2   Every nonvertical line L in the XY plane has an equation of the form (2),

$$y = mx + b,$$

where m is the slope of L and b is the vertical intercept of L. Equation (2) is called the **slope-intercept equation of L**.

THEOREM 2.3.3   If A and B are not both zero, then the graph of equation (1)

$$Ax + By + C = 0,$$

in the XY plane is a line.

PROOF   If $B = 0$, then $A \neq 0$, so $x = -C/A$, which is an equation of the vertical line having horizontal intercept $-C/A$. If $B \neq 0$, let L be the line determined by the points $(0, -C/B)$ and $(1, -C/B - A/B)$. Then the vertical intercept of L is $-C/B$ and its slope is

$$\frac{(-C/B - A/B) - (-C/B)}{1 - 0} = \frac{-A}{B},$$

so its slope-intercept equation is

$$y = (-A/B)x + (-C/B),$$

which is equivalent to (1).

COROLLARY   If $B \neq 0$, then the line in the XY plane having $Ax + By + C = 0$ as an equation has slope $-A/B$ and vertical intercept $-C/B$.

Let us now return to the questions posed earlier. A line L is generally determined by its slope and one of its points or by two distinct points of the line. If the line L in the XY plane is determined by a point $P_1 = (x_1, y_1)$ and the slope m of L, then for any point $P = (x, y) \neq (x_1, y_1)$ of L, the slope of the line segment $P_1 P$ must be m. Thus,

$$\frac{y - y_1}{x - x_1} = m, \quad \text{or}$$

(4) $$y - y_1 = m(x - x_1).$$

Thus, the coordinates of every point of L distinct from P_1 satisfy equation (4). But the coordinates of P_1 also satisfy (4), so the line L is contained in the graph of equation (4). Equation (4) can be rewritten in the form

$$mx + (-1)y + (y_1 - mx_1) = 0,$$

which by Theorem 2.3.3 is an equation of a line in the XY plane. Hence, Equation (4) is an equation of L.

Equation (4) is called a **point-slope equation of L** and furnishes a simple formula for finding an equation of a line L if a point of L and the slope of L are known. Note that every nonvertical line L has many point-slope equations—one corresponding to each point of L. If a line is determined by two points having different horizontal coordinates, its slope can be computed from the definition and an equation found using (4).

For the second question, an equation of type (1) with $B = 0$ is an equation of a vertical line with horizontal intercept $-C/A$. If $B \neq 0$, it is an equation of the line having slope $m = -A/B$ and vertical intercept $b = -C/B$. In this latter case, it is the line through the points $P_1 = (0, b)$ and $P_2 = (1, b + m)$; *i.e.*, the line with vertical intercept b and slope

$$m = \frac{(b + m) - b}{1 - 0}.$$

Example 1 Find an equation of the line through $(-4, 3)$ with slope $\frac{1}{2}$ in the XY plane.

We use (4) with $x_1 = -4$, $y_1 = 3$ and $m = \frac{1}{2}$ to get

$$y - 3 = \tfrac{1}{2}(x + 4)$$

as an equation of the line.

Example 2 Find an equation of the line through $(1, -7)$ and $(2, 5)$ in the XY plane.

The line has slope

$$m = \frac{5 - (-7)}{2 - 1} = 12$$

and contains the point $(1, -7)$, so it has an equation

$$y + 7 = 12(x - 1).$$

Had the other point been used we would have obtained the equivalent equation

$$y - 5 = 12(x - 2).$$

Example 3 Sketch the graph of the equation $x - 5y + 7 = 0$ in the XY plane.

We rewrite the equation in the form of equation (2),

$$y = (1/5)x + 7/5,$$

and conclude that its graph is a line with slope $1/5$ and vertical intercept $7/5$. Hence, it passes through the points $(0, 7/5)$ and $(1, 8/5)$. (See Figure 2.)

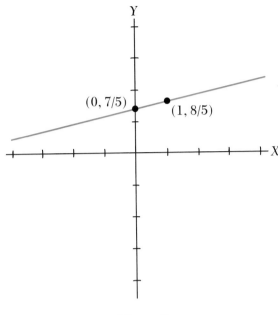

Figure 2

Example 4 Sketch the graph of the equation $2s + t + 1 = 0$ in the ST plane.
We rewrite this equation in the form

$$t = -2s - 1,$$

which is an equation of the line having slope -2 and vertical intercept -1.
Thus, the line contains the points $(0, -1)$ and $(1, -3)$. (See Figure 3.)

The geometric significance of the slope of a line or line segment is probably
clear to the reader by now. If a line L has slope m and contains the point
$P_0 = (x_0, y_0)$, then it also contains the point $Q = (x_0 + 1, y_0 + m)$ since the
slope of the segment from P_0 to Q is

$$\frac{y_0 + m - y_0}{x_0 + 1 - x_0} = m.$$

Thus, the slope is the change of vertical position per unit change of horizontal position along the line. If m is positive, the line rises from left to
right. If m is negative, the line falls from left to right. The magnitude or
absolute value of m is a measure of the rate at which the line is rising or
falling.

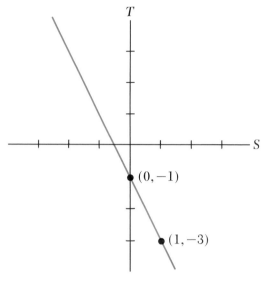

Figure 3

Figure 4 shows sketches of the graphs of the equations $y = mx$, for $m = -10, -2, -1, 0, 1, 2, 3$, in the XY plane, to illustrate how the "directions" of the lines vary with their slopes.

The preceding discussion suggests the relation between parallel lines L_1 and L_2 and slope. (To simplify many statements we will agree to think of a line as being parallel to itself). If both lines are vertical, then neither has slope. If not, let the lines have slope-intercept equations

$$y = m_1 x + b_1$$

and

$$y = m_2 x + b_2$$

respectively, in the XY plane. Either L_1 and L_2 are coincident, in which case their equations above are identical and $m_1 = m_2$, or they have no point in common. In the latter case, if $m_1 \neq m_2$, then we can solve their equations simultaneously to get

$$x = \frac{b_2 - b_1}{m_1 - m_2}, \qquad y = m_1 \left[\frac{b_2 - b_1}{m_1 - m_2} \right] + b_1.$$

Hence, the point

$$Q = \left(\frac{b_2 - b_1}{m_1 - m_2}, \quad m_1 \left[\frac{b_2 - b_1}{m_1 - m_2} \right] + b_1 \right)$$

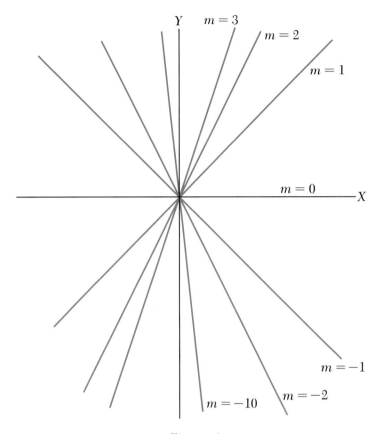

Figure 4

satisfies the equation for each of L_1 and L_2. That is, the lines L_1 and L_2 each contain the point Q so they intersect in the point Q. This contradicts the fact that they had no point in common, so the hypothesis that $m_1 \neq m_2$ must be false; *i.e.*, $m_1 = m_2$. Therefore, if L_1 and L_2 are parallel, they have the same slope.

Conversely, if L_1 and L_2 have equal slopes m_1 and m_2, they are parallel. For if they intersected in a point (x', y'), then

$$y' = m_1 x' + b_1$$

and
$$y' = m_2 x' + b_2.$$

When corresponding members of these equations are subtracted,

we obtain
$$0 = (m_1 - m_2)x' = b_2 - b_1$$

or $$b_1 = b_2.$$

That is, the lines have the same slope-intercept equation so they coincide. The combination of the above results proves:

THEOREM 2.3.4 Two nonvertical lines are parallel if and only if they have the same slope.

THEOREM 2.3.5 Let two lines L_1 and L_2 have slopes m_1 and m_2 respectively. L_1 is perpendicular to L_2 if and only if $m_1 = -1/m_2$.

PROOF Let $T = (a_1, b_1)$ and $S = (a_2, b_2)$ be two distinct points of L_2 and let L be the perpendicular bisector of the segment TS. As shown on page 62, an equation of L in the XY plane is

$$2(a_2 - a_1)x + 2(b_2 - b_1)y + (a_1^2 + b_1^2 - a_2^2 - b_2^2) = 0.$$

Thus, by the corollary to Theorem 2.3.3, L has slope

$$m = -\frac{a_2 - a_1}{b_2 - b_1}.$$

Note also that the slope m_2 of L_2 is

$$m_2 = \frac{b_2 - b_1}{a_2 - a_1} = -\frac{1}{m}.$$

("Only if" part) Let L_1 and L_2 be perpendicular. Since L and L_1 are each perpendicular to L_2 they are parallel. By Theorem 2.3.4 then, the slope m_1 of L_1 is equal to m. Hence,

$$m_1 = m = -\frac{a_2 - a_1}{b_2 - b_1} = -\frac{1}{m_2}.$$

("If" part) If $m_1 = -1/m_2$, then L_1 and L are parallel by Theorem 2.3.4. But L is perpendicular to L_2, so L_1 is also perpendicular to L_2. (See Figure 5.)

Example 5 In the XY plane, find an equation of the tangent line L to the circle

$$x^2 + y^2 = 25$$

at the point $Q = (4, -3)$.

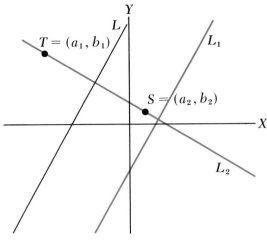

Figure 5

To find the slope of L, note that L is perpendicular to the radius OQ. (See Figure 6.)

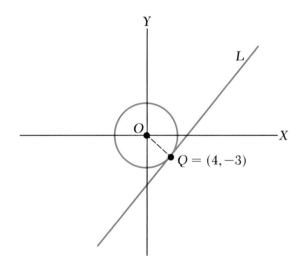

Figure 6

$$\text{Slope of } OQ = \frac{-3-0}{4-0} = -\frac{3}{4}.$$

$$\text{Slope of } L = -\frac{1}{\text{slope } OQ} = \frac{4}{3}.$$

Since the point $(4, -3)$ is on L, a point-slope equation of L is

$$y + 3 = \frac{4}{3}(x - 4).$$

Example 6 Sketch the graph of the inequality $0 \le v \le |u|$ in the UV plane.

For $u \ge 0$, $|u| = u$ and the inequality is $0 \le v \le u$. Thus, for $u \ge 0$, the graph consists of all points above or on the horizontal axis and below or on the line $v = u$. If $u < 0$, then $|u| = -u$ and the inequality is $0 \le v \le -u$. Thus, to the left of the vertical axis the graph consists of all points above or on the horizontal axis and below or on the line $v = -u$. A sketch of the graph appears in Figure 7.

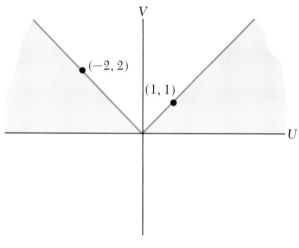

Figure 7

Example 7 Find the distance from the point $P = (1, 4)$ to the line L in the WZ plane having equation $z = 2w - 1$.

L has slope 2 and vertical intercept -1. An equation of the line L' through P and perpendicular to L is

$$z - 4 = (-1/2)(w - 1).$$

Let Q be the point of intersection of L and L'. Then the distance sought is $|PQ|$. (See Figure 8.)

The coordinates of Q must satisfy the equations of both L and L'. If we solve their equations simultaneously, we find that $Q = (11/5, 17/5)$. Hence,

$$|PQ| = \sqrt{(1 - 11/5)^2 + (4 - 17/5)^2} = 3\sqrt{5}/5.$$

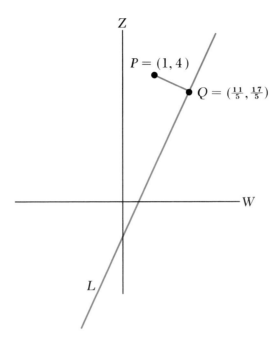

$P = (1, 4)$

$Q = (\frac{11}{5}, \frac{17}{5})$

Z

W

L

Figure 8

EXERCISES

1. Find an equation of the line
   (a) having slope -12 and vertical intercept $-2/7$ in the XY plane.
   (b) through $(5,0)$ and having slope 27 in the PQ plane.
   (c) through $(-6,-5)$, parallel to the line $4s - 5t + 6 = 0$ in the TS plane.
   (d) through the points $(2,1)$ and $(-1,3)$ in the HK plane.
   (e) through $(-7,0)$, perpendicular to the line $x = -7$ in the XY plane.
   (f) through the point of intersection of the lines $2x + 3y = 1$ and $x - y + 5 = 0$ and perpendicular to the line $2x + \pi y = 0$ in the XY plane.

2. Find the slope and vertical intercept, if possible, of each of the following lines and sketch their graphs.
   (a) $x = 9y + 7$ in the XY plane.
   (b) $5x + 2y - 7 = 0$ in the YX plane.
   (c) $5x + 2y - 7 = 0$ in the XY plane.
   (d) $a/2 - b/3 = 1$ in the AB plane.
   (e) $2z + 3 = 4z - 8$ in the ZY plane.
   (f) $3t + 5s - 6 = s + 7 + 3t$ in the TS plane.

3. Sketch the graph of each of the following conditions in the XY plane.
   (a) $4x - 5y \geq 2$
   (b) $-1 \leq 2x + 3y \leq 3$
   (c) $|5x - y| = 1$
   (d) $|x| + |y| = 1$
   (e) $|y| - |x| \leq 1$
   (f) $|x| + |y| > |x + y|$
   (g) If $|x - 2| < 1/2$, then $y = x + 3$.

4. Show that a line in the XY plane with horizontal intercept a and vertical intercept b, with $ab \neq 0$,

has equation

$$\frac{x}{a} + \frac{y}{b} = 1.$$

5. Find at least one point P such that the quadrilateral with vertices $A = (0, 0)$, $B = (1, 1)$, $C = (2, -3)$ and P is a parallelogram.

6. Sketch the graph of each of the following conditions in the XY plane.

(a) $x + |x| + y + 1 = 0$
(b) $|2x - 5| + |y + 3| < 1$
(c) $x + 5y \geq 1$ and $2x - 5y < 7$
(d) $(x + y + 1)(x - y - 1) = 0$ or $(x - 3)^2 + (y + 4)^2 \leq 4$
(e) If $|x - 1| < 2$ then $|y| < |x|$
(f) $|x - 1| \geq 2$ or $|y| < |x|$

7. Find a condition for each of the following graphs.

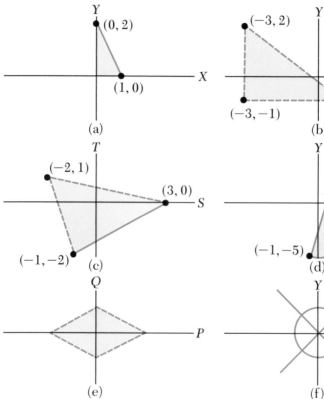

(a)

(b)

(c)

(d)

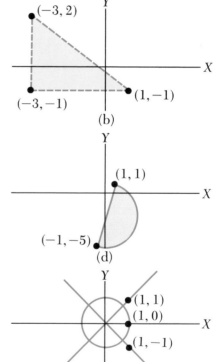

(e)

(f)

8. Let P be a point and L be a line. The **projection** of P on L is the point of intersection Q of L and the line L' that contains P and is perpendicular to L. (See Figure 9.) Note that in Example 7 (Figure 8), the projection of the point $(1, 4)$ on the line $z = 2w - 1$ in the WZ plane was found to be $\left(\frac{11}{5}, \frac{17}{5}\right)$.

(a) Let $P = (x_0, y_0)$ be a point in a natural coordinate plane. What is the projection of P on the horizontal axis? The vertical axis?

(b) In the XY plane, find the projection of the point $(-2, 3)$ on the line $4x - 2y + 5 = 0$.

(c) In the XY plane, find the projection of the point (x_0, y_0) on

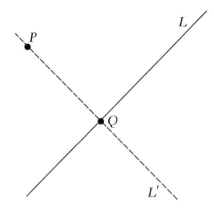

$Figure\ 9$

the line $Ax + By + C = 0$.
(d) Use the result in part (c) to show that the distance from the point (x_0, y_0) to the line $Ax + By + C = 0$ is

$$\frac{|Ax_0 + By_0 + C|}{\sqrt{A^2 + B^2}}.$$

9. Find an equation of the circle with center $(-2, 3)$ that is tangent to the line $x - 2y - 4 = 0$ in the XY plane.
10. Find equations of all lines through the point $(0, 13)$ that are tangent to the circle with center at the origin and radius 5 in the XY plane.
11. Let L_1 be the line with equation

$2x + 3y + 4 = 0$ in the XY plane, and for each real number r, let L_r be the line having equation $2x + 3y + 4r = 0$.
(a) On the same piece of graph paper, sketch the graphs of L_1, L_2, L_3, $L_{1/2}$, L_0, L_{-1}, and L_{-2}.
(b) What is the relation between any two lines L_{r_1} and L_{r_2}?
(c) How would you describe the set $\{L_r : r \in R\}$?
12. Let L_1 be the line with equation $Ax + By + C = 0$ in the XY plane, and for each real number r, let L_r be the line with equation $Ax + By + Cr = 0$. Discuss the set $\{L_r : r \in R\}$.

■ 2.4 Symmetry

The graph of a condition can be sketched fairly accurately if a sufficient number of points are plotted. Frequently, however, so many points are required to furnish an adequate notion of the graph that the point plotting method becomes extremely tedious. Moreover, as was seen in Example 6 of Section 2.2, this method supplies little or no information about some of the salient properties of the graph. Some of these properties are easily detected and enable the graph to be sketched with a minimum of effort. In the next few sections we will discuss several graphing aids that can often increase the accuracy of our graphing and decrease the work involved.

DEFINITION   Two points A and B are **symmetric** with respect to a point M provided M is the midpoint of the line segment joining A and B. Each of the points A and B is called the **reflection** of the other in the point M. The reflection of a point A in itself is the point A. A set S of points is **symmetric** with respect to a point M provided it contains the reflection in M of each of its elements.

Examples of sets of points that are symmetric with respect to a point are easy to find. Clearly, the endpoints of a diameter of a circle are symmetric with respect to its center and the set of points on the circle is symmetric with respect to the center of the circle. A line segment is symmetric with respect to its midpoint, while a line is symmetric with respect to each of its points.

DEFINITION   Two points A and B are **symmetric** with respect to a line L provided L is the perpendicular bisector of the line segment AB. Each of the points A and B is called the **reflection** of the other in the line L. If C is a point of L, the reflection of C in L is C. A set S of points is **symmetric** with respect to a line L provided it contains the reflection in L of each of its elements.

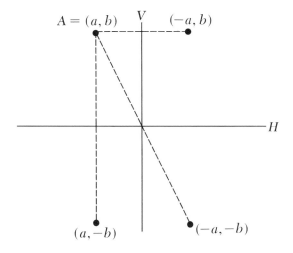

Figure 1

Examples of sets that are symmetric with respect to a line are also plentiful. A circle is symmetric with respect to each line through its center, a rectangle is symmetric with respect to a line containing the midpoints of a pair of opposite sides, and a square is symmetric with respect to a line containing one of its diagonals.

Our problem now is to find ways of recognizing symmetry properties of the graph of a condition directly from the condition.

Let $A = (a, b)$ be a point in a coordinate plane. It is readily seen that: (i) the point $(-a, b)$ is the reflection of A in the vertical axis, (ii) the point $(a, -b)$ is the reflection of A in the horizontal axis, and (iii) the point $(-a, -b)$ is the reflection of A in the origin. (See Figure 1.)

Now let S be a set of points in a coordinate plane. These remarks and the definitions then yield the following test for symmetry:

THEOREM 2.4.1

(i) S is symmetric with respect to the vertical axis provided $(-a, b) \in S$ whenever $(a, b) \in S$.

(ii) S is symmetric with respect to the horizontal axis provided $(a, -b) \in S$ whenever $(a, b) \in S$.

(iii) S is symmetric with respect to the origin provided $(-a, -b) \in S$ whenever $(a, b) \in S$.

Thus, if G is the graph of a condition in the XY plane, G is symmetric with respect to the vertical axis if the replacement of x by $-x$ in the condition yields an equivalent condition. It is symmetric with respect to the horizontal axis if the replacement of y by $-y$ yields an equivalent condition, and is symmetric with respect to the origin if the replacement of x and y by $-x$ and $-y$, respectively, yields an equivalent condition.

Example 1 Let G be the graph of the condition $x^2 + 4y^2 = 1$ in the XY plane.

When x is replaced by $-x$, we obtain $(-x)^2 + 4y^2 = 1$, which is clearly equivalent to $x^2 + 4y^2 = 1$. Hence, G is symmetric with respect to the Y-axis. Similarly, the replacement of y by $-y$, or each of x and y by its negative yields an equivalent condition. Thus, the graph is also symmetric with respect to the X-axis and the origin. Therefore, we need only sketch the graph of this condition in the first quadrant, the portions of the graph in the remaining quadrants being determined by symmetry.

Before sketching the graph, note that if (x, y) is a point of the graph in the first quadrant, then $y = \frac{1}{2}\sqrt{1 - x^2}$. If (x_1, y_1) and (x_2, y_2) are any two points on this part of the graph with $x_1 < x_2$, then $x_1^2 < x_2^2$ by Theorem 1.3.2; $-x_1^2 > -x_2^2$ by Theorem 1.3.1, and finally $\sqrt{1-x_1^2} > \sqrt{1-x_2^2}$ by Exercise 5 of Section 1.3. Therefore, $y_1 = \frac{1}{2}\sqrt{1-x_1^2} > \frac{1}{2}\sqrt{1-x_2^2} = y_2$, so the graph is falling from left to right. Finally, we plot a few points to obtain in Figure

x	$\dfrac{1}{4}$	$\dfrac{1}{2}$	$\dfrac{3}{4}$	$\dfrac{7}{8}$
y	$\dfrac{\sqrt{15}}{8}$	$\dfrac{\sqrt{3}}{4}$	$\dfrac{\sqrt{7}}{8}$	$\dfrac{\sqrt{15}}{16}$

2(a) a fairly accurate sketch of the graph in the first quadrant and complete the graph in Figure 2(b) by symmetry.

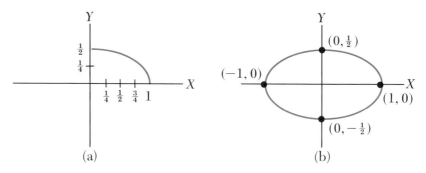

Figure 2

Example 2   Let G be the graph of the inequality $x < |y|$ in the XY plane.

The replacement of y by $-y$ gives an equivalent condition because $|-y| = |y|$. Therefore G is symmetric with respect to the X-axis. It is not, however, symmetric with respect to the Y-axis or the origin. Thus, we need only determine the points (x, y) of G for which $y \geq 0$; the rest will be obtained by symmetry.

If $y \geq 0$ then $|y| = y$ and the condition reduces to $x < y$. The graph of the equation $y = x$ in the XY plane is the line that bisects the first and third quadrants. Thus, a point (x_1, y_1), with $y_1 \geq 0$ will be on the graph G if and only if it is above the point (x_1, x_1); *i.e.*, if and only if it lies above the line $y = x$. The portion of G in the upper half-plane appears in Figure 3(a) and all of G, obtained by symmetry, in Figure 3(b).

Example 3   Sketch the graph of the equation $t = s|s|$ in the ST plane.

If we replace s by $-s$, the resulting condition is $t = -s|-s| = -s|s|$, which is not equivalent to $t = s|s|$. (Why?) Therefore the graph is not symmetric with respect to the T-axis. Similarly, if t is replaced by $-t$ it is seen that the graph is not symmetric with respect to the S-axis. But the replacement of

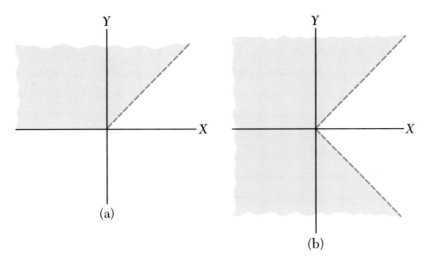

Figure 3

each of s and t by its negative gives $-t = -s|-s|$ or $t = s|s|$, so the graph *is* symmetric with respect to the origin. It suffices, therefore, to find that portion of the graph for which $s \geq 0$. Now, if $s \geq 0$, the condition becomes $t = s^2$, so $t \geq 0$. Note also that if $0 \leq s_1 < s_2$, then $s_1^2 < s_2^2$, so the graph is rising from left to right. By plotting a few points, we sketch the portion of the graph in the right half-plane in Figure 4(a) and complete the graph in Figure 4(b) by symmetry.

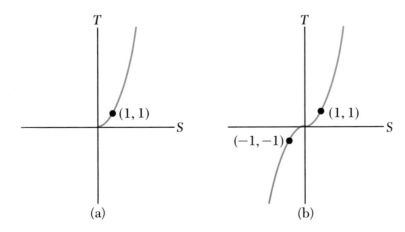

Figure 4

EXERCISES

1. For each given point, find its reflection in (i) the origin, (ii) the
vertical axis, and (iii) the horizontal
axis.
   (a) $P_1 = (1, 3)$
   (b) $P_2 = (-5, 2)$
   (c) $P_3 = (0, -4)$
   (d) $P_4 = (0, 0)$
   (e) $P_5 = (-\pi, \pi^2)$
   (f) $P_6 = (1, 1)$

2. In Figure 5 there are portions of
the graphs of six sets. For each one,
complete the graph if the set is
   (i)   symmetric with respect to
          the vertical axis.
   (ii)   symmetric with respect to
          the horizontal axis.
   (iii) symmetric with respect to
          the origin.

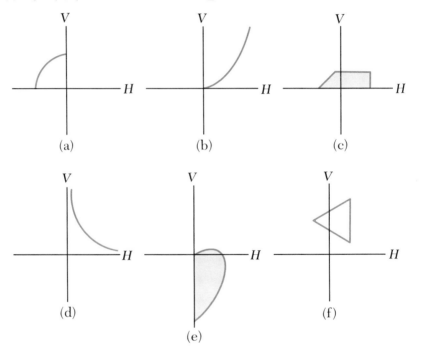

Figure 5

3. (a) Show that a set of points that is
symmetric with respect to each
coordinate axis is also symmetric with respect to the origin.
   (b) If a set of points is symmetric
with respect to the origin and
one of the coordinate axes, is
it necessarily symmetric with
respect to the other coordinate
axis?

*4. Show that the points (a, b) and
(b, a) are symmetric with respect
to the line $y = x$ in the XY plane.
State a test for symmetry of a set
of points with respect to the line
$y = x$ in the XY plane.

5. Show that the graph of the equation $x^2 y^2 - xy = 0$ in the XY plane
is symmetric with respect to the
line $y = x$. Sketch the graph.

6. Let M be a point, L a line, and S a set of points in a plane. Define the **reflection** of S in the point M to be the set of all points in the plane that are reflections in M of some point in S, and the **reflection** of S in L to be the set of points that are reflections in L of some point of S. Figure 6 shows the graphs of four sets in the XY plane. Sketch the reflection of each in (i) the horizontal axis, (ii) the vertical axis, (iii) the origin, and (iv) the line $y = x$.

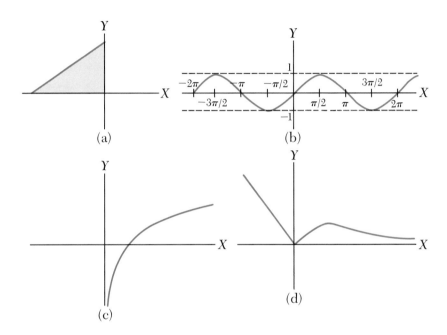

(a) (b) (c) (d)

Figure 6

7. If S is a set of points in a coordinate plane, show that
  (a) the reflection of S in the vertical axis is
      $\{(x, y): (-x, y) \in S\}$.
  (b) the reflection of S in the horizontal axis is
      $\{(x, y): (x, -y) \in S\}$.
  (c) the reflection of S in the origin is $\{(x, y): (-x, -y) \in S\}$.
  (d) the reflection of S in the line bisecting the first and third quadrants is
      $\{(x, y): (y, x) \in S\}$.
8. In each of the following, let G denote the graph of the given condition in the XY plane. Find a condition whose graph is
  (i) the reflection of G in the vertical axis.
  (ii) the reflection of G in the horizontal axis.
  (iii) the reflection of G in the origin.
  (iv) the reflection of G in the line $y = x$.
  (a) $2x + 3y + 1 = 0$
  (b) $(x + y + 1)(x + y - 1) = 0$
  (c) $|x - 1| \le 2$
  (d) $y = x^2$
  (e) $x^2 + y^2 = 1$
  Sketch the graphs of each condition in the XY plane.
9. Devise a test for symmetry with

respect to the line $x = 2$ in the XY plane. Do the same for the lines (i) $x = h$, and (ii) $y = k$.

10. A **parabola** is defined as the set of all points in a plane which are equidistant from a fixed point F and a fixed line L in the plane.

(a) Give a geometric argument to show that a parabola is symmetric with respect to the line through F which is perpendicular to L.

(b) Verify the result of part (a) using the symmetry tests in this section if for some number p, $F = (p, 0)$ and $L = \{(x, y) : x = -p\}$. *Hint:* Find an equation of the parabola in the XY plane first.

(c) Sketch the graph of the parabola in (b) for each of the following values of p.

(i) $p = 1$　(iii) $p = -1$
(ii) $p = 4$　(iv) $p = -4$

(d) Find an equation for the reflection of the parabola in part (b) in the line $y = x$. Is this reflection also a parabola? If your answer is "yes," what is the fixed line and the fixed point corresponding to the definition?

11. An **ellipse** $\mathscr{E}$ is the set of all points in a plane for which the sum of its distances from two fixed points is a constant. That is, if the fixed points, called the **foci** of $\mathscr{E}$, are F_1 and F_2 and the constant is d, with $d > |F_1 F_2|$, then $\mathscr{E} = \{P : |PF_1| + |PF_2| = d\}$.

(a) Give a geometric argument to show that $\mathscr{E}$ is symmetric with respect to both the line determined by F_1 and F_2 and the perpendicular bisector of the segment $F_1 F_2$.

(b) Use the symmetry tests of this section to show that an ellipse with foci $F_1 = (c, 0)$ and $F_2 = (-c, 0)$, $c > 0$, corresponding to the number $d = 2a$, $a > c$,

is symmetric with respect to each coordinate axis and the origin. *Hint:* First derive an equation for $\mathscr{E}$ in the XY plane.

(c) Show that the equation you found for the ellipse in part (b) is equivalent to the equation $\dfrac{x^2}{a^2} + \dfrac{y^2}{b^2} = 1$, where $b = \sqrt{a^2 - c^2}$.

(d) Sketch the graph of the ellipse in (c) in each of the following cases.

(i) $c = 1$, $a = 2$
(ii) $a = 3$, $b = 1$
(iii) $c = 7$, $a = 9$
(iv) $b = 5$, $c = 3$

(e) Find an equation for the reflection of the ellipse of parts (b) and (c) in the line $y = x$. Show that this reflection is also an ellipse and find its foci and the constant d of the definition.

(f) Show that if $F_1 = F_2$, the ellipse is a circle.

12. A **hyperbola** $\mathscr{H}$ is the set of all points in a plane for which the absolute value of the difference of its distances to two fixed points F_1 and F_2 in the plane is a positive constant d. That is, if the fixed points, called the **foci** of $\mathscr{H}$, are F_1 and F_2 and the constant is d, then $\mathscr{H} = \{P : ||PF_1| - |PF_2|| = d\}$.

(a) Give a geometric argument to show that a hyperbola is symmetric with respect to both the line determined by F_1 and F_2 and the perpendicular bisector of the line segment $F_1 F_2$.

(b) Verify the results of part (a) using the symmetry tests of this section if $F_1 = (c, 0)$, $F_2 = (-c, 0)$, and $d = 2a$ where $0 < a < c$. *Hint:* Find an equation of the hyperbola in the XY plane.

(c) Show that the equation you found for the hyperbola in part (b) is equivalent to the equation

$\dfrac{x^2}{a^2} - \dfrac{y^2}{b^2} = 1$, where

$b = \sqrt{c^2 - a^2}$.

(d) Sketch the graph of the hyperbola in part (c) in each of the following cases.
  (i) $c = 5,\ a = 3$
  (ii) $c = 5,\ a = 4$
  (iii) $a = 1,\ b = 1$
  (iv) $b = 1,\ c = 2$

(e) Find an equation of the reflection of the hyperbola of part (c) in the line $y = x$. Show that the reflection is also a hyperbola and find its foci and the constant d of the definition.

Note: Any plane curve that is either a parabola, ellipse, or hyperbola is called a **conic section.** It can be shown that each of them is the intersection of a right circular cone with a plane that does not pass through the vertex of the cone. The intersection is a parabola if the plane is parallel to a generator of the cone, an ellipse if the plane intersects only one nappe of the cone and is not parallel to a generator, and a hyperbola if the plane intersects both nappes of the cone. (See the accompanying figure.) The interested reader is referred to the first chapter of the book "Geometry and the Imagination," by D. Hilbert and S. Cohn-Vossen, Chelsea Publishing Company, 1952.

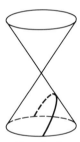
Parabola

Ellipse

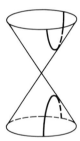
Hyperbola

■ 2.5 Intercepts and Extent

In sketching the graph of a condition, it is usually necessary to plot some points by assigning a value to one of the coordinates and determining the values of the other coordinate for which the condition is satisfied. In many cases the easiest points to determine are those on the coordinate axes. Since these will also play an important role in future discussions, we introduce the following terminology.

DEFINITION Let G be the graph of a condition in a coordinate plane. A number a is a **horizontal intercept** of G provided $(a, 0)$ is a point of G. A number b is a **vertical intercept** of G provided $(0, b)$ is a point of G.

To say that a number a is a horizontal intercept of a graph G means that the point $(a, 0)$ on the horizontal axis is also on the graph. To say that a number b is a vertical intercept of G means that the point $(0, b)$ on the vertical axis is also on the graph. Therefore, the horizontal and vertical intercepts of G are the horizontal and vertical coordinates, respectively, of the points of intersection of the graph and the coordinate axes. In the XY plane they are frequently called the X- and Y-intercepts, respectively. If G is the graph of a condition in the XY plane, the horizontal intercepts are found by setting $y = 0$ and solving for x; the vertical intercepts are found by setting $x = 0$ and solving for y.

For example, to find the horizontal intercepts of the graph of the equation $x^2 + 4y^2 = 1$ in the XY plane, we set $y = 0$ and solve the resulting equation, $x^2 = 1$, for x. Hence, the horizontal intercepts are 1 and -1. If $x = 0$ then $4y^2 = 1$, so the vertical intercepts are $\frac{1}{2}$ and $-\frac{1}{2}$.

The horizontal intercepts of the graph of the inequality $x^2 + 4y^2 \leq 1$ in the XY plane are all numbers in the closed interval $[-1, 1]$. For, if $y = 0$, then $x^2 \leq 1$, or equivalently, $|x| \leq 1$, and the solution set of this inequality is $[-1, 1]$. (Recall Theorem 1.5.1.) Similarly, the set of vertical intercepts is $[-1/2, 1/2]$.

It may be, of course, that there are no horizontal or vertical intercepts, as in the graph of $\{(x, y): xy = 1\}$. For $x = 0$, the equation $0 \cdot y = 1$ has no solutions. Similarly, for $y = 0$, $x \cdot 0 = 1$ has no solution. This information is also useful, because it tells us that the graph does *not* intersect the coordinate axes, and knowledge of where the graph isn't increases our knowledge of where it is.

This suggests that before we start assigning values to one of the coordinates to plot points of the graph, it might be well to have some idea of where points of the graph might be found, or equivalently, where there are no points of the graph. The graph of the equation $x^2 + 4y^2 = 1$ in the XY plane was found to be approximately the oval sketched in Figure 1. (If you have

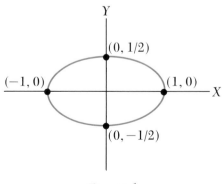

Figure 1

worked Exercise 11 of Section 2.4, you should recognize this as the graph of an ellipse.)

It would be fruitless to try to determine points (x, y) on this graph by assigning values to x that were greater than 1 in absolute value, or values of y that were greater than 1/2 in absolute value, because no such points exist.

Thus, we are led to ask the question: For what numbers a does the line $x = a$ contain a point of the graph and for what numbers b does the line $y = b$ contain a point of the graph?

DEFINITION   Let G be the graph of a set in a coordinate plane. The **horizontal extent** of G is the set

$$E_H = \{x : (x, y) \in G \text{ for some } y\}.$$

The **vertical extent** of G is the set

$$E_V = \{y : (x, y) \in G \text{ for some } x\}.$$

Observe that in the XY plane, $a \in E_H$ if and only if there is a point of the graph on the vertical line $x = a$; that is, $(a, 0)$ is the projection onto the horizontal axis of some point of the graph. Hence, E_H is the set of all numbers that are horizontal coordinates of points of the graph. Similarly, in the XY plane, $b \in E_V$ if and only if there is a point of the graph on the horizontal line $y = b$; that is, $(0, b)$ is the projection onto the vertical axis of some point of the graph. Hence, E_V is the set of all numbers which are vertical coordinates of points of the graph.

Example 1   Sketch the graph of the condition $x^2 - y^2 = 1$ in the XY plane.

We first determine the intercepts of the graph. If $y = 0$, then $x^2 = 1$, whence it is seen that 1 and -1 are X-intercepts of the graph. If $x = 0$, then $-y^2 = 1$, which has no solution, so there is no Y-intercept.

To find the horizontal extent of the graph, note that a number x_0 is in the horizontal extent if and only if there is a number y such that $x_0^2 - y^2 = 1$, that is, if and only if the equation $x_0^2 - y^2 = 1$ can be solved for y. The horizontal extent, then, is the set of all numbers x for which the equation $x^2 - y^2 = 1$ can be solved for y. Hence, to find the horizontal extent we try to solve for y. Thus, $y^2 = x^2 - 1$ or $y = \pm\sqrt{x^2 - 1}$. This can be done, however, only when $x^2 - 1 \geq 0$, that is when $|x| \geq 1$. Thus, we see that the horizontal extent is $\{x : |x| \geq 1\}$.

Similarly, a number y is in the vertical extent if and only if the equation $x^2 - y^2 = 1$ can be solved for x. But, if we solve for x, we obtain $x^2 = 1 + y^2$ or $x = \pm\sqrt{1 + y^2}$. This can be done no matter what y is since $1 + y^2 \geq 0$.

Therefore, the vertical extent is the set R of all real numbers.

Therefore, the graph must lie in the regions on or to the left of the line $x = -1$ and on or to the right of the line $x = 1$. (See Figure 2.) We note that

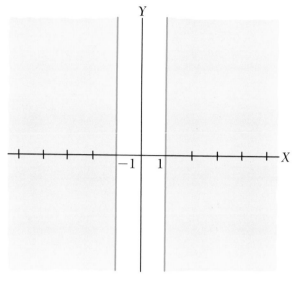

Figure 2

the graph is symmetric with respect to each coordinate axis, so we need only determine that portion in the first quadrant. Now, compute several points of the graph in the first quadrant.

x	$y = \sqrt{x^2 - 1}$
1	0
2	$\sqrt{3}$
3	$2\sqrt{2}$
4	$\sqrt{15}$
3/2	$\sqrt{5/4}$

If we plot these points we obtain in Figure 3(a) a sketch of the graph in the first quadrant. The graph is completed in Figure 3(b) by symmetry. (If you have worked problem 12 of Section 2.4, you should recognize this as the graph of a hyperbola.)

The vertical extent in Example 1 was found by solving the equation for x and determining all values of y for which the resulting equation was defined. Similarly, the horizontal extent was found by solving for y and determining the values of x for which the resulting equation was meaningful. This method

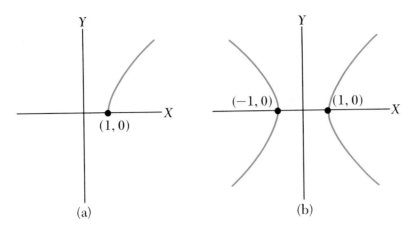

Figure 3

is convenient if it is possible to solve the condition in this way. There will be cases, however, where this approach is impractical or impossible.

Example 2   Sketch the graph of the equation

$$y^2 = (x - 1)(x - 2)(x - 3)$$

in the XY plane.

We observe first that the graph is symmetric with respect to the X-axis, so it suffices to sketch that portion in the upper half plane. In order that a number x be in the horizontal extent, $(x - 1)(x - 2)(x - 3)$ must be nonnegative, whence an odd number of the factors $x - 1$, $x - 2$, and $x - 3$ must be nonnegative. Now

$$x - 1 \geq 0 \quad \text{if and only if} \quad x \geq 1,$$
$$x - 2 \geq 0 \quad \text{if and only if} \quad x \geq 2,$$
$$x - 3 \geq 0 \quad \text{if and only if} \quad x \geq 3.$$

From an examination of the several possibilities and the fact that every nonnegative number has a nonnegative square root, it is seen that

$$E_H = \{x : x \in [1, 2] \quad \text{or} \quad x \in [3, \infty)\}.$$

A number $y_0 \in E_V$ provided the cubic equation $(x - 1)(x - 2)(x - 3) = y_0^2$ can be solved for x. It will be seen in Chapter 4 that every cubic equation has a real solution. Hence, $E_V = R$, so the graph is contained in the set $\{(x, y) : x \in [1, 2] \text{ or } x \in [3, \infty)\}$ as shown in Figure 4.

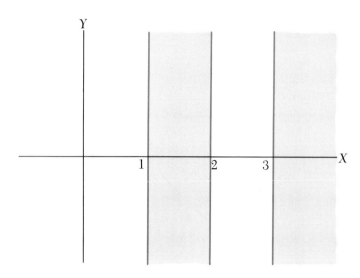

Figure 4

If $y = 0$, then $x = 1$ or $x = 2$ or $x = 3$, so 1, 2, and 3 are horizontal intercepts.

x	$\dfrac{5}{4}$	$\dfrac{3}{2}$	$\dfrac{7}{4}$	4	5
y	$\dfrac{\sqrt{21}}{8}$	$\dfrac{\sqrt{3}}{2\sqrt{2}}$	$\dfrac{\sqrt{15}}{8}$	$\sqrt{6}$	$2\sqrt{6}$

Now, we plot a few points with $x \in E_{II}$ and $y > 0$ and note, by a straight-forward exercise with inequalities, that for $x > 3$ and $y > 0$ the graph rises. We thus obtain a sketch of the graph in the upper half-plane in Figure 5(a) and complete the graph in Figure 5(b) by symmetry.

Example 3   Sketch the graph of the equation

$$y = \frac{x|x|}{x^2 + 1}$$

in the XY plane.

The replacement of x and y by their negatives gives the equivalent condition

$$-y = \frac{-x|-x|}{(-x)^2 + 1} = -\frac{x|x|}{x^2 + 1}$$

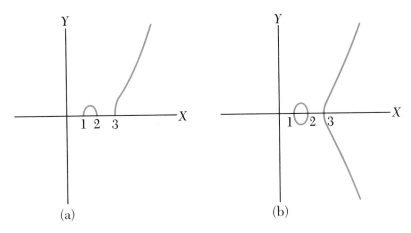

(a)   (b)

Figure 5

so the graph is symmetric with respect to the origin. There is no symmetry with respect to either axis. Also, 0 is the only vertical intercept and the only horizontal intercept.

From the symmetry, we need only consider the extent in the right half-plane.

If (x, y) is on the graph, then for

$$x \geq 0, \ |x| = x \quad \text{so} \quad y = \frac{x^2}{x^2 + 1}.$$

Now $\qquad 0 \leq x^2 < x^2 + 1 \quad \text{so} \quad 0 \leq y = \frac{x^2}{x^2 + 1} < 1.$ \qquad (Theorem 1.3.1.)

Thus, we can conclude that the vertical extent in the right half-plane is contained in the interval $[0, 1)$. From the symmetry then, $E_V \subset (-1, 1)$. The horizontal extent is clearly R. Each point of the graph is therefore contained in one of the sets

$$U = \{(x, y) : x \geq 0 \quad \text{and} \quad y \in [0, 1)\}$$

or $\qquad W = \{(x, y) : x \leq 0 \quad \text{and} \quad y \in (-1, 0]\}.$

(See Figure 6.)

Before plotting some points, we observe that if (x_1, y_1) and (x_2, y_2) are points of the graph with $0 < x_1 < x_2$, then

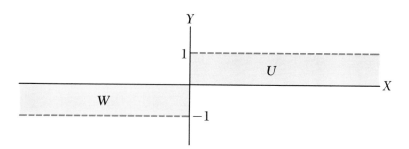

Figure 6

$$y_2 - y_1 = \frac{x_2|x_2|}{x_2^2 + 1} - \frac{x_1|x_1|}{x_1^2 + 1}$$

$$= \frac{x_1^2 x_2^2 + x_2^2 - x_1^2 x_2^2 - x_1^2}{(x_2^2 + 1)(x_1^2 + 1)}$$

$$= \frac{x_2^2 - x_1^2}{(x_2^2 + 1)(x_1^2 + 1)},$$

which is positive. That is, the graph is rising in the right half-plane.
If we compute a few points of the graph with $x > 0$

x	1	2	3	$\frac{1}{2}$	$\frac{1}{4}$
y	$\frac{1}{2}$	$\frac{4}{5}$	$\frac{9}{10}$	$\frac{1}{5}$	$\frac{1}{17}$

and combine all these results, we obtain the graph in Figure 7.

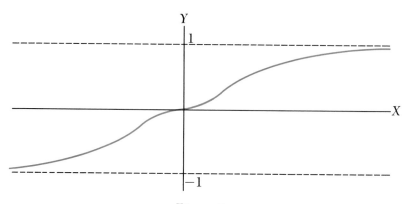

Figure 7

In Example 3 we never actually determined the vertical extent E_V, but found a set that contained E_V. This will often suffice for graphing a condition. Indeed, in many instances it will be impossible to determine exactly the extent and we must content ourselves with whatever limitations on the extent can be readily established.

EXERCISES

1. Use the graphing aids discussed in this and the previous section to sketch the graph of the following sets and conditions. In each case, find all intercepts and as much information about the horizontal and vertical extents as you can. Don't forget symmetry.
   (a) $xy = 1$ in the XY plane.
   (b) $u^3 = w^2$ in the UW plane.
   (c) $4x^2 + 9y^2 \leq 1$ in the YX plane.
   (d) $y = x\sqrt{9 - x^2}$ in the XY plane.
   (e) $y = \dfrac{2}{x^2 + 1}$ in the XY plane.
   (f) $y^2 = \dfrac{2}{x^2 + 1}$ in the XY plane.
   (g) $x^2 - 2y^2 = 8$ in the XY plane.
   (h) $2y^2 - x^2 = 8$ in the XY plane.
   (i) $y^2 = t(t + 1)(t - 1)$ in the TY plane.
   (j) $x^2 = y(y^2 - 1)(y - 2)$ in the XY plane.

2. For the graph of the equation $(x - 3)^2 + 4(y + 1)^2 = 4$ in the XY plane, show that
   (i) $E_H = [1, 5]$,
   (ii) $E_V = [-2, 0]$.

3. For the graph of the equation $\dfrac{(x + 1)^2}{6} + \dfrac{(y - 5)^2}{4} = 1$ in the XY plane, show that
   (i) $E_H = [-1 - \sqrt{6}, -1 + \sqrt{6}]$,
   (ii) $E_V = [3, 7]$.

4. If you worked Exercise 11 in Section 2.4 you should recognize the equation $x^2/a^2 + y^2/b^2 = 1$ as having an ellipse for its graph in the XY plane.
   (a) Find the horizontal and vertical intercepts of this ellipse.
   (b) Find the horizontal and verti-

cal extents of the ellipse.
   (c) Use parts (a) and (b) and symmetry properties to sketch the graph of the ellipse in each of the following cases.
   (i) $a = 1$, $b = 2$
   (ii) $a = 2$, $b = 1$
   (iii) $a = 2$, $b = 2$
   (iv) $a = 7$, $b = 1$

5. If you worked Exercise 12 in Section 2.4, you should recognize each of the equations
   (1) $x^2/a^2 - y^2/b^2 = 1$
   and
   (2) $y^2/a^2 - x^2/b^2 = 1$
   as equations of hyperbolas in the XY plane.
   (a) Find the horizontal and vertical intercepts of the graph of (1).
   (b) Show that the horizontal and vertical extents of the graph of (1) are
   $$E_H = \{x : |x| \geq |a|\}$$
   and
   $$E_V = R, \quad \text{respectively.}$$
   (c) Use the fact that the graph of (2) is the reflection of the graph of (1) in the line $y = x$ to determine the intercepts and extents for (2).
   (d) Sketch the graphs of (1) and (2) for each of the following choices of a and b.
   (i) $a = 1$, $b = 1$
   (ii) $a = 2$, $b = 1$
   (iii) $a = 1$, $b = 2$
   (iv) $a = 5$, $b = 1/2$

6. Show that the portion of the graph of the equation $y = x + 1/x$ in the XY plane for which $x > 0$ is con-

tained in $\{(x, y) : y > x\}$. What can you conclude about the portion of the graph in the left half-plane? Sketch the graph. How can you use the line $y = x$ to aid in graphing the equation when $|x|$ is large?

7. Compare the graphs of the conditions
   (i) $y = x + 1/x$ and $x > 0$,
   (ii) $y = x + 1/x^2$ and $x > 0$,
   (iii) $y = x + 1/x^3$ and $x > 0$
   in the XY plane. Sketch the graphs of each if the condition $x > 0$ is dropped.

8. Let a and b be positive numbers and let G be the graph of the equation $x^2/a^2 - y^2/b^2 = 1$ in the XY plane. (See Exercise 5.)
   (a) Show that the portion of G that is in the first quadrant lies below the line $y = (b/a)x$. *Hint:* If $(x, y) \in G$ and $y > 0$, then $(b/a)x - y$ is positive.
   (b) Explain why the portion of G in the first quadrant is "close" to the line $y = (b/a)x$ when x is "large."
   (c) What do the results of parts (a) and (b) tell you about the portions of G in each of the other quadrants? *Hint:* Use symmetry.
   (d) What do the results of parts (a), (b), and (c) tell you about the graph of the equation $y^2/a^2 - x^2/b^2 = 1$ in the XY plane? *Hint:* Consider a reflection in the line $y = x$.

■ 2.6 Translations

In attempting to solve many problems in a plane, one introduces a coordinate system in such a way that the problem becomes a fairly straightforward algebra problem. For example, if we want to prove that the diagonals of a rectangle $ABCD$ are equal in length and bisect each other, we might introduce a natural coordinate system with origin at one vertex A, the positive horizontal axis containing the side AB, and the positive vertical axis containing side AD as in Figure 1.

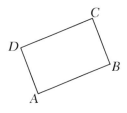 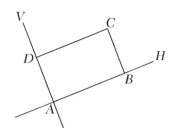

Figure 1

No matter how we choose the unit segment, the vertices can be described algebraically as $A = (0, 0)$, $B = (w, 0)$, $D = (0, h)$ and $C = (w, h)$, where w and h are the width and height, respectively, of the rectangle using the unit segment as a unit of length. From the distance formula,

$$|AC| = \sqrt{(w-0)^2 + (h-0)^2} = \sqrt{h^2 + w^2}$$

and
$$|BD| = \sqrt{(0-w)^2 + (h-0)^2} = \sqrt{h^2 + w^2},$$

so the diagonals are equal in length. By applying the results of Exercise 9, Section 2.1, we determine the midpoints M of AC and N of BD to be

$$M = \left(\frac{0+w}{2}, \frac{0+h}{2}\right) = \left(\frac{w}{2}, \frac{h}{2}\right)$$

and
$$N = \left(\frac{w+0}{2}, \frac{0+h}{2}\right) = \left(\frac{w}{2}, \frac{h}{2}\right)$$

and hence the diagonals bisect each other.

This problem was easy to solve because the coordinate system was introduced in a very convenient manner. Had we set up a coordinate system in a random way (Figure 2), we might never have been able to determine coordi-

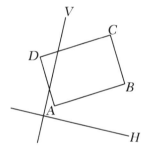

Figure 2

nates of the vertices, much less prove the desired conclusion. Thus, it is seen that an astute choice of a coordinate system can greatly simplify the work involved in solving a given problem.

In the same vein, the algebraic description of a set with respect to one coordinate system may be very complicated, whereas its description with respect to another coordinate system is quite simple. In Figure 3 for example, the circle with center $(3, 4)$ and radius 2 in the XY plane has the equation $(x-3)^2 + (y-4)^2 = 4$, while its equation in the UV plane is $u^2 + v^2 = 4$.

A less obvious, but more striking, example is illustrated in Figure 4, where an equation of the set S in the UV plane is $u^2 + 2v^2 = 8$, but its equation in the XY plane is $34x^2 - 24xy + 41y^2 = 200$. However, we will not try to justify this at present.

The question, then, is if we are given a complicated algebraic description of a set in a coordinate plane, can we introduce another coordinate system in which the set can be described in a simpler manner? If the answer is

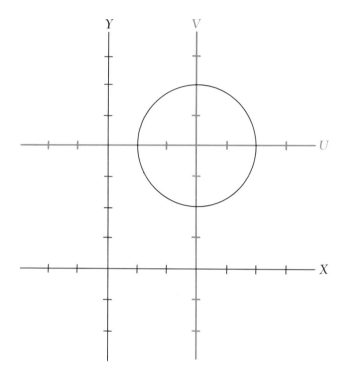

Figure 3

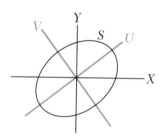

Figure 4

"yes," we want to know how, and to be able to interpret information obtained relative to one system in terms of the other. In the remainder of this section we consider a special case of this problem.

Let us consider a plane in which a natural coordinate system has been defined, say the XY system. Suppose that a second coordinate system, the UV system, is introduced so that its origin is at the point (h, k) of the XY plane, its horizontal and vertical axes are parallel, respectively, to the horizontal and vertical axes of the XY plane, the positive directions on the corresponding axes of the two systems are the same (as indicated in Figure 5),

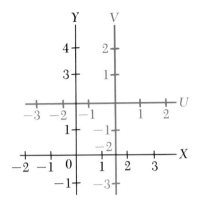

Figure 5

and the two systems have congruent unit segments.

If P is a point in the plane, then it has coordinates with respect to each coordinate system. To distinguish between them, if P has coordinates (a, b) in the XY plane, we write $P = (a, b)_{XY}$, whereas if P has coordinates (c, d) in the UV plane, we write $P = (c, d)_{UV}$. For example, the origin of the UV plane has coordinates (h, k) considered as a point of the XY plane. Thus we have $(0, 0)_{UV} = (h, k)_{XY}$. Since the unit segments are congruent, we note also, for example, that $(-7, 2)_{UV} = (-7 + h, 2 + k)_{XY}$, and that $(7, 8)_{XY} = (7 - h, 8 - k)_{UV}$. These points are plotted in Figure 6 on page 96.

If two coordinate systems are related as above, each is called a **translation** of the other, and if $(0, 0)_{UV} = (h, k)_{XY}$ so that $(0, 0)_{XY} = (-h, -k)_{UV}$, we say that the UV plane is a translation of the XY plane determined by the condition $(0, 0)_{UV} = (h, k)_{XY}$ and that the XY plane is a translation of the UV plane determined by $(0, 0)_{XY} = (-h, -k)_{UV}$.

Let the UV plane be a translation of the XY plane determined by $(0, 0)_{UV} = (h, k)_{XY}$. Let P be a point of the plane with $P = (x, y)_{XY}$ and $P = (u, v)_{UV}$, as in Figure 7 on page 97. Then the projection of P on the U-axis is the point $Q = (x, k)_{XY} = (u, 0)_{UV}$ and the projection of P on the V-axis is $Q' = (h, y)_{XY} = (0, v)_{UV}$. If we can determine the relation between the coordinates of Q with respect to the two coordinate systems and the relation between the different coordinates of Q', then we can do the same for the arbitrary point P.

Since u and x are the horizontal coordinates of Q in the UV and XY planes, respectively, the distance d between the origin of the UV plane and Q is

$$d = |u| = |x - h|.$$

If $u > 0$, then Q is to the right of the V-axis, so $x > h$ and $x - h > 0$. If $u < 0$,

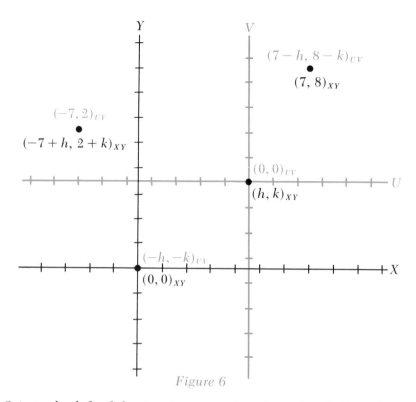

Figure 6

then Q is to the left of the V-axis, so $x < h$ and $x - h < 0$. In either case, $u = x - h$. In a similar manner it is seen that $v = y - k$. Since these relations hold between the coordinates of the projections of P on the U- and V-axes, they must also hold for the coordinates of P. Therefore, if $(u, v)_{UV} = (x, y)_{XY}$, then

$$u = x - h$$

(#)

$$v = y - k.$$

Equations (#) spell out exactly the relationship between the coordinates of any point with respect to the two coordinate systems. Thus,

$$P = (u, v)_{UV} = (x - h, y - k)_{UV}.$$

By solving the equations (#) for x and y,

$$x = u + h$$

(##)

$$y = v + k,$$

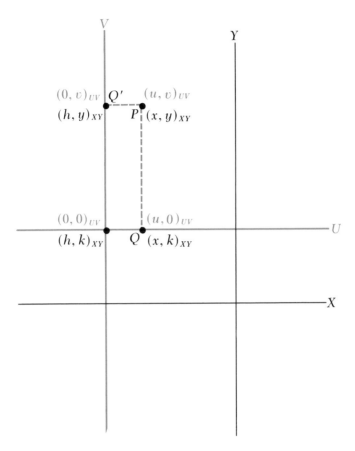

Figure 7

we have $(x, y)_{XY} = (u + h, v + k)_{XY}$.

Example 1 Let the UV plane be a translation of the XY plane determined by $(0, 0)_{UV} = (2, -3)_{XY}$.

The relation between the axes is shown in Figure 8.

If	$P = (x, y)_{XY}$
then	$P = (x - 2, y + 3)_{UV}$,
and if	$Q = (u, v)_{UV}$
then	$Q = (u + 2, v - 3)_{XY}$.

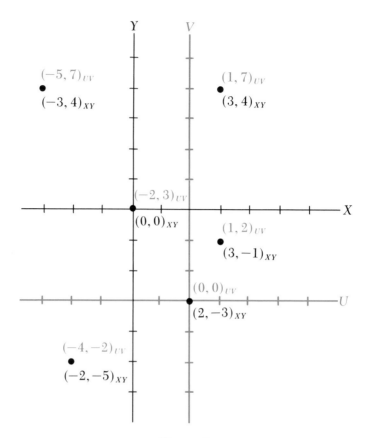

Figure 8

Thus
$$(-3, 4)_{XY} = (-3 - 2, 4 + 3)_{UV} = (-5, 7)_{UV};$$
$$(3, -1)_{XY} = (1, 2)_{UV};$$
$$(-4, -2)_{UV} = (-4 + 2, -2 - 3)_{XY} = (-2, -5)_{XY};$$
$$(1, 7)_{UV} = (3, 4)_{XY}$$

Example 2   Let G be the graph of the equation $x^2 + y^2 = 4$ in the XY plane. If the UV plane is a translation of the XY plane with $(0, 0)_{UV} = (-1, 3)_{XY}$, then G is the graph of what condition in the UV plane?

If $P = (x, y)_{XY}$ and also $P = (u, v)_{UV}$, then by (##), $x = u - 1$ and $y = v + 3$.

Now, $P \in G$ if and only if its coordinates $(x, y)_{XY}$ satisfy the equation $x^2 + y^2 = 4$; that is, if and only if $(u - 1)^2 + (v + 3)^2 = 4$. Therefore, $P \in G$ if and only if its coordinates $(u, v)_{UV}$ satisfy the equation

$$(u - 1)^2 + (v + 3)^2 = 4.$$ (See Figure 9.)

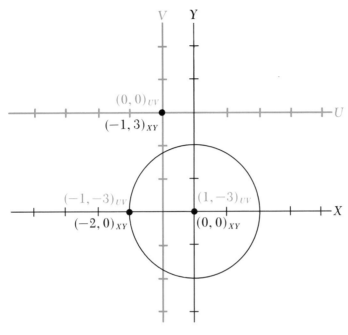

Figure 9

In general, if G is the graph of a condition $\mathscr{C}$ in the XY plane and the UV plane is a translation of the XY plane with $(0,0)_{UV} = (h, k)_{XY}$, then the condition having G as its graph in the UV plane is found by replacing x and y in $\mathscr{C}$ by $u + h$ and $v + k$, respectively. Thus, for the coordinate planes in Example 2, the graph of $y = 3x - 5$ in the XY plane is the graph of $v + 3 = 3(u - 1) - 5$, or equivalently, $v = 3u - 11$ in the UV plane. Similarly, the graph of

$$x^2 + 2x + 2y^2 - 12y = -15$$

in the XY plane is the graph of

$$(u - 1)^2 + 2(u - 1) + 2(v + 3)^2 - 12(v + 3) = -15,$$

or equivalently, $$u^2 + 2v^2 = 4$$

in the UV plane.

Example 3 Sketch the graph of $(x - 5)^2 + 4(y + 2)^2 = 1$ in the XY plane.

Clearly this equation can be simplified if we can find a new coordinate system, say the UV system, that is a translation of the XY system for which $u = x - 5$ and $v = y + 2$. From equations (#) we see that this can be done by taking $(0, 0)_{UV} = (5, -2)_{XY}$. That is, we choose h and k so that $x - 5 = x - h$ and $y + 2 = y - k$. In the UV plane, the graph is described by the equation

$$u^2 + 4v^2 = 1.$$

This equation was discussed in Example 1 of Section 2.4 and its graph sketched in Figure 2 of that section. The graph G is sketched in the UV plane in Figure 10. But G is also the graph of $(x - 5)^2 + 4(y + 2)^2 = 1$ in the XY plane, so the problem is solved.

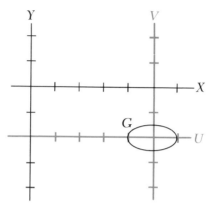

Figure 10

In many graphing problems it will be convenient to introduce a translation of the given coordinate system to simplify the work involved. The graph is just a set of points in the plane and as such is independent of the coordinate system we are using. A coordinate system simply gives us a way to describe that set of points. Thus, a graph found with respect to a translation of a given coordinate system is *also* the graph with respect to the given coordinate system.

One of the most useful graphing aids we have is symmetry, but the tests for symmetry at our disposal are for symmetry with respect to a coordinate axis, the origin, and the line bisecting the first and third quadrants. With the aid of translations of coordinate systems it is possible to detect symmetry with respect to any horizontal or vertical line and with respect to any point.

Example 4   Sketch the graph of $x^2 - 8x - y + 15 = 0$ in the XY plane.

It is not obvious here that a translation will help. If, however, we could rewrite this equation in terms of $(x - h)$ and/or $(y - k)$ for some constants h and k, the outlook would be brighter. This suggests completing the square in x to obtain

$$x^2 - 8x + 16 - y - 1 = 0$$

or $$(x - 4)^2 - (y + 1) = 0,$$

and finally, $$y + 1 = (x - 4)^2.$$

Now introduce a UV coordinate system that is a translation of the XY system so that $u = x - 4$ and $v = y + 1$; *i.e.*, so that $(0,0)_{UV} = (4,-1)_{XY}$. In the UV plane the condition becomes $v = u^2$. The graph is symmetric with respect to the V-axis, so we need only consider points for which $u \geq 0$. (Note that symmetry with respect to the V-axis implies symmetry with respect to the line $x = 4$ in the XY plane.) For $u \geq 0$, the graph of $v = u^2$ has already been found in Example 3 of Section 2.4. The graph is thus obtained in the UV plane and so too, in the XY plane. (See Figure 11.)

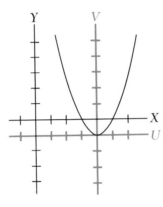

Figure 11

The reader's appreciation of the use of translation will increase as he develops a collection of rather simple conditions whose graphs he can recognize by inspection.

EXERCISES

1. Let the UV plane be a translation of the XY plane with $(0,0)_{UV} = (-3,-2)_{XY}$.
   (a) For each point given with respect to one coordinate system, find its coordinates with respect to the other.
      (i) $(0,0)_{XY}$
      (ii) $(-5,16)_{UV}$
      (iii) $(4,0)_{XY}$
      (iv) $(-1,3/2)_{XY}$
      (v) $(\pi, \sqrt{2})_{UV}$

      (vi) $(a, a)_{XY}$
      (vii) $(3, 2)_{UV}$
      (viii) $(c, c^2)_{XY}$
      (ix) $(d, d^3)_{UV}$
   (b) Each of the following conditions is given in terms of the XY coordinate system. Find each of them in terms of the UV system.
      (i) $x = 2$
      (ii) $y = -5$
      (iii) $y = x$

(iv) $|x| < y$
(v) $x^2 + y^2 = 7$
(vi) $xy = 1$
(vii) $x^3 + 9x^2 + 27x + y^2 + 4y + 31 = 0$
(viii) $y = x^2 + yx + 7$

(c) Each of the following conditions is given with respect to the UV system. Express each one as a condition with respect to the XY system.
  (i) $u = 0$
  (ii) $u^2 + 5v^2 - 6u - 20v + 28 = 0$
  (iii) $v = u$
  (iv) $2u - 3v = 4$

2. Sketch the graph of each of the following conditions in the XY plane.
  (a) $(x + 2)^2 + 4(y - 6)^2 = 1$
  (b) $(x - 4)^2 + 4(y - 1)^2 = 1$
  (c) $x^2 + 4(y - 2)^2 = 1$
  (d) $(x + 3)^2 + 4y^2 = 1$

3. Sketch the graph of each of the following conditions in the XY plane.
  (a) $y = x^2 - 6x + 12$
  (b) $y = x^2 + x$
  (c) $x^2 + 10x - y^2 + 6y + 15 = 0$
  (d) $x^2 + 4y^2 + x - 2y + 1 = 0$
  (e) $x^2 + 4y^2 + x - 2y - 30 = 0$
  (f) $|x - 3| < y + 2$

4. (a) Let the UV plane be a translation of the XY plane with $(0, 0)_{UV} = (1, 7)_{XY}$ and let the ST plane be a translation of the UV plane with $(0, 0)_{ST} = (2, -4)_{UV}$. What is the relation between the ST plane and the XY plane? Draw the three sets of coordinate axes to illustrate.
  (b) Do part (a) if $(0, 0)_{UV} = (h_1, k_1)_{XY}$ and $(0, 0)_{ST} = (h_2, k_2)_{UV}$.

5. (a) Devise a test for symmetry with respect to the line $x = 3$ in the XY plane. *Hint:* Introduce a translation whose vertical axis is this line.
  (b) Devise a test for symmetry with respect to the line $x = a$ in the XY plane.

(c) Devise a test for symmetry with respect to the line $y = b$ in the XY plane.
(d) Devise a test for symmetry with respect to the point (a, b) in the XY plane.

6. Let the ST plane be a translation of the XY plane with $(0, 0)_{ST} = (h, k)_{XY}$.
  (a) Find a condition in the XY plane whose graph is the first quadrant of the ST plane. Do the same for the second, third, and fourth quadrants of the ST plane.
  (b) Find a condition in the XY plane whose graph is (i) the right half-plane, (ii) the left half-plane, (iii) the upper half-plane, (iv) the lower half-plane of the ST plane.
  (c) Let W be a set of points in the plane with horizontal and vertical extents $\{s : s \in [-2, 2]\}$ and $\{t : t \in [-3, 3]\}$ respectively, in the ST plane. Find the horizontal and vertical extents of W in the XY plane.
  (d) Do part (c) if the horizontal and vertical extents in the ST plane are respectively, $\{s : |s| \geq 1\}$ and $\{t : t \in R\}$.

Exercises 7 and 8 assume that you have worked Exercises 10–12 in Section 2.4 and Exercises 4, 5, and 8 in Section 2.5.

7. Discuss the graphs of each of the following five equations in the XY plane. Give as much information as you can about the graphs, keeping in mind the exercises in Sections 2.4 and 2.5 dealing with conic sections.
  (1) $(y - k)^2 = 4p(x - h)$
  (2) $(x - h)^2 = 4p(y - k)$
  (3) $(x - h)^2/a^2 + (y - k)^2/b^2 = 1$
  (4) $(x - h)^2/a^2 - (y - k)^2/b^2 = 1$
  (5) $(y - k)^2/a^2 - (x - h)^2/b^2 = 1$

8. Identify the graph in the XY plane of each of the following equations as a circle, parabola, ellipse, or hyperbola, and sketch its graph.

(a) $(x-1)^2 + 2(y+3)^2 = 8$
(b) $(y+1)^2 = 6x$
(c) $x^2 - y^2 + 4x - 9y + 1 = 0$
(d) $x^2 + y^2 + 8y + 16 = 0$
(e) $x^2 + 3x + 1 = y^2 - 6x + 2$
(f) $x^2 + 3y^2 - 5 = 4x - 12y$
(g) $y = 4x^2 + 5x - 7$

†9. Let there be given a plane with a natural coordinate system, say the XY system. Now put a second, UV coordinate system in the plane so that the horizontal and vertical axes of the two systems coincide, but so that the unit segment in the UV system is twice the length of the unit segment of the XY system. Then it is clear that

$$(0,0)_{UV} = (0,0)_{XY},$$
$$(1,0)_{UV} = (2,0)_{XY} \quad \text{and}$$
$$(0,1)_{UV} = (0,2)_{XY}.$$

(Refer to Figure 12.)

(a) Find coordinates in the XY system of each of the points:
$(-1,0)_{UV}$, $(2,0)_{UV}$, $(7,0)_{UV}$,
$(a,0)_{UV}$, $(0,2)_{UV}$, $(0,-3)_{UV}$,
$(0,b)_{UV}$.

(b) Show that if
$$P = (u,v)_{UV} \text{ and } P = (x,y)_{XY},$$
then
$$x = 2u \text{ and } y = 2v,$$
or equivalently,
$$u = \frac{x}{2} \text{ and } v = \frac{y}{2}.$$

(c) Work Exercise 1 if the XY and UV coordinate systems are related as described above.

†10. Work Exercise 9 if the coordinate systems are the same except the length of the unit segment in the UV system is c times the length of the unit segment in the XY sys-

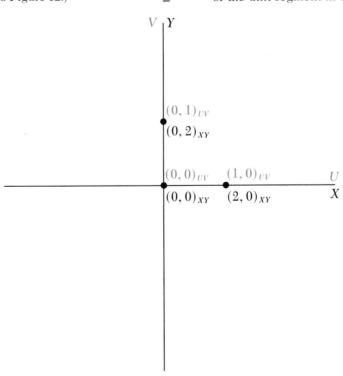

Figure 12

tem, where $c > 0$. Start by observing that $(0,0)_{UV} = (0,0)_{XY}$, $(1,0)_{UV} = (c,0)_{XY}$, and $(0,1)_{UV} = (0,c)_{XY}$. The equations in (b) will, of course, have to be modified.

Note: Each of the coordinate systems in this exercise is called a **similarity** of the other. In particular, we will say that the UV system is a similarity of the XY system with (or determined by) $(1,0)_{UV} = (c,0)_{XY}$ and the XY system is a similarity of the UV system with $(1,0)_{XY} = (1/c,0)_{UV}$. Can you explain why the word *similarity* was chosen?

†11. Let C be a circle with center $(0,0)$, radius r in the UV system of Exercise 10. It will, of course, be a circle in the XY system as well,

but what is its radius there? *Note:* A similarity simply involves a change in the unit of length. For example, if we decide to use an inch as our basic unit of length, we can speak of a circle with radius 6, meaning radius 6 inches. But if the basic unit of length is a foot, the same circle has radius 1/2, *i.e.*, 1/2 foot.

†12. Suppose we have three coordinate systems in a plane, the XY, UV, and ST systems. Suppose further that the UV system is a translation of the XY system with $(0,0)_{UV} = (h,k)_{XY}$, and the ST system is a similarity of the UV system with $(1,0)_{ST} = (c,0)_{UV}$. If $P = (x,y)_{XY} = (u,v)_{UV} = (s,t)_{ST}$, determine equations for changing from any one of these systems to any other.

CHAPTER 3

FUNCTIONS

■ 3.1 Basic Definitions

An intuitively appealing way to think of what is meant by a function is to think of it as a rule, or correspondence, that assigns to each member of a given set of objects a member of a second set. However, if the word *function* is to become a useful technical term in mathematics, it must have a precise definition. And words such as *rule*, *correspondence*, and *assigns* are not technical words in terms of which *function* can be defined legitimately. Fortunately, this does not mean that a legitimate definition of the term *function* has to be very complicated. In fact, the one we will use is not at all complicated, and it also has the advantage that there are many settings in which its use makes the explanation of certain ideas quite easy.

To see how the definition we are going to choose fits with our intuitive notion of what a function is, consider the following correspondences:

(1) The one that assigns to the diameter d of a circle the circumference πd of the circle;

(2) The one that assigns to each real number x the point of a coordinate line whose coordinate is x;

(3) The one that computes the square of each of the numbers -2, -1, 0, 1, 2, 3.

−2	−1	0	1	2	3
4	1	0	1	4	9

Figure 1

Before reading further, take a look at Figure 1. It is likely that you observed that there is a pattern in this diagram, that each number in the second row is found by squaring the number above it in the first row. Thus, the diagram is a table that exhibits the third correspondence described in our list of correspondences.

This sort of scheme is not available for either the first or second correspondence listed. We can't make a table for (1) that lists all the possible values of the diameter d of a circle in one row and the corresponding values of the circumference πd in the second row, because we would have to be able to make a list of all the positive numbers d. In (2), we can't list all the values of the real number x, so it is impossible to make a table that exhibits the correspondence.

Now, suppose that instead of the table in Figure 1, you were confronted with this set of ordered pairs of numbers:

$$\{(-2,4),\ (-1,1),\ (0,0),\ (1,1),\ (2,4),\ (3,9)\}.$$

You should discover that the pattern here is that for each ordered pair in this set, the second coordinate is the square of the first coordinate. Moreover, the first coordinate of any ordered pair in this set is one of the numbers in $\{-2,-1,0,1,2,3\}$. So, this set of ordered pairs exhibits the third correspondence listed in the same way that Figure 1 does.

If we try this approach with the first correspondence, we again have difficulties, because we can't make a list of all the ordered pairs (d,c) where d is the diameter of a circle and c is its circumference. But we do have a way of describing a set other than by the "listing" method, and that is by using the classifier symbol. For correspondence (1), the appropriate set is

$$\{(d,c): d > 0 \quad \text{and} \quad c = \pi d\},$$

so that the correspondence is "known" by examining this set of ordered pairs. Similarly, if L is a coordinate line, then

$$\{(x,P): x \text{ is a real number and } P \text{ is the point} \\ \text{of } L \text{ whose coordinate is } x\}$$

serves the same purpose for correspondence (2).

Thus, our first conclusion is that one way to get at the essence of a correspondence is to use a set of ordered pairs that really exhibits what the correspondence says.

Now, we must ask whether *any* set of ordered pairs of objects is suitable
for this purpose. Returning to our three examples of correspondences, we
notice that

(1) The circumference of a circle is determined *uniquely* by its diameter;
(2) A real number x determines *uniquely* the point of a given coordinate
     line whose coordinate is x, that is, no two distinct points of a coordinate
     line have the same coordinate;
(3) If any one of the numbers $-2, -1, 0, 1, 2, 3$ is squared, the answer is
     unique, that is, one cannot legitimately find two different ways of squaring
     one of these numbers so as to obtain two different answers.

It appears then, that if a correspondence is to be exhibited by a set of
ordered pairs, and (x, y) is one of those ordered pairs, then y should be
uniquely determined by x in the sense that there should be no ordered pair
in the set of the form (x, y') with $y' \neq y$. It can then be said with some con-
viction that y is *the* object assigned to x by the correspondence.

Our conclusions are formalized in the following definition.

DEFINITION A **function** is a nonempty set f of ordered pairs of objects
such that if $(x, y_1) \in f$ and $(x, y_2) \in f$, then $y_1 = y_2$.

Remembering that to say that an ordered pair (x, y) is equal to an ordered
pair (u, v) is to say that both $x = u$ and $y = v$, we have that a function is a
nonempty set f of ordered pairs such that no two unequal members of f have
the same first coordinate.

DEFINITION Let f be a function. The set of all first coordinates of the
members of f is called the **domain** of f, and is denoted $\mathscr{D}_f$. The set of all
second coordinates of the members of f is called the **range** of f, and is denoted $\mathscr{R}_f$. Thus,

$$\mathscr{D}_f = \{x : \text{For some } y, \ (x, y) \in f\},$$
$$\mathscr{R}_f = \{y : \text{For some } x, \ (x, y) \in f\}.$$

Notice that if f is a function and $x \in \mathscr{D}_f$, then there is at *least* one element y
in $\mathscr{R}_f$ such that $(x, y) \in f$. But by the definition of what it means to be a
function, there can be at *most* one such element y.

DEFINITION   If f is a function and $x \in \mathcal{D}_f$, then the unique element y such that $(x, y) \in f$ is denoted by $f(x)$ and is called the **value** of f at x.

Hence, if f is a function, then the statements "$y = f(x)$" and "$(x, y) \in f$" mean the same thing. Also, if we agree that the term *correspondence* is a synonym for the term *function*, then it is reasonable to agree that if f is a function and $y = f(x)$, then y **corresponds** to x, and that f **assigns** the element y of $\mathcal{R}_f$ to the element x of $\mathcal{D}_f$.

With a few notable exceptions, the functions we shall deal with are **real functions**, that is, functions f such that $\mathcal{D}_f \subset R$ and $\mathcal{R}_f \subset R$. Practically speaking, we make no distinction between a real function and what one would expect to call the graph of the function. This is because we have agreed not to distinguish between a point of a natural coordinate plane and the ordered pair of coordinates of that point, at least when a fixed natural coordinate system in the plane is being used. Since, however, a function f can always be written as $\{(x, y) : y = f(x)\}$, it follows that the graph of a real function f in the XY plane is the graph of the condition $y = f(x)$ in the XY plane.

Thus, no matter how we choose to label the coordinate axes, it is understood that the domain of a real function f is the horizontal extent of the graph of f, while its range is the vertical extent of the graph of f.

Example 1   Let $f = \{(x, y) : x \in R \text{ and } y = x^2\}$.

(i) f is a function, because if $(x, y_1) \in f$ and $(x, y_2) \in f$, then $y_1 = x^2$ and $y_2 = x^2$, so $y_1 = y_2$.

(ii) $\mathcal{D}_f = R$, for every member of $\mathcal{D}_f$ is said explicitly to be in R, while for every x in R, x^2 is defined, so $x \in \mathcal{D}_f$ and $f(x) = x^2$.

(iii) $\mathcal{R}_f = \{y : y \geq 0\}$. To see this, let $y \in \mathcal{R}_f$. Then for some x in R, $y = x^2$, so $y \geq 0$. Conversely, if $y \geq 0$, then $(\sqrt{y}, y) \in f$, so $y \in \mathcal{R}_f$.

Example 2   Let $g = \{(x, y) : x > 2 \text{ and } y = x^2\}$.

Then g is also a function, but notice that if f is the function of Example 1, then f and g are not the same because $\mathcal{D}_f \neq \mathcal{D}_g$.

Sketches of the graphs of f and g in the XY plane are shown in Figure 2.

Notice that if f and g are the functions of Examples 1 and 2, then that fact that $f \neq g$ could be shown by realizing that f and g are *sets*, and that there are members of f, $(-1, 1)$ for example, that are not members of g. Thus, $f \neq g$ by the definition of equality of sets given in Section 1.1.

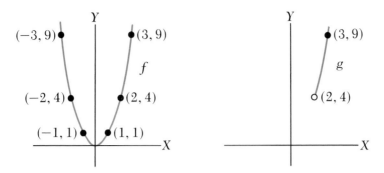

Figure 2

However, this is not the usual way of deciding whether or not two functions are equal. The following test is more practical:

To say that functions f and g are equal is to say that both of the following conditions are satisfied:

(i) $\mathcal{D}_f = \mathcal{D}_g$

(ii) For every x that belongs to both $\mathcal{D}_f$ and $\mathcal{D}_g$, $f(x) = g(x)$.

The functions f and g of Examples 1 and 2 illustrate the importance of verifying *both* conditions (i) and (ii) before being certain that two functions are equal, because f and g *do* satisfy (ii), but they do not satisfy (i).

Example 3 Let $h = \{(u, v) : u \in R, v \le 0, \text{ and } u^2 + v^2 = 1\}$.

(i) h is a function, because if $(u, v_1) \in h$ and $(u, v_2) \in h$, then $v_1^2 = 1 - u^2 = v_2^2$, so $|v_1| = |v_2|$. But both $v_1 \le 0$ and $v_2 \le 0$, so $v_1 = v_2$.

(ii) $\mathcal{D}_h = [-1, 1]$. To see this, notice first that if $u \in \mathcal{D}_h$, then for some $v \le 0$, $v^2 = 1 - u^2$, so $1 - u^2 \ge 0$. Hence, $|u| \le 1$ so $u \in [-1, 1]$. Conversely, if $u \in [-1, 1]$, then $1 - u^2 \ge 0$ and $(u, -\sqrt{1 - u^2}) \in h$, so $u \in \mathcal{D}_h$ and $h(u) = -\sqrt{1 - u^2}$.

(iii) $\mathcal{R}_h = [-1, 0]$, by an argument similar to the one for (ii).

Defining a function by means of the classifier symbol is precise, but often clumsy. Agreeing that only real functions are to be discussed unless something to the contrary is specifically indicated, we will use the device suggested by the following description of the function h of Example 3:

$$h : h(u) = -\sqrt{1 - u^2}.$$

This statement is to be read

"h is the function defined by $h(u) = -\sqrt{1 - u^2}$,"

and it is to be understood from this that h is the function whose domain is the set of all *real* numbers u such that $-\sqrt{1 - u^2}$ is also a *real* number, and for each such number u, the value of h at u is $-\sqrt{1 - u^2}$.

Similarly, the function f of Example 1 can be described by

$$f: f(x) = x^2,$$

which may be read

"f is the function defined by $f(x) = x^2$,"

or   "f is the function whose value at any number x is x^2."

However, the function g of Example 2 will be described by

$$g: g(x) = x^2, \; x > 2,$$

which may be read

"g is the function defined by $g(x) = x^2$ for $x > 2$"

or   "g is the function whose value at x is x^2 for $x > 2$."

One word of warning: you will undoubtedly encounter phrases such as "the function $y = f(x)$," or "the function $f(x)$." These are obvious abuses of the word *function*, because a function is not an equation, nor is a function the same thing as the value of that function at some element of its domain. The notation introduced here is to emphasize that a function f is to be distinguished from some formula that may be used to calculate the values of f.

Example 4   For each real number x, let $[x]$ denote the unique integer n such that $n \leq x < n + 1$. The number $[x]$ is usually called the **greatest integer in x**, and if $f: f(x) = [x]$, then f is called the **greatest integer function**. A sketch of part of its graph is shown in Figure 3.

Example 5   Let $g = \{(x, y) : x \in R, \, y \in R, \text{ and } x = y^2\}$.

Then g is not a function, because the unequal ordered pairs $(1, 1)$ and $(1, -1)$ are in g, but they have the same first coordinate.

You will probably notice that in the exercises that follow and in those of later sections there is a fair amount of emphasis placed on determining the domain of a function. The reason is simple: it would be silly, for example, to make a lot of noises about the value of the function $f: f(x) = x^3/(4x - x^2)^{1/2}$ at the number 5 or at the number 0 when, in fact, neither 0 nor 5 is in the domain of f.

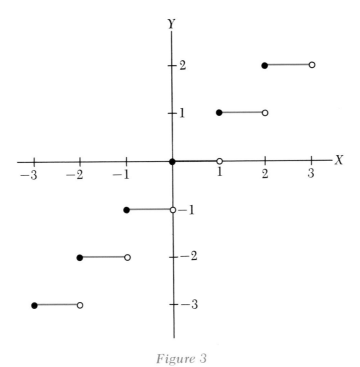

Figure 3

You will also notice that hardly anything is said about determining the range of a function. One reason is that this problem is not, at this stage, as critical as that of determining a function's domain. In fact, it is not until Chapter 6 that this becomes a crucial issue. Moreover, finding the range of a function f is usually difficult, since it amounts to finding all y such that the equation $y = f(x)$ has at least one solution. Ordinarily, one is able to give a reasonable estimation of what the range of a function is, just as in estimating the extent of a graph in Section 2.5. If you are interested in a more challenging type of exercise, see what you can do with the determination of the ranges of the functions in Exercises 4 and 5.

EXERCISES

1. Use the definition to decide whether or not the given set is a function. If it is, use the notation introduced after Example 3 to describe the function.
   (a) $\{(x, y): x \in R$ and $3y - 2x + 1 = 0\}$

   (b) $\{(s, t): s \in R,\ t \in R,$ and $s^2 + t^2 = 1\}$
   (c) $\{(u, v): u \in R,\ v \in R,$ and $u^2 - v^2 = 0\}$
   (d) $\{(x, y): x \in R,\ y \in R,$ and $x^3 - y^3 = 0\}$
   (e) $\{(x, y):$ Either $x \leq 1$ and

$y = x + 3,$ or $x > 1$ and
$y = 2\}$

(f) $\{(s, t) : s \in R, t \in R,$ and
$s^4 + 2s^2 t + t^2 = 0\}$

(g) $\{(y, x) : y \in R, x \in R,$ and
$y^2 = x^3\}$

(h) $\{(x, y) : x \in R, y \in R,$ and
$y^2 = x^3\}$

(i) $\{(u, v) : u \in R, v \geq 0,$ and
$u^2 - v^2 = 1\}$

(j) $\{(u, v) : u \geq 0, v \in R,$ and
$u^2 - v^2 = 1\}$

*2. Let G be a nonempty subset of a coordinate plane.

 (a) Give a geometric description of the condition that G be the graph of a function.

 (b) Give a geometric description of the condition that G *not* be the graph of a function.

 (c) Sketch the graph of each set in Exercise 1 that is *not* a function, and use the test you found in part (b) to show why the graph you have sketched is not the graph of a function.

*3. Let f be a real function such that $-x \in \mathscr{D}_f$ whenever $x \in \mathscr{D}_f$.

 (a) Prove that the graph of f is symmetric with respect to the vertical coordinate axis if, and only if, $f(-x) = f(x)$ for every number $x \in \mathscr{D}_f$.

 (b) State and prove an algebraic condition that is equivalent to the statement that the graph of f be symmetric with respect to the origin.

 (c) Can the graph of a real function be symmetric with respect to the horizontal coordinate axis?

4. For each function, find its domain and use the information from Exercise 3 to test its graph for symmetry with respect to the vertical coordinate axis and the origin.

 (a) $f : f(y) = \sqrt{y^2 - 4}$

 (b) $g : g(x) = \sqrt{\dfrac{x - 1}{x + 1}}$

 (c) $h : h(x) = (x^2 - 4)^{3/2}$

 (d) $f : f(t) = (5 - 2t^3)^{-1/2}$

 (e) $g : g(u) = \dfrac{u}{u^2 + 1}$

 (f) $h : h(t) = \dfrac{|t|}{1 - t^2}$

5. For each function, find its domain, describe the function by using the classifier symbol, and sketch its graph.

 (a) $f : f(x) = 3x + 2$

 (b) $g : g(x) = |3x + 2|$

 (c) $F : F(t) = \sqrt{t - 4}$

 (d) $H : H(x) = [x] - x, \dfrac{1}{2} \leq x < 3$

 (e) $h : h(t) = \begin{cases} t^2, & \text{if } t > 1, \\ 3 - 2t, & \text{if } t \leq 1 \end{cases}$

 (f) $g : g(y) = ||y| - y|$

 (g) $F : F(x) = x^4$

 (h) $h : h(x) = x^4 + 2$

 (i) $f : f(u) = \dfrac{u^2 - 1}{u + 1}$

 (j) $G : G(t) = \dfrac{1}{t^2 + 1}$

6. Let $g : g(x) = \sqrt{\dfrac{x - 1}{x + 1}}$ as in Exercise 4(b). Let $f : f(x) = \dfrac{\sqrt{x - 1}}{\sqrt{x + 1}}$. Is it true that $f = g$?

7. Suppose $f : f(x) = x^2$. Compute:

 (a) $f(-1)$

 (b) $f(3)$

 (c) $f(t)$

 (d) $f(4y)$

 (e) $f(2x)$

 (f) $f(x + h)$

 (g) $f(f(x))$

 (h) $f(\sqrt{u})$

8. Let m and b be real numbers with $m \neq 0$, and let $g : g(x) = mx + b$. Compute:

 (a) $g(2x)$

 (b) $g(xy)$

 (c) $g(t + h)$

 (d) $g(x^2)$

 (e) $g(g(u))$

 (f) $g(y/m - b/m)$

9. Suppose $f : f(x) = 4x^2 - 3x + 1$. Calculate $\dfrac{f(x + h) - f(x)}{h}$. For which values of x and h is this

expression defined?
10. Repeat Exercise 9 for
    $f \colon f(x) = \sqrt{2x + 5}$.
11. Use the notation introduced after
    Example 3 to describe the corre-
    spondence that
    (a) Assigns the area of a circle to
        its radius.
    (b) Assigns the radius of a circle
        to its area.
    (c) Assigns the area of a square to
        the length of one of its sides.
    (d) Assigns the length of a side of
        a square to its perimeter.
    (e) Assigns the distance traveled
        by a car to the length of time
        traveled, assuming the car
        moves at a constant rate of 60
        miles per hour.
    (f) Assigns the area of a rectangle
        to its width, given that the rec-
        tangle has perimeter 8 inches.
    (g) Assigns the perimeter of an
        isosceles triangle of area 4

square inches to its altitude.
    (h) Assigns the area of a rectangle
        to its length, given that the rec-
        tangle is inscribed in a circle
        of radius r.
    †(i) Assigns the area of an isosceles
        triangle to its altitude, given
        that the triangle is inscribed in
        a circle of radius r.
    †(j) Assigns the area of an isosceles
        triangle to its altitude, given
        that the triangle is circum-
        scribed about a circle of ra-
        dius r.
12. Show that the test for equality of
    two functions stated in the dis-
    cussion of Example 2 (page 109)
    is valid, that is, prove that a func-
    tion f equals a function g if, and
    only if,
    (i) $\mathscr{D}_f = \mathscr{D}_g$ and
    (ii) For every x that belongs to
        both $\mathscr{D}_f$ and $\mathscr{D}_g$, $f(x) = g(x)$.

■ 3.2 One-to-One Functions

If we return for a moment to the notion of a coordinate system for a line L as defined at the beginning of Section 1.4, we see that part (i) of the definition says that a coordinate system for L is a function f whose domain is the set R of real numbers and whose range is a subset of L, that is, f assigns to each real number exactly one point of L.

But part (ii) of that definition imposes two more restrictions on f. One is that given any point P on L, there is *at least one* x in R such that $f(x) = P$, so that the range of f is actually equal to L. The second restriction is that given P on L, there is *only one* x in R that satisfies $f(x) = P$. It is this second restriction on f that allows us to define x as being *the* coordinate of the point P. Another way of stating this condition on f is that if $x_1 \in R$, $x_2 \in R$, and $x_1 \neq x_2$, then $f(x_1) \neq f(x_2)$, so that any two different real numbers are assigned by f to two different points of L.

Functions that have the property that they assign distinct elements of their range to distinct elements of their domain are quite useful, and we will examine this property further in Chapter 6. At present, we will content our-selves with getting some practice in the use of the following definition.

DEFINITION   A function f is **one-to-one** if, and only if, whenever x_1 and x_2 are in $\mathscr{D}_f$ and $f(x_1) = f(x_2)$, it follows that $x_1 = x_2$.

The statement that f is one-to-one clearly means that if x_1 and x_2 are in $\mathscr{D}_f$ and $x_1 \neq x_2$, then $f(x_1) \neq f(x_2)$. The definition is stated in its given form because it states what must be done to actually show that a function f is one-to-one; it says essentially that it must be shown that the equation $f(x_1) = f(x_2)$ has only $x_1 = x_2$ as a solution.

Example 1   Let $f: f(x) = 3x + 5$.
Then f is one-to-one, because,

if $$f(x_1) = f(x_2)$$

then $$3x_1 + 5 = 3x_2 + 5.$$

Hence, $$3x_1 = 3x_2,$$

so $$x_1 = x_2.$$

Example 2   Let $f: f(x) = \dfrac{x}{x-1}$.

If x_1 and x_2 are both different from 1,

and $$f(x_1) = f(x_2),$$

then
$$\frac{x_1}{x_1 - 1} = \frac{x_2}{x_2 - 1},$$
$$x_1(x_2 - 1) = x_2(x_1 - 1),$$
$$x_1 x_2 - x_1 = x_2 x_1 - x_2,$$
$$-x_1 = -x_2,$$

so $$x_1 = x_2.$$

Hence, f is one-to-one.

Example 3   Let $g: g(t) = t^2 + 2t$.
If we attempt to show that g is one-to-one, we have

$$g(t_1) = g(t_2) \quad \text{implies}$$
$$t_1^2 + 2t_1 = t_2^2 + 2t_2,$$
$$(t_1^2 - t_2^2) + 2(t_1 - t_2) = 0,$$
$$(t_1 - t_2)(t_1 + t_2) + 2(t_1 - t_2) = 0,$$

so $$(t_1 + t_2 + 2)(t_1 - t_2) = 0.$$

It appears that we are stuck, because although $t_1 = t_2$ is a solution of this last equation, so is $t_1 = -t_2 - 2$. Thus, we suspect that g is not one-to-one, and our suspicions are confirmed if, for example, we let $t_2 = 1$, $t_1 = -1 - 2 = -3$. Then $t_1 \neq t_2$, but

$$g(t_1) = g(-3) = 3$$

and

$$g(t_2) = g(1) = 3,$$

so

$$g(t_1) = g(t_2).$$

A final example is more of a problem of recognition than anything else.

Example 4   Let $h: h(u) = \dfrac{u^2}{1 + u}$, $u > 0$.

Suppose u_1 and u_2 are in $\mathscr{D}_h$, so that both $u_1 > 0$ and $u_2 > 0$, and suppose that $h(u_1) = h(u_2)$. Then,

$$\frac{u_1^2}{1 + u_1} = \frac{u_2^2}{1 + u_2},$$
$$u_1^2(1 + u_2) = u_2^2(1 + u_1),$$
$$u_1^2 + u_1^2 u_2 = u_2^2 + u_2^2 u_1.$$

Things are not as pleasant here as they were in Example 2, for instance, because the "odd" terms $u_1^2 u_2$ and $u_2^2 u_1$ won't cancel. However, the last equation can be written

$$u_1^2 - u_2^2 = u_2^2 u_1 - u_1^2 u_2,$$
$$(u_1 - u_2)(u_1 + u_2) = u_1 u_2 (u_2 - u_1),$$
$$(u_1 - u_2)(u_1 + u_2 + u_1 u_2) = 0.$$

But both $u_1 > 0$ and $u_2 > 0$, so $u_1 + u_2 + u_1 u_2 > 0$ as well. Hence, the last equation implies $u_1 = u_2$, so h is one-to-one.

There is a more elegant method of showing that the function of Example 4 is one-to-one, but that method uses calculus. So, the point of including Example 4 here is as a test of ability to perform some algebraic manipulations. You will find some similar examples in the Exercises.

EXERCISES

1. Without referring to the text, state carefully what it means for a function to be one-to-one.
2. Realizing that a function f is a set of ordered pairs, state what it means for a function f to be one-to-one in terms of the ordered pairs which belong to f.
3. Show that each of these functions is one-to-one.
   (a) $f: f(x) = 4x - 5$
   (b) $g: g(x) = x^3$

(c) $h: h(t) = \dfrac{2t}{3t+1}$

(d) $f: f(u) = au + b$, where $a \neq 0$

(e) $g: g(x) = \dfrac{x}{x-1}$

(f) $h: h(z) = \dfrac{z}{1-z^2}$, $|z| < 1$

(g) $F: F(x) = \dfrac{x^3}{1+x}$, $x > 0$

4. For each of the functions in Exercises 4 and 5 of Section 3.1, decide whether or not the function is one-to-one. Keep in mind that to show that a function f is *not* one-to-one amounts to finding members x_1 and x_2 in the domain of f with $f(x_1) = f(x_2)$ but $x_1 \neq x_2$.

5. In Exercise 2(a) of Section 3.1, you should have found that the graph G of a function has the property that no vertical line contains more than one point of G. When is G the graph of a one-to-one function?

°6. A real function f is called an **increasing function** provided that whenever $x_1 \in \mathcal{D}_f$, $x_2 \in \mathcal{D}_f$, and $x_1 < x_2$, then also $f(x_1) < f(x_2)$. It is called a **decreasing function** provided that whenever $x_1 \in \mathcal{D}_f$, $x_2 \in \mathcal{D}_f$, and $x_1 < x_2$, then $f(x_1) > f(x_2)$. A real function is **monotone** if either it is an increasing function or it is a decreasing function.
Prove that every monotone function is one-to-one.

7. Show that each of these functions is one-to-one by showing that it is monotone:

(a) $f: f(x) = 6x - 1$

(b) $f: f(x) = -2x + 5$

(c) $g: g(x) = ax + b$, where $a \neq 0$

(d) $h: h(x) = \dfrac{1}{x}$, $x > 0$

(e) $G: G(x) = x^2$, $x \leq 0$

(f) $F: F(x) = \dfrac{x}{1-x^2}$, $|x| < 1$

8. Show that none of these functions is monotone, that is, show that each function is neither an increasing function nor a decreasing function. Notice what this means: for each function f, you must find numbers $x_1 < x_2$ in $\mathcal{D}_f$ such that $f(x_1) \geq f(x_2)$ (which shows that f is not an increasing function), and you must find numbers $x_3 < x_4$ in $\mathcal{D}_f$ such that $f(x_3) \leq f(x_4)$ (which shows that f is not a decreasing function.)

(a) $f: f(x) = x^2$

(b) $f: f(x) = |x|$

(c) $f: f(x) = \dfrac{1}{x}$

(d) $f: f(x) = \dfrac{2x}{3x+1}$

°9. Give an example of a one-to-one real function that is not monotone. (If you can't think of an example right away, try to draw the graph of such a function, and then try for an algebraic description of an example.)

†10. If A and B are sets, then A and B are said to be in **one-to-one correspondence** if there is a one-to-one function whose domain is A and whose range is B. For example, if

$f: f(n) = 2n$, n a natural number,

then f is a one-to-one function whose domain is the set A of all natural numbers and whose range is the set B of all even natural numbers, so A and B are in one-to-one correspondence.
Show that the following sets A and B are in one-to-one correspondence.

(a) $A = \{n: n$ is a natural number$\}$,
$B = \{m: m$ is an odd natural number$\}$.

(b) $A = \{n: n$ is a natural number$\}$,
$B = \{m: m$ is an integer$\}$.

(c) $A = \{0, 1, 1/2, 1/3, 1/4, \ldots\}$,
$B = \{1, 1/2, 1/3, 1/4, 1/5, \ldots\}$.

(d) $A = [-1, 3]$, $B = [2, 5]$.

(e) $A = [a, b]$, $B = [a', b']$, where a, b, a', and b' are any real numbers with $a < b$ and $a' < b'$.

(f) $A = \{x: x > 0\}$,
$B = \{y: 0 < y < 1\}$.
Hint: Consider

$$f: f(x) = \frac{x}{1+x}, \ x > 0.$$

(g) $A = [0, 1], \quad B = (0, 1]$.
Hint: Part (c) of this exercise is useful here.

(h) $A = [0, 1], \quad B = (0, 1)$.

■ 3.3 Algebra of Functions

The basic operations of addition, subtraction, multiplication, and division as applied to the set R of real numbers can be extended in a natural way to the set of real functions. In fact, the operations on the real functions are so closely related to the operations on R that the same symbol is used for a given operation in either of the two settings.

DEFINITION   Let each of f and g be a real function. Then

(i) $f + g = \{(x, y): y = f(x) + g(x)\}$
(ii) $f - g = \{(x, y): y = f(x) - g(x)\}$
(iii) $fg = \{(x, y): y = f(x)g(x)\}$
(iv) $f/g = \{(x, y): y = f(x)/g(x)\}$

provided that the indicated set of ordered pairs is nonempty.

It follows from the definition of function given in Section 3.1 that in each of (i), (ii), (iii), and (iv), if the given set of ordered pairs is nonempty, then it is a function. For example, if $fg = \{(x, y): y = f(x)g(x)\}$ is nonempty, and both (x, y_1) and (x, y_2) are members of fg, then $y_1 = f(x)g(x) = y_2$, so fg is a function.

Notice that the **sum** $f + g$, the **difference** $f - g$, and the **product** fg all have the same domain, namely,

$$\{x: x \in \mathscr{D}_f \ \text{and} \ x \in \mathscr{D}_g\},$$

and for each number x in this set,

$$(f + g)(x) = f(x) + g(x),$$
$$(f - g)(x) = f(x) - g(x),$$
$$(fg)(x) = f(x)g(x).$$

However, the domain of the **quotient** f/g is

$$\{x: x \in \mathscr{D}_f, \ x \in \mathscr{D}_g, \ \text{and} \ g(x) \neq 0\},$$

and if x is any number in this set, then

$$(f/g)(x) = f(x)/g(x).$$

Example 1   Let $f\colon f(x) = 2x + 1$, $g\colon g(x) = 3x^2 + 4$.
Then $\mathscr{D}_f = \mathscr{D}_g = R$, so each of the functions $f + g$, $f - g$, and fg has domain R, and

$$
\begin{aligned}
f + g\colon (f + g)(x) &= (2x + 1) + (3x^2 + 4) = 3x^2 + 2x + 5, \\
f - g\colon (f - g)(x) &= (2x + 1) - (3x^2 + 4) = -3x^2 + 2x - 3, \\
fg\colon (fg)(x) &= (2x + 1)(3x^2 + 4) = 6x^3 + 3x^2 + 8x + 4.
\end{aligned}
$$

Moreover, $\{x\colon x \in R \quad \text{and} \quad g(x) = 0\} = \varnothing$,   so $\mathscr{D}_{f/g} = R$,   and

$$f/g\colon (f/g)(x) = (2x + 1)/(3x^2 + 4).$$

Example 2   Let $f\colon f(x) = 1/(x - 1)$, $g\colon g(x) = \sqrt{x + 1}/(x^2 + 3x - 4)$.

Then $\mathscr{D}_f = \{x\colon x \in R \quad \text{and} \quad x \neq 1\}$,

and
$$
\begin{aligned}
\mathscr{D}_g &= \{x\colon x + 1 \geq 0 \quad \text{and} \quad x^2 + 3x - 4 \neq 0\} \\
&= \{x\colon x \geq -1 \quad \text{and} \quad (x - 1)(x + 4) \neq 0\} \\
&= \{x\colon x \geq -1 \quad \text{and} \quad x \neq 1 \quad \text{and} \quad x \neq -4\} \\
&= \{x\colon x \geq -1 \quad \text{and} \quad x \neq 1\}.
\end{aligned}
$$

Also, $\{x\colon g(x) = 0\} = \{-1\}$.

Therefore,
$$
\begin{aligned}
\mathscr{D}_{f/g} &= \{x\colon x \geq -1 \quad \text{and} \quad x \neq 1 \quad \text{and} \quad x \neq -1\} \\
&= \{x\colon x > -1 \quad \text{and} \quad x \neq 1\},
\end{aligned}
$$

and for each x in $\mathscr{D}_{f/g}$,

$$(f/g)(x) = (x + 4)/\sqrt{x + 1}.$$

Notice that if $h\colon h(x) = (x + 4)/\sqrt{x + 1}$, then $\mathscr{D}_h = \{x\colon x > -1\}$, so that the functions h and f/g are different because they do not have the same domain.

Just as important as being able to perform manipulations as in Examples 1 and 2 is being able to recognize a given real function as an algebraic combination of other real functions.

Example 3   Let $h\colon h(x) = \dfrac{3x - 2}{x^2 - 4}$.

Then $h = f/g$, where $f\colon f(x) = 3x - 2$ and $g\colon g(x) = x^2 - 4$. Not quite as obvious is the fact that

$$h = F + G, \quad \text{where} \quad F\colon F(x) = \frac{1}{x - 2} \quad \text{and} \quad G\colon G(x) = \frac{2}{x + 2}.$$

Other examples of this sort appear in Exercises 5–9.

Appearances can sometimes be deceiving in the formation of algebraic combinations of functions.

Example 4   Let $f: f(x) = (1 - x^2)^{-1/2}$, $g: g(x) = (x^2 - 4)^{1/2}$.

Then $\mathscr{D}_f = \{x: |x| < 1\}$ and $\mathscr{D}_g = \{x: |x| \geq 2\}$,

so there is no real number that is in both $\mathscr{D}_f$ and $\mathscr{D}_g$. Hence, $f + g$ is not defined, even though the expression

$$(1 - x^2)^{-1/2} + (x^2 - 4)^{1/2}$$

looks as if it is the value at x of $f + g$.

Examples 2 and 4 have this much in common: one can get into difficulties if he does not pay close attention to the domains of the functions involved. This is another example of the idea that a potentially valuable concept is not going to be valuable at all unless it is treated with a reasonable amount of care.

Finally, we introduce a class of functions that play a special role in the algebra of functions.

Example 5   Let c be a real number. If

$$f: f(x) = c,$$

then f is called a **constant function**. Its graph is the horizontal line whose vertical intercept is c. It is more or less universal practice to let the symbol c stand for this function as well as for the real number it represents. This, of course, is an abuse of the function concept, but it is one that shouldn't cause much confusion.

Then, if f and g are real functions, by the statement $f + g = 0$ is meant that $f + g$ is defined, and for each number x in $\mathscr{D}_{f+g}$, $f(x) + g(x) = (f + g)(x) = 0$. Similarly, $fg = 1$ means that fg is defined, and for each x in $\mathscr{D}_{fg}$, $f(x)g(x) = (fg)(x) = 1$.

Finally, if c is a real number and f is a real function, then

$$cf: (cf)(x) = c \cdot f(x),$$

and $$c/f: (c/f)(x) = c/f(x).$$

EXERCISES

1. Let $f: f(x) = 1/(3x^2 - 2)$, $g: g(x) = \sqrt{x + 7}$. Find each of the follow- ing, and for each expression find the set of all numbers for which the

expression is defined.
(a) $(f + 4g)(x)$
(b) $(fg)(x)$
(c) $(f/g)(u)$
(d) $(f - g)(2t)$
(e) $(g/2f)(y)$
(f) $g(f(x))$
(g) $f(g(z))$
(h) $(f \cdot f)(x)$
(i) $(g \cdot g)(t)$

2. Repeat Exercise 1 for the functions
$f\colon f(x) = \frac{1}{2}x - \frac{1}{3}$,
$g\colon g(x) = \sqrt{2 - x^2}$.

3. Let $f\colon f(x) = -2$.
Compute: $f(3)$, $f(t)$, $f(f(1))$.

4. Suppose f is a real function and c is a constant function. What is the relationship between the graph of f and the graph of $f + c$ if c is positive? negative?

Exercises 5–9 illustrate a technique that you will examine more thoroughly in calculus. The technique has a fancy name—*decomposition into partial fractions*—but its purpose is easy to state, namely, that of writing a given function h as a sum of functions that are rather less complicated than h itself.

5. Let $h\colon h(x) = \frac{5x + 9}{x^2 - 9}$. Find constants A and B such that
$h\colon h(x) = \frac{A}{x - 3} + \frac{B}{x + 3}$.

6. Let $h\colon h(x) = \frac{x - 10}{x^2 - 4}$. Find constants A and B such that
$h\colon h(x) = \frac{A}{x + 2} + \frac{B}{x - 2}$.

7. Let $h\colon h(x) = \frac{4x^2 + 3x - 3}{x(x^2 - 1)}$. Find constants A, B, and C such that
$h\colon h(x) = \frac{A}{x} + \frac{B}{x + 1} + \frac{C}{x - 1}$.

8. Let $h\colon h(x) = \frac{x - 2}{x^2(x - 1)}$. Find constants A, B, and C such that
$h\colon h(x) = \frac{A}{x} + \frac{B}{x^2} + \frac{C}{x - 1}$.

9. Let $h\colon h(x) = \frac{2x^2 - 5}{(x - 3)(x^2 + x + 1)}$. Find constants A, B, and C such that $h\colon h(x) = \frac{Ax + B}{x^2 + x + 1} + \frac{C}{x - 3}$.

10. Suppose n is a positive integer, and each of $f_0, f_1, \ldots, f_n$ is a real function. Is there a "natural" way to define the sum and the product of these functions?

11. For each of the following, give examples of one-to-one real functions f and g such that
(a) $f + g$ is not one-to-one.
(b) $f - g$ is not one-to-one.
(c) fg is not one-to-one.
(d) f/g is not one-to-one.

12. (a) Prove that if f and g are increasing functions, then so is $f + g$.
(b) Prove that the sum of two decreasing functions is a decreasing function.
(c) Is the sum of any two monotone functions a monotone function?

*13. (a) Let f and g be increasing functions such that for each number x common to $\mathscr{D}_f$ and $\mathscr{D}_g$, $f(x) > 0$ and $g(x) > 0$. Prove that the product fg is an increasing function.
(b) Is the product of any two increasing functions an increasing function?
(c) Is the product of any two monotone functions a monotone function?

■ 3.4 Composition of Functions

In Section 3.1, we defined a function to be a set of ordered pairs having certain properties, motivated by the fact that a function should be a certain kind of correspondence between two sets of objects. It is sometimes more natural to take a more dynamic view of what a function is, and imagine that if g is a function, then $g(x)$ is the result of "acting on" the element x in the domain of g. Figure 1 may help in keeping this viewpoint in mind.

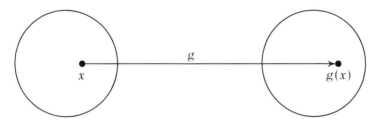

Figure 1

One should not infer from Figure 1 that $\mathscr{D}_g$ and $\mathscr{R}_g$ are necessarily different sets. If, for example, g is the function whose value $g(P)$ at each point P of a coordinate plane is the reflection of P in the vertical coordinate axis, then $\mathscr{D}_g$ and $\mathscr{R}_g$ are the same set, and we might illustrate the "action" of g as in Figure 2 on page 122.

The problem we wish to deal with now is that of *successive action* of functions. That is, if f and g are functions, what happens when g acts on an element x of its domain and then f acts on $g(x)$? Can the result be interpreted as the action of some new function on the object x? Our answer is formalized in the following definition.

DEFINITION   If each of f and g is a function, then the **composite** of f and g, denoted $f \circ g$, is

$$\{(x, y) : y = f(g(x))\},$$

provided this set is nonempty.

It is easy to see that if $\{(x, y) : y = f(g(x))\}$ is nonempty, then it is a function. Its domain is

$$\{x : x \in \mathscr{D}_g \quad \text{and} \quad g(x) \in \mathscr{D}_f\},$$

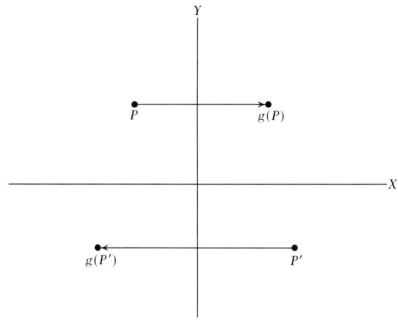

Figure 2

and for each x in this set,

$$(f \circ g)(x) = f(g(x)).$$

In particular, if f and g are real functions, then either $f \circ g$ is undefined, or else it is also a real function.

This definition answers the questions that have been raised. The "action" of $f \circ g$ on an element x of its domain produces the element $(f \circ g)(x)$ of its range, and $(f \circ g)(x)$ is the result of first acting on x with g, and then acting on $g(x)$ with f. Figure 3 illustrates this situation.

The following examples emphasize that one must be careful not to confuse $f \circ g$ with $g \circ f$, because the order in which the functions f and g act is important.

Example 1   Let $f: f(x) = 2x + 1$, $g: g(x) = x^2 - 2$.

Since $\mathscr{D}_f = \mathscr{D}_g = R$, it follows that

$$\mathscr{D}_{f \circ g} = \{x: x \in \mathscr{D}_g \quad \text{and} \quad g(x) \in \mathscr{D}_f\} = R,$$

$$\mathscr{D}_{g \circ f} = \{x: x \in \mathscr{D}_f \quad \text{and} \quad f(x) \in \mathscr{D}_g\} = R,$$

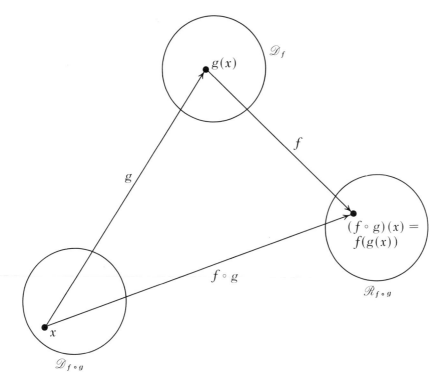

Figure 3

and
$$f \circ g \colon (f \circ g)(x) = f(g(x)) = 2 \cdot g(x) + 1 =$$
$$= 2(x^2 - 2) + 1 = 2x^2 - 3,$$
$$g \circ f \colon (g \circ f)(x) = g(f(x)) = (f(x))^2 - 2 =$$
$$= (2x + 1)^2 - 2 = 4x^2 + 4x - 1.$$

Example 2   Let $f \colon f(x) = 1/(x - 2)$, $g \colon g(x) = \sqrt{x + 4}$.

Then $\mathscr{D}_f = \{x \colon x \in R \quad \text{and} \quad x \neq 2\}$, $\mathscr{D}_g = \{x \colon x \geq -4\}$.

Therefore, $\mathscr{D}_{f \circ g} = \{x \colon x \geq -4 \quad \text{and} \quad \sqrt{x + 4} \neq 2\}$
$$= \{x \colon x \geq -4 \quad \text{and} \quad x \neq 0\},$$

and for each x in $\mathscr{D}_{f \circ g}$, $(f \circ g)(x) = f(g(x)) = 1/(\sqrt{x + 4} - 2)$.

Example 3   Let f and g be as in Example 2, and find $g \circ f$.

$$\mathscr{D}_{g \circ f} = \{x \colon x \neq 2 \quad \text{and} \quad 1/(x - 2) \geq -4\}$$
$$= \{x \colon x \neq 2 \quad \text{and} \quad (4x - 7)/(x - 2) \geq 0\}$$

$$= \{x: 4x - 7 \geq 0 \quad \text{and} \quad x > 2, \text{ or } 4x - 7 \leq 0 \quad \text{and} \quad x < 2\}$$
$$= \{x: x > 2 \text{ or } x \leq 7/4\},$$

and for each x in $\mathscr{D}_{g \circ f}$,
$$(g \circ f)(x) = g(f(x)) = \sqrt{1/(x-2) + 4} = \sqrt{(4x-7)/(x-2)}.$$

Example 4   Let $f: f(x) = \sqrt{1-x}$, $g: g(x) = x^2 + 2$.
   Then $f \circ g$ is undefined, because if $x \in \mathscr{D}_g$, then $g(x) \geq 2$, so $g(x) \notin \mathscr{D}_f$.

Example 5   Let f and g be as in Example 4.

$$\mathscr{D}_f = \{x: x \leq 1\} \quad \text{and} \quad \mathscr{D}_g = R, \quad \text{so} \quad \mathscr{D}_{g \circ f} = \{x: x \leq 1\},$$

and for each $x \leq 1$, $(g \circ f)(x) = (\sqrt{1-x})^2 + 2 = 3 - x$. Thus,

$$g \circ f: (g \circ f)(x) = 3 - x, \, x \leq 1.$$

This indicates that the domain of $g \circ f$ cannot, in general, be found by calculating $g(f(x))$, willy-nilly, and then finding those values of x for which the resulting expression is defined, else we might come to the erroneous conclusion in Example 5 that $\mathscr{D}_{g \circ f} = R$ because the expression $3 - x$ is defined for *all* real numbers x.

Example 6   Let $f: f(x) = \sqrt{x}$, $g: g(x) = |x|$.
   For any number $x \geq 0$, we have that

$$g(f(x)) = |\sqrt{x}| = \sqrt{x} = \sqrt{|x|} = f(g(x)).$$

But it is not correct to conclude from this that $g \circ f = f \circ g$.

For, $\mathscr{D}_f = \{x: x \geq 0\} \quad \text{and} \quad \mathscr{D}_g = R.$

Moreover, if $x \in \mathscr{D}_g,$

then $g(x) \geq 0, \quad \text{so} \quad g(x) \in \mathscr{D}_f.$

Hence, $\mathscr{D}_{f \circ g} = \mathscr{D}_g = R.$

By similar reasoning, we see that $\mathscr{D}_{g \circ f} = \{x: x \geq 0\}$, so that $f \circ g$ and $g \circ f$ have different domains. Hence, the two functions cannot be equal.

Example 7   Let $h: h(x) = (x-3)^2 + 1.$
   If $f: f(u) = u^2 + 1$ and $g: g(x) = x - 3$, it follows that $h = f \circ g$. This fact can be used to sketch the graph of h in the XY plane.
   First introduce the UV coordinate system that is the translation of the XY coordinate system such that $(0,0)_{UV} = (3,0)_{XY}$. This means that the UV coordinates of a point are related to the XY coordinates of the same point by the equations

$$u = x - 3$$
$$v = y.$$

Then, if the U and V axes are drawn in the XY plane, the graph of h in the XY plane will appear as the graph of f in the UV plane, as shown in Figure 4.

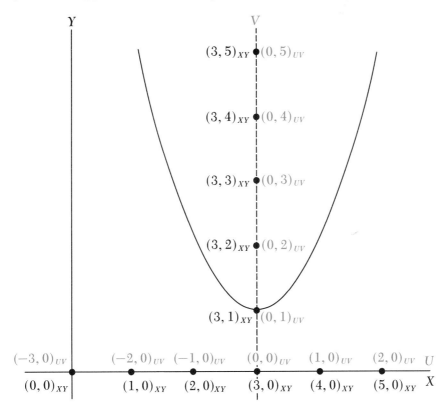

Figure 4

Graph of h: $h(x) = (x - 3)^2 + 1$
in the XY plane

Example 8   The whole idea behind the translation of a coordinate system can be described in terms of the composition of functions.

To begin with, a coordinate system for a plane is a one-to-one function f whose domain is the set of all points P of the plane and whose range is the set of all ordered pairs (x, y) of real numbers. To obtain a natural coordinate system for a plane, we select a horizontal coordinate line X and a vertical coordinate line Y in the plane, as described in Section 2.1, and then define a function f as follows:

For each point P in the plane, let

$$f(P) = (x, y),$$

where x is the coordinate of the projection of P on X and y is the coordinate of the projection of P on Y. (See Figure 5.)

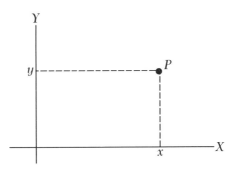

Figure 5

The resulting coordinate plane is called the XY plane.

Now, suppose that a UV coordinate system is introduced in this same plane, and it is a translation of the XY system. First of all, this new system will be a natural coordinate system, so it will be described by the function g defined by:

For each point P in the plane, let

$$g(P) = (u, v),$$

where u is the coordinate of the projection of P on the coordinate line U and v is the coordinate of the projection of P on the coordinate line V. (See Figure 6.)

Next, there is a definite relationship between the functions f and g, for suppose the origin $(0, 0)_{UV}$ in the UV system is the point $(h, k)_{XY}$ in the XY system. Then, for any point P in the plane, if

$$f(P) = (x, y) \quad \text{and} \quad g(P) = (u, v),$$

we know from Section 2.6 that

$$u = x - h$$
$$v = y - k.$$

This means that if

$$H : H((x, y)) = (x - h, y - k), x \in R, y \in R,$$

then for every point P in the plane, $g(P) = H(f(P))$, so that $g = H \circ f$.

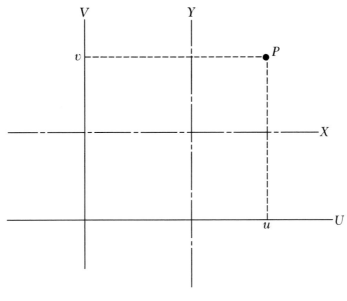

Figure 6

Thus, the "new" coordinate system g is obtained from the "old" coordinate system f by finding the composite of the function H with f. For this reason, H is called a **change of coordinates.**

Example 9.   Let $f = \{(d, c) : d > 0 \text{ and } c = \pi d\}$, and let $g = \{(r, c) : r > 0 \text{ and } c = 2\pi r\}$. Then

$$f : f(d) = \pi d,\, d > 0, \quad \text{and}$$
$$g : g(r) = 2\pi r,\, r > 0,$$

so f is the function that gives the circumference of a circle in terms of its diameter, and g gives the circumference of a circle in terms of its radius. When someone says, rather imprecisely, that "the circumference of a circle is a function of its diameter," he is talking about the function f, while if he says that "the circumference of a circle is a function of its radius," he refers to the function g.

Now, f and g are clearly not the same function, but there is a close relationship between them. For, if

$$h : h(r) = 2r,\, r > 0,$$

then $g = f \circ h$. That is, if h is the function that gives the diameter of a circle in terms of its radius, then g is the composite of f and h.

In many problems of calculus, especially those that involve applications to physical situations, this technique of recognizing one function as the composite of other functions is quite important. Some samples of these problems are given in the exercises.

EXERCISES

1. Find $f \circ g$ and $g \circ f$ in each of the following. Remember to calculate $\mathscr{D}_{f \circ g}$ and $\mathscr{D}_{g \circ f}$.
   (a) $f \colon f(x) = x^2 - 2$,
       $g \colon g(x) = 1/(x+1)$
   (b) $f \colon f(x) = |x| + 1$,
       $g \colon g(x) = \sqrt{x-3}$
   (c) $f \colon f(x) = 5x^2 - 2x - 2$,
       $g \colon g(x) = (x-1)^{1/2}$
   (d) $f \colon f(x) = 1/x$,
       $g \colon g(x) = 1 - 1/x$.

2. For each given function h, find functions f and g such that $h = f \circ g$. Use this to draw the graph of h in the XY plane.
   (a) $h \colon h(x) = (x+4)^2 - 1$
   (b) $h \colon h(x) = (x-2)^2 + 2$
   (c) $h \colon h(x) = x^2 + 4x + 5$
   (d) $h \colon h(x) = x^2 - 2x - 3$
   (e) $h \colon h(x) = \sqrt{x+3}$
   (f) $h \colon h(x) = 1/(x+2)$
   (g) $h \colon h(x) = |2x - 4|$
   (h) $h \colon h(x) = \sqrt{2x-5}$

3. Prove that if H is the function defined in Example 8, then H is one-to-one, and $\mathscr{R}_H = \{(u,v) : u \in R \text{ and } v \in R\}$.

4. Let f and g be the functions defined in Example 8. Find a function K such that $f = K \circ g$.

5. Let f and g be the functions defined in Example 9. Find a function k such that $f = g \circ k$. What does the function k which you have found "do"?

6. Let f be the function that gives the area of a circle in terms of its radius, and let g be the one that gives the area of a circle in terms of its diameter. Give algebraic formulations of f and g, and find functions

h and k such that $g = f \circ h$ and $f = g \circ k$.

7. Let F be the function that gives the area of a square in terms of the length of one of its diagonals. In finding an algebraic formulation of F, you almost automatically discover that F is the composite of two other functions. What are they?

8. A baseball diamond is a 90-foot square. A ball is hit down the third-base line at a rate of 100 feet per second. Let d be the function that gives the distance in feet of the ball from first base in terms of time in seconds. Write d as the composite of two other functions to get an algebraic formulation of d.

9. Let F be the function defined as follows:

   For each ordered pair (x, y) of real numbers, let

$$F((x, y)) = (-x, y).$$

If the ordered pair (x, y) is regarded as a point of a coordinate plane, what does F "do" to each point (x, y)? What is the result of $F \circ F$?

10. Let G be the function defined on the set of all points (x, y) of a coordinate plane as follows:

   For each point (x, y), let $G((x, y))$ be the reflection of (x, y) in the origin.

   Give an algebraic formulation of G, and compute $G \circ G$. If F is the function defined in Exercise 9, what is $F \circ G$? What is $G \circ F$?

$^{\circ}$**11.** Let f and g be monotone functions. (See Exercise 6 of Section 3.2.)

Prove that if $f \circ g$ is defined, then it is a monotone function also.

12. If $g: g(x) = x^2$ and $f: f(x) = \sqrt{x}$, then $(g \circ f)(x) = x$ whenever $x \geq 0$. Find several other examples of real functions f and g such that for every x in $\mathscr{D}_f$, $(g \circ f)(x) = x$. Can you discover a property that we have studied that all the functions f you have found have in common?

13. Suppose f and g are real functions whose graphs appear in the following diagram. Find the coordinates of each of the four points A, B, C, D.

14. Use the result of Exercise 13 to state a recipe for constructing the graph of $f \circ g$, given the graphs of the real functions f and g.

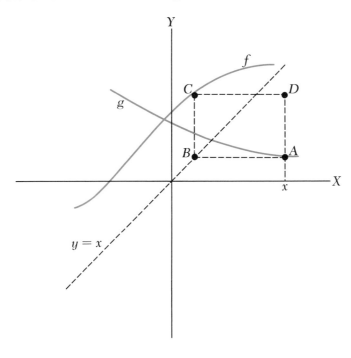

CHAPTER 4

POLYNOMIAL AND RATIONAL FUNCTIONS

■ 4.1 Polynomial Functions

The remainder of our study is devoted to a class of functions called *elementary functions*. These are the functions that the reader will encounter most often in his study of calculus. Of the elementary functions, those that are used most frequently are the *polynomial functions*, to which we now turn our attention.

DEFINITION A **polynomial function** is a function

$$p: p(x) = a_0 + a_1 x + a_2 x^2 + \cdots + a_n x^n,$$

where n is a nonnegative integer and $a_0, a_1, a_2, \ldots, a_n$ are real numbers.

Notice that no restriction has been placed on the domain of p, so the domain of every polynomial function is the set of all real numbers.

DEFINITION If $p: p(x) = a_0 + a_1 x + a_2 x^2 + \cdots + a_n x^n$ is a polynomial function with all of the coefficients $a_0, a_1, a_2, \ldots, a_n$ equal to zero, p is called the **zero polynomial**. If p is not the zero polynomial, the largest integer k, $0 \leq k \leq n$, for which $a_k \neq 0$ is called the **degree** of p and a_k is called the **leading coefficient** of p. The number a_0 is called the **constant term** of p.

Example 1 $f: f(x) = 3 + x - 5x^2 + (\tfrac{1}{2})x^3$ is a polynomial function of degree 3, with leading coefficient $\tfrac{1}{2}$ and constant term 3.

$g: g(x) = 7 - \sqrt{2}x^5 + 4/3x^2 + 0x^7$ is a polynomial function of degree 5, with leading coefficient $-\sqrt{2}$ and constant term 7.

$h: h(x) = 2 + x + 5x^{3/2}$ is *not* a polynomial function. We may suspect that this is the case because the exponent on x in the third term is not a non-negative integer. To verify our suspicion on this basis is not exactly a trivial matter, however, since we sould have to show that there is *no* way of choosing a nonnegative integer n and real numbers $a_0, a_1, \ldots, a_n$ such that $h: h(x) = a_0 + a_1 x + \cdots + a_n x^n$. (For more enlightenment on this subject, see Exercises 12, 13, and 14 of Section 4.3.) For this particular example, however, we can see that $\mathscr{D}_h = \{x: x \geq 0\}$, so h is not a polynomial function because $\mathscr{D}_h \neq R$.

Example 2 $f: f(x) = -6$ is a polynomial having degree zero, leading coefficient -6 and constant term -6. If c is a nonzero real number, the function $p: p(x) = c$ is a polynomial function of degree 0 and leading coefficient c. Thus, polynomial functions of degree 0 and the zero polynomial function are constant functions. (Recall Example 5 of Section 3.3.)

Example 3   Every **linear function** $L: L(x) = mx + b$, $m \neq 0$, is a polynomial function of degree 1, with leading coefficient m and constant term b. Its graph is a nonvertical line with slope m and vertical intercept b.

Example 4   A polynomial function

$$q: q(x) = ax^2 + bx + c \quad \text{with} \quad a \neq 0$$

of degree two is called a **quadratic function**.

Completing the square in x, one has

$$q(x) = a\left[x^2 + \frac{b}{a}x + \frac{b^2}{4a^2} + \frac{c}{a} - \frac{b^2}{4a^2}\right]$$

$$= a\left(x + \frac{b}{2a}\right)^2 + \frac{4ac - b^2}{4a}.$$

For each real number x, $\left(x + \dfrac{b}{2a}\right)^2 \geq 0$. Hence, if $a > 0$,

$$q(x) \geq \frac{4ac - b^2}{4a} = q\left(-\frac{b}{2a}\right)$$

and if $a < 0$,

$$q(x) \leq \frac{4ac - b^2}{4a} = q\left(-\frac{b}{2a}\right).$$

Therefore, the graph lies above or on the line $y = q\left(-\frac{b}{2a}\right)$ if $a > 0$ as shown in Figure 1, and below or on this line if $a < 0$.

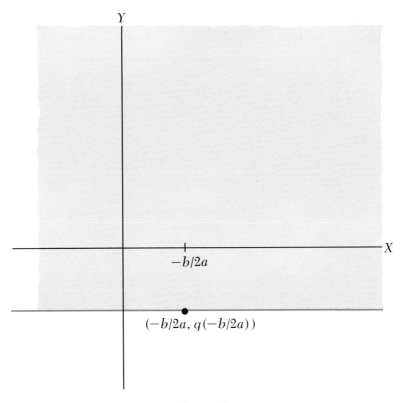

Figure 1

Since
$$\left(x + \frac{b}{2a}\right)^2 > 0 \quad \text{if} \quad x \neq -\frac{b}{2a},$$

we see that the point

$$\left(-\frac{b}{2a}, \, q\left(-\frac{b}{2a}\right)\right)$$

is the highest or lowest point on the graph of q depending on whether

$$a < 0 \quad \text{or} \quad a > 0.$$

Let us consider several specific quadratic functions.

Let $f\colon f(x) = x^2 + 4x - 3.$

Here, $a = 1, b = 4$ and $c = -3,$

so the lowest point on the graph of f is

$$(-2, f(-2)) = (-2, -7).$$

The graph of f appears in Figure 2(a).

Let $g\colon g(x) = -3x^2 + 4x - 1$. The highest point of the graph of g is

$$\left(-\frac{4}{2(-3)}, g\left(-\frac{4}{2(-3)}\right)\right) = (2/3, 1/3).$$

The graph appears in Figure 2(b). If $h\colon h(x) = 5x^2 - 10x + 6$, the graph has $(1,1)$ as its lowest point. See Figure 2(c) for the graph of h.

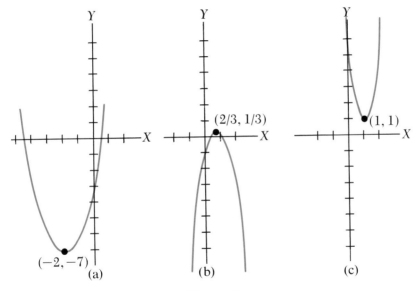

Figure 2

Example 5   Let $f_n\colon f_n(x) = x^n$, where n is a positive integer. That is, $f_1\colon f_1(x) = x$, $f_2\colon f_2(x) = x^2$, $f_3\colon f_3(x) = x^3$, and so on.

If n is an even integer, $f_n(x) \geq 0$ for all $x \in R$ and equality holds if and only if $x = 0$. If n is an odd integer, $f_n(x) > 0$ for $x > 0$, $f_n(x) < 0$ for $x < 0$ and $f_n(0) = 0$. Notice also that for n even, the graph of f_n is symmetric with respect to the vertical axis. Similarly, for n odd, the graph of f_n is symmetric with respect to the origin. Consequently, to graph any of these functions, we need only determine the graph in the first quadrant.

Now if $0 \le x_1 < x_2$ then by Theorem 1.3.2,

$$f_n(x_1) = x_1^n < x_2^n = f_n(x_2).$$

That is, each of the functions f_n is increasing on the ray $[0, \infty)$. (Recall Exercise 6, Section 3.2.)

To compare the graphs of these functions, note that each contains the points $(0,0)$ and $(1,1)$. For $0 < x < 1$, $0 < f_n(x) = x^n < 1$ and for $x > 1$, $f_n(x) = x^n > 1$. Now consider two of these functions, say f_i and f_j, where each of i and j is a positive integer and $i < j$. Then for $0 < x < 1, 0 < x^{j-i} < 1$ and $0 < x^i$, so that

$$f_j(x) = x^j = x^{j-i} \cdot x^i < x^i = f_i(x).$$

For $x > 1$, $1 < x^i$ and $1 < x^{j-i}$, so

$$f_i(x) = x^i < x^i \cdot x^{j-i} = x^j = f_j(x).$$

Thus, we see that when $i < j$, the graph of f_i lies above the graph of f_j on the interval $(0, 1)$, and below the graph of f_j on the ray $(1, \infty)$. The graphs of f_1, f_2, f_3, f_4 and f_7 appear in Figure 3.

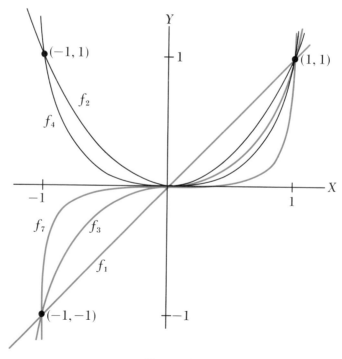

Figure 3

EXERCISES

1. Which of the following functions are polynomial functions? For each polynomial function, state, if possible, its degree, leading coefficient, and constant term. Which, if any, of these functions have graphs that are symmetric with respect to (i) the vertical axis, (ii) the horizontal axis, (iii) the origin?
   (a) $f: f(x) = 3x^2 - 5x^3 + 4x$
   (b) $g: g(x) = (-1/\sqrt{17})\, x^4 - \pi x^2$
   (c) $h: h(x) = 0$
   (d) $G: G(x) = 47/3 + x^{13}$
   (e) $H: H(a) = \sqrt{2}\, a + 2\sqrt{a}$
   (f) $p: p(s) = 2s^7 + 3s^5 - 5s$
   (g) $q: q(x) = 1/x$
   (h) $P: P(x) = 4x^2 + 3x^{-1} + 2$
   (i) $Q: Q(x)$
     $= (x+5)(x-3)^2(x+1)$
   (j) $F: F(z) = (z^2 - 1)^{-1}$

2. (a) On a large piece of graph paper sketch the graphs of the functions f_3, f_4, f_5 and f_6 of Example 5 on the interval $[-3/2, 3/2]$.
   (b) Sketch the graphs of the functions f_{15} and f_{20} of Example 5 on the interval $[-1, 1]$.

3. Sketch the graph of each of the following quadratic polynomial functions after rereading Example 4.
   (a) $P: P(x) = x^2 - 2x - 3$
   (b) $P: P(x) = -3x^2 + 5x - 4$
   (c) $f: f(x) = 1 + x + x^2$
   (d) $g: g(x) = (2x + 3)(1 - 2x)$
   (e) $h: h(x) = -(x - 1)^2$

4. (a) Show that the range of the function $q: q(x) = 2x^2 - 4x + 5$ is $[3, \infty)$.
   (b) Show that the range of the function $p: p(x) = -x^2 + 3x + 1$ is $(-\infty, \frac{13}{4}]$.

5. In Example 4, it was seen for a quadratic polynomial function $q: q(x) = ax^2 + bx + c$ with $a \neq 0$, that

$\mathcal{R}_q \subset \left[\dfrac{4ac - b^2}{4a}, \infty \right)$ if $a > 0$, and

$\mathcal{R}_q \subset \left(-\infty, \dfrac{4ac - b^2}{4a} \right]$ if $a < 0$.

In each case, show that set inclusion can be replaced by set equality. That is, for $a > 0$, show that if d is any number greater than or equal to $\dfrac{4ac - b^2}{4a}$, then there is a number x such that $q(x) = d$, and for $a < 0$, if $d' \leq \dfrac{4ac - b^2}{4a}$ then there is a number x' such that $q(x') = d'$.

6. For each real number a, let $g_a: g_a(x) = ax^2$. On the same large piece of graph paper sketch the graphs of g_{-2}, g_{-1}, $g_{1/2}$, g_1, g_2, and g_3.

7. With the aid of the previous examples and exercises of this section and the method of Example 7 of Section 3.4, sketch the graphs of each of the following polynomial functions.
   (a) $f: f(x) = (x - 3)^3$
   (b) $g: g(x) = (x - 3)^3 - 2$
   (c) $h: h(x) = -2(x + 1)^2$
   (d) $F: F(x) = -2(x + 1)^2 + 3$
   (e) $G: G(x) = 3\left(x - \dfrac{1}{2}\right)^5 + 1$

8. Let q be a quadratic function. Show that there is a vertical line L such that the graph of q is symmetric with respect to L.

9. (a) Find a quadratic polynomial function whose graph contains the points $(-1, 0)$, $(2, 0)$ and $(1, 1)$.
   (b) Find a quadratic polynomial function whose graph contains the points $(0, 0)$, $(1, 2)$ and $(3, 1)$.
   (c) Given three points (x_1, y_1),

(x_2, y_2), and (x_3, y_3), does there necessarily exist a quadratic polynomial function whose graph contains these points?

10. Let $p: p(x) = x^2 - 3x - 28$.
    (a) Show that if $x > 7$ then $p(x) > 0$.
    (b) Show that if $x > 20$ then $p(x) > 300$.
    (c) Find a number x_0 such that $p(x) > 1{,}000$ whenever $x > x_0$.
    (d) Let N be a positive number. Does there exist another positive number d such that $p(x) > N$ whenever $x > d$? Is there a negative number t such that $p(x) > N$ whenever $x < t$?
    (e) What do the above results tell you about the graph of p?

11. Let $q: q(x) = ax^2 + bx + c$, where $a > 0$, and let N be a positive number. Show that there is a positive number d such that if $|x| > d$ then $q(x) > N$. What does this tell you about the graph of q? What conclusions can you draw if the leading coefficient a is negative?

°12. Let P be a polynomial function of degree m and let Q be a polynomial function of degree n. Consider the functions $P + Q$, $P - Q$, $P \cdot Q$, P/Q and $P \circ Q$. Which of these functions will necessarily be polynomial functions? For those that are, what, if anything, can you say

about their degrees?

13. Let R be a rectangle of perimeter 8 inches.
    (a) Give an algebraic description of the function A that gives the area of R in terms of the length of one side of R.
    (b) Show that the point $(2, 4)$ is the highest point of the graph of A. What is the significance of this result?

14. Let $L = \{(x, y) : y = x + 4\}$ and let $P = (1, 2)$.
    (a) Give an algebraic formulation of the function d that assigns to each real number x the distance between the point P and the point $(x, x + 4)$ on L.
    (b) Let $q: q(x) = (d(x))^2$, and show that the point $(-1/2, 9/2)$ is the lowest point of the graph of q. What is the significance of this result?

15. Let $L = \{(x, y) : y = 3x + 1\}$, and let $P_1 = (2, 1)$, $P_2 = (4, 3)$.
    (a) Give an algebraic formulation of the function f that assigns to each real number x the square of the distance between the point P_1 and the point $(x, 3x + 1)$ plus the square of the distance between the point P_2 and the point $(x, 3x + 1)$.
    (b) Show that the point $(\frac{3}{5}, \frac{84}{5})$ is the lowest point of the graph of f. What is the significance of this result?

■ 4.2 Zeros of Polynomials

Let P and D be polynomial functions. If there is a unique polynomial function Q such that $P = D \cdot Q$, D is said to **divide** P, or be a **factor** of P. For example, if $P: P(x) = 6x^3 + 17x^2 + 2x - 15$ and $D: D(x) = 2x + 3$, then $P = D \cdot Q$ where $Q: Q(x) = 3x^2 + 4x - 5$, so D is a factor of P. Similarly, in the example, Q is a factor of P. Clearly, any polynomial function of degree 0 is a factor of every polynomial function, and each polynomial function other than the zero polynomial is a factor of itself. In the light of Exercise 12 of

Section 4.1, it is seen that if D is a factor of P, then the degree of D is less than or equal to the degree of P.

The reader is probably familiar with the process of dividing one polynomial by another to obtain a quotient and remainder. That this can always be done is guaranteed by the following theorem.

THEOREM 4.2.1 (Division Algorithm) Let each of P and D be polynomial functions with D not the zero polynomial. There exist unique polynomial functions Q and R such that

$$P = Q \cdot D + R$$

and R is either the zero polynomial or has degree less than the degree of D. Q is called the **quotient** and R the **remainder** when P is divided by D.

To prove this theorem would take us too far afield and contribute little to the reader's understanding at present so its validity will be accepted.

It is now clear that D is a factor of P if and only if the remainder when P is divided by D is the zero polynomial. To illustrate, let $P: P(x) = x^5 + 4x^2 - 6x + 1$ and $D: D(x) = x - 1$. Then, using long division to divide P by D, it is found that $P = D \cdot Q + R$, where

$$Q: Q(x) = x^4 + x^3 + x^2 + 5x - 1$$

and R is the zero polynomial. Hence, D is a factor of P. If $D': D'(x) = x - 2$, then $P = D' \cdot Q' + R'$ where $Q': Q'(x) = x^4 + 2x^3 + 4x^2 + 12x + 18$ and $R': R'(x) = 37$. Thus, D' is not a factor of P.

DEFINITION A number c is a **zero** of a function f provided $f(c) = 0$.

Geometrically, the zeros of a real function are the horizontal intercepts of its graph. A constant function $f: f(x) = c$ has no zeros if $c \neq 0$. However, if $c = 0$, then every real number is a zero of f. A linear function $L: L(x) = mx + b$, with $m \neq 0$, has exactly one zero, namely, $-b/m$.

Example 1 Let $q: q(x) = ax^2 + bx + c$, $a \neq 0$. It was shown in Section 4.1 that

$$q(x) = a(x + b/(2a))^2 + (4ac - b^2)/(4a).$$

Hence, $$\{x: q(x) = 0\} = \left\{ x: \left(x + \frac{b}{2a} \right)^2 = \frac{b^2 - 4ac}{4a^2} \right\}.$$

There are three possibilities:

(i)   If $b^2 - 4ac < 0$, then $\{x : q(x) = 0\} = \varnothing$ so q has no zeros.

(ii) If $b^2 - 4ac = 0$, then $\{x : q(x) = 0\} = \left\{-\dfrac{b}{2a}\right\}$, so q has exactly one zero.

(iii) If $b^2 - 4ac > 0$, then

$$\{x : q(x) = 0\} = \left\{\frac{-b + \sqrt{b^2 - 4ac}}{2a}, \frac{-b - \sqrt{b^2 - 4ac}}{2a}\right\}$$

and there are exactly two zeros of q.

The number $b^2 - 4ac$ is called the **discriminant** of q and Example 1 shows that it can be used to ascertain the number of zeros of a quadratic polynomial function without actually computing them.

Example 2   In Example 1 it was seen that a quadratic polynomial function can have at most two zeros. Consider the graph of $q : q(x) = ax^2 + bx + c$ with $a \neq 0$ in the XY-plane. Let k be a constant and $p : p(x) = ax^2 + bx + (c - k)$. Now $p(x) = q(x) - k$ and there are at most two zeros of p, so there are at most two numbers r such that $q(r) = k$. That is, the graph of q intersects any horizontal line $y = k$ in at most two points.

Let P be any polynomial function, c a real number, and $D : D(x) = x - c$. By the Division Algorithm (Theorem 4.2.1) there are unique polynomial functions Q and R, with R a constant function, such that $P = Q \cdot D + R$. Thus, for any number x,

$$P(x) = Q(x)D(x) + R(x).$$

In particular,

$$P(c) = Q(c)(c - c) + R(c) = R(c).$$

Since R is a constant function, and its value at the number c is known to be $P(c)$, it follows that the value of R at any number x must be $P(c)$. Thus, $R : R(x) = P(c)$, so we have proved the following theorem.

THEOREM 4.2.2   (Remainder Theorem) If P is a polynomial function and c is a real number, then $P(c)$ is the constant remainder found upon dividing P by the polynomial function $D : D(x) = x - c$.

An immediate corollary of Theorem 4.2.2 is

THEOREM 4.2.3   (Factor Theorem)   A number c is a zero of the polynomial function P if and only if $D: D(x) = x - c$ is a factor of P.

Example 3   Suppose r_1 and r_2 are distinct zeros of a polynomial function P. First of all, the Factor Theorem implies that there is a polynomial function Q_1 such that

$$P: P(x) = (x - r_1)Q_1(x).$$

In particular, $0 = P(r_2) = (r_2 - r_1)Q_1(r_2)$. Since $r_2 - r_1 \neq 0$, $Q_1(r_2) = 0$ so applying the Factor Theorem again, there is a polynomial function Q_2 such that $Q_1: Q_1(x) = (x - r_2)Q_2(x)$, whence

$$P: P(x) = (x - r_1)(x - r_2)Q_2(x).$$

If $r_1, r_2, \ldots, r_n$ are distinct zeros of P, then the above argument can be extended by induction to obtain a polynomical function Q_n such that

$$P: P(x) = (x - r_1)(x - r_2) \cdots (x - r_n)Q_n(x).$$

From this it is seen that if P has degree n, then there are at most n distinct zeros of P. For if there were more, choose $n + 1$ of them, say $r_1, r_2, \ldots, r_n$, r_{n+1}. There is a polynomial function Q_{n+1} such that

$$P: P(x) = (x - r_1)(x - r_2) \cdots (x - r_n)(x - r_{n+1})Q_{n+1}(x).$$

From Exercise 12 of Section 4.1, the degree of P is at least $n + 1$, which is a contradiction. Thus, a polynomial function of degree n has at most n zeros. Arguing exactly as in Example 2, it follows that any horizontal line can intersect the graph of P in at most n points.

Example 4   Find a polynomial function f having degree 3 and leading coefficient 1, whose zeros are $-1, 5$ and 7.

If $-1, 5$ and 7 are zeros of f, then each of $x + 1$, $x - 5$, and $x - 7$ must be a factor of $f(x)$. Hence,

$$f: f(x) = (x + 1)(x - 5)(x - 7)Q(x)$$

for some polynomial function Q. The degree of Q must be zero, so Q is a constant function. To obtain the leading coefficient 1 for f, $Q: Q(x) = 1$. Thus,

$$f: f(x) = (x + 1)(x - 5)(x - 7) = x^3 - 11x^2 + 23x + 35.$$

Had we been seeking a polynomial function f having degree 3, zeros -1, 5, and 7 and leading coefficient -2, we would choose $Q: Q(x) = -2$ so that

$$f: f(x) = -2(x+1)(x-5)(x-7) = -2x^3 + 22x^2 - 46x - 70.$$

Example 5   Find a polynomial function Z of degree 3 and leading coefficient 1, having -2 as its only zero.

This can be done in many ways. One way is to pick $Z: Z(x) = (x+2)^3$. Another is to let

$$Z: Z(x) = (x+2)Q(x)$$

where Q is a polynomial function of degree 2 with leading coefficient 1 that has no zeros. Thus, we could choose Q to be any quadratic polynomial whose discriminant is negative and whose leading coefficient is 1, say

$$Q: Q(x) = x^2 + x + 5$$

or

$$Q: Q(x) = x^2 - 6x + 11.$$

Example 6   Find a polynomial function g having degree 4, leading coefficient 6 and such that

$$g(-5) = g(1) = g(2) = g(5/2) = -1.$$

The polynomial function

$$h: h(x) = 6(x+5)(x-1)(x-2)(x-5/2)$$

is of degree 4, has leading coefficient 6 and zeros -5, 1, 2, and 5/2. Let $j: j(x) = -1$ and $g = h + j$.

Then

$$g: g(x) = h(x) + j(x) = 6(x+5)(x-1)(x-2)(x-5/2) - 1$$

so we have

$$g(-5) = g(1) = g(2) = g(5/2) = -1,$$

and g has the desired degree and leading coefficient.

EXERCISES

1. For each of the following pairs P, D of polynomial functions, find the quotient Q and remainder R, when P is divided by D.
   (a) $P: P(x) = 2x^3 + x^2 - 5x + 1,$
   $D: D(x) = -x^2 + 1$
   (b) $P: P(x) = x^5 + x^4 + x^3 + x^2 + x + 1,$ $D: D(x) = x + 1$
   (c) $P: P(x) = -(x-2)^3,$
   $D: D(x) = x - 2$

(d) $P: P(x) = 4x^4 - 3x^2 + 5x + 2$,
$\quad D: D(x) = x^3 - x$

(e) $P: P(x) = x - 1$,
$\quad D: D(x) = x^2 + 2x - 3$

(f) $P: P(x) = x^2 + 5x - 1$,
$\quad D: D(x) = 2$

2. Find the zeros of each of the following functions.

(a) $f: f(x) = 2x - 3$

(b) $g: g(x) = 4x^2 - 2x - 1$

(c) $h: h(s) = s^3 - s^2 + s$

(d) $F: F(a) = \dfrac{a - 1}{2a + 3}$

(e) $G: G(x)$
$\quad = \dfrac{(x - 1)(3x^2 + 5x + 3)}{x^2 - 2x + 1}$

(f) $H: H(x) = x^4 + 4x^2 - 21$

3. Let $P: P(x) = x^2 - x - 6$.

(a) Find the zeros of P.

(b) Find $\{x: P(x) = 2\}$.

(c) Find $\{x: P(x) = -10\}$.

(d) Let (a, b) be any open interval that contains no zeros of P. Show that for all pairs of numbers x_1 and x_2 in (a, b), $P(x_1)P(x_2) > 0$. Give a geometric interpretation of this result.

(e) Sketch the graph of P.

4. Let $q: q(x) = ax^2 + bx + c$. Let (α, β) be any open interval that contains no zeros of q. Show that if x_1 and x_2 are any elements of (α, β) then $q(x_1)q(x_2) > 0$. What does this tell you about the graph of q?

5. Find polynomial functions having the indicated degree, leading coefficient, and zeros.

(a) degree 4, leading coefficient 3, zeros $1, \frac{1}{2}, \frac{1}{3}, \frac{1}{4}$.

(b) degree 2, leading coefficient 1, zeros $1 - \sqrt{2}, 1 + \sqrt{2}$.

(c) degree 6, leading coefficient 1, zeros $1 \pm \sqrt{17}, 2 \pm \sqrt{6}, 0, 1$.

(d) degree 4, leading coefficient -1, zeros $1, 3$.

(e) degree 3, leading coefficient -5, zeros $-\frac{1}{2}, \frac{4}{3}, \pi$.

Exercises 6 and 7 outline a scheme, called **synthetic division**, for finding the quotient and remainder when a polynomial function P is divided by $D: D(x) = x - d$.

6. Let $C: C(x) = a_3x^3 + a_2x^2 + a_1x + a_0$, $a_3 \neq 0$. For each real number d, show that $C(d) = d[d(a_3d + a_2) + a_1] + a_0$. This suggests the following scheme or algorithm for computing the value of C at any number d.

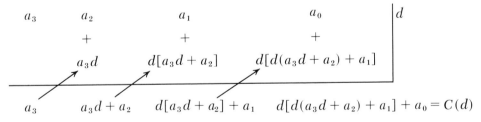

Let us try this scheme if $C: C(x) = 3x^3 - 4x^2 - x + 7$ and $d = 2$.

3	-4	-1	7	2
	$+$	$+$	$+$	
	6	4	6	
3	2	3	$13 = C(2)$	

To find $C(-3)$,

$$
\begin{array}{c|ccccc}
3 & -4 & -1 & 7 & \big|{-3} \\
  & -9 & 39 & -114 & \\
\hline
3 & -13 & 38 & -107 = C(-3) &
\end{array}
$$

Use this scheme to compute $C(1)$, $C(-1)$, $C(4)$ and $C(1/2)$. Extend this scheme to apply to polynomials of degrees 4 and 5.

7. (Continuation of Exercise 6) By Theorem 4.2.2, it is seen that $C(d)$ is the remainder obtained when C is divided by D: $D(x) = x - d$. Observe that if C is divided by D_1: $D_1(x) = x - 2$, the quotient is

$$Q_1 : Q_1(x) = 3x^2 + 2x + 3;$$

if C is divided by D_2: $D_2(x) = x + 3$, the quotient is

$$Q_2 : Q_2(x) = 3x^2 - 13x + 38.$$

Show that if C: $C(x) = a_3x^3 + a_2x^2 + a_1x + a_0$ is divided by D: $D(x) = x - d$, then the quotient is

$$
Q : Q(x) = a_3x^2 + (a_3d + a_2)x \\
+ [d(a_3d + a_2) + a_1].
$$

The first diagram in Exercise 6 indicates that the terms that appear in the last row of the computational scheme under discussion are exactly the coefficients of the quotient and the remainder when C is divided by D. State a similar result for polynomials of degree 4, 5, and n.

Use this process of synthetic division to find the quotient and remainder when P is divided by D in each of the following.

(a) P: $P(x) = -2x^3 + x^2 - 5x + 1$, D: $D(x) = x + 7$
(b) P: $P(x) = x^3 + 5x$, D: $D(x) = x - 1$
(c) P: $P(x) = x^7 + 4x^6 - 5x^3 - 7x^2 + 2$, D: $D(x) = x + 1$

8. It can be shown that if P: $P(x) = a_nx^n + a_{n-1}x^{n-1} + \cdots + a_1x + a_0$, $a_n \neq 0$, where each of coefficients $a_n, a_{n-1}, \ldots, a_1, a_0$ is an integer and c/d is a zero of P, where c and d are integers having no common factor, then c is a factor of the constant term a_0 and d is a factor of the leading coefficient a_n. That is, the only possible rational zeros c/d in lowest terms of P are those for which c is a factor of a_0 and d is a factor of a_n. Use this to aid in finding the zeros of each of the following polynomial functions.

(a) f: $f(x) = x^5 + 4x^4 + 7x^3 + 7x^2 + 4x + 1$
(b) g: $g(x) = 4x^3 + 8x^2 + x - 3$
(c) h: $h(t) = 7t^3 - 6t^2 + 6t + 1$

■ 4.3 The Intermediate Value Property

Except where there have been obvious "breaks" in the graph of a function, as was the case with the greatest integer function g: $g(x) = [x]$ and several others, its graph has been sketched by determining some basic properties — symmetry, intercepts, where it is increasing or decreasing, where it is positive or negative, and so on — plotting a few points, and connecting these points with a curve having no "jumps" or "holes" or other unusual aspects. In doing this several fundamental assumptions were made concerning the graph, or equivalently, the function. One of these was the assumption that if $(x_1, f(x_1))$

and $(x_2, f(x_2))$ are points of the graph of f, and every number between x_1 and x_2 is in the domain of f, then for each number y_0 between $f(x_1)$ and $f(x_2)$, the horizontal line $y = y_0$ intersects the graph at some point between the vertical lines $x = x_1$ and $x = x_2$. (See Figure 1.)

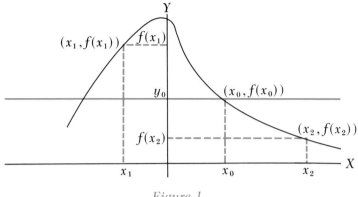

Figure 1

This property of a function is formalized in the following definition.

DEFINITION   Let f be a function and I an interval or ray contained in the domain of f. Then f is said to have the **intermediate value property on I** provided that for each pair of numbers x_1 and x_2 in I, if y_0 is any number between $f(x_1)$ and $f(x_2)$, then there is at least one number x_0 between x_1 and x_2 such that $f(x_0) = y_0$.

Geometrically, this means that any horizontal line $y = y_0$ that lies between the lines $y = f(x_1)$ and $y = f(x_2)$ will intersect the graph of f in at least one point between the lines $x = x_1$ and $x = x_2$. As is seen in Figure 2, there may be more than one number between x_1 and x_2 at which the value of f is y_0.

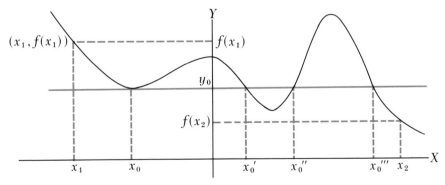

Figure 2

Example 1   Let f be the function whose graph is sketched as follows.

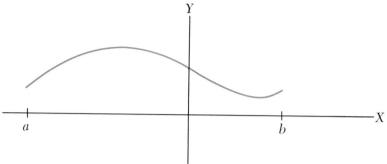

Then f appears to have the intermediate value property on the interval $[a, b]$. Practically speaking, it is impossible to verify that it does, because to do so entails looking at *all* pairs of numbers x_1 and x_2 in $[a, b]$, and for *each* such pair looking at *all* possible numbers y_0 that lie between $f(x_1)$ and $f(x_2)$ to see if the equation $f(x) = y_0$ has a solution x_0 lying between x_1 and x_2. Since we are not given an algebraic description of f, there is no way for us to carry out a rigorous verification of our intuitive guess that f indeed has the intermediate value property on $[a, b]$.

Example 2   Let $f: f(x) = 2x - 5$.

Then f has the intermediate value property on the set R of all real numbers. For, suppose x_1 and x_2 are two real numbers, with the notation chosen so that $x_1 < x_2$, and let y_0 be any number between $f(x_1) = 2x_1 - 5$ and $f(x_2) = 2x_2 - 5$, so that

$$2x_1 - 5 < y_0 < 2x_2 - 5.$$

The equation $f(x) = y_0$ has the unique solution

$$x_0 = \frac{1}{2}(y_0 + 5),$$

and the question becomes whether $x_1 < x_0 < x_2$ or not.

Since $2x_1 - 5 < y_0 < 2x_2 + 5,$

we have $2x_1 < y_0 + 5 < 2x_2,$

so $x_1 < \frac{1}{2}(y_0 + 5) < x_2,$

that is, $x_1 < x_0 < x_2.$

A graphical demonstration can often be given to show that a given function does *not* have the intermediate value property on a given interval.

Example 3   Let f be the function whose graph is sketched as follows:

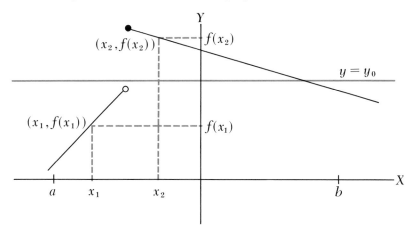

Here, we can find numbers $x_1 < x_2$ in $[a, b]$ and a number y_0 between $f(x_1)$ and $f(x_2)$ such that the horizontal line $y = y_0$ does not intersect the graph of f anywhere between the vertical lines $x = x_1$ and $x = x_2$. Hence, f fails to have the intermediate value property on $[a, b]$.

Beware of the following trap on examples like this one. Evidently, any horizontal line $y = y_0$ lying between the lines $y = f(a)$ and $y = f(b)$ will intersect the graph somewhere between the vertical lines $x = a$ and $x = b$.

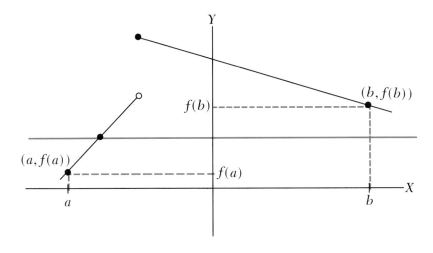

But it is not correct to conclude that f has the intermediate value property on $[a, b]$, since the test given in the definition must be applied to *all* pairs of numbers x_1, x_2 in $[a, b]$, and we have found above at least one pair of numbers in $[a, b]$ for which the test fails.

Example 4   Figure 3 shows the graphs of four functions. The function whose graph appears in (i) does not have the intermediate value property on any interval that contains the number -2 in its interior or as its right endpoint. It does have the intermediate value property on all other intervals. The functions whose graphs appear in (ii) and (iii) have the intermediate value property on every interval contained in their domains. The function whose graph appears in (iv) has the intermediate value property on every interval that does not contain either of the numbers -3 or 0. Notice that a function may have the intermediate value property on some intervals contained in its domain, but not on others as in (i) and (iv) and that if it has the intermediate value property on an interval I in its domain then it will also have this property on any subinterval of I.

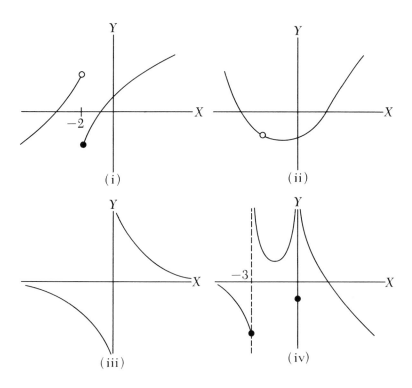

Figure 3

Suppose f is a function that has the intermediate value property on an interval I contained in its domain and suppose further that a and b are numbers in I with $f(a)f(b) < 0$. Then one of $f(a)$ and $f(b)$ must be positive and the other negative, and hence 0 is between $f(a)$ and $f(b)$. Consequently, there is a number c between a and b such that $f(c) = 0$; that is, there is a zero of f between a and b. Therefore, if f has the intermediate value property on the interval $[a, b]$ and the points $(a, f(a))$ and $(b, f(b))$ lie on opposite sides of the horizontal axis, then the graph of f must cross the horizontal axis at some point between a and b, as shown in Figure 4 (i). That this is not necessarily the case for a function that does not have the intermediate value property is seen in Figure 4 (ii).

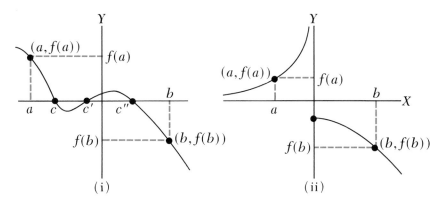

Figure 4

A second important result is that if a function f has the intermediate value property on an interval I in its domain that contains no zeros of f, then f has **constant sign** on I. That is, for any pair of numbers x_1 and x_2 in I, $f(x_1)f(x_2) > 0$. If this were not the case, there would be numbers x_1 and x_2 in I such that $f(x_1) > 0$ and $f(x_2) < 0$. Then, by the intermediate value property there would be a number c between x_1 and x_2 (and hence in I) such that $f(c) = 0$. This contradicts the assumption that I contains no zeros of f.

The following theorem, whose proof is beyond our present capabilities, will be used freely.

THEOREM 4.3.1 Each polynomial function has the intermediate value property on every interval.

In Section 1.2 it was indicated that the system of real numbers must obey some conditions other than the axioms for addition, multiplication, and order that were stated, because, for example, the system of rational numbers satisfies all those axioms. The reason that we are forced to accept Theorem 4.3.1 without proof at this stage is that its proof is based upon an additional axiom for the real number system that is beyond the scope of our discussion at present. We can, however, give a simple illustration to show that the truth of Theorem 4.3.1 involves more than the axioms of Section 1.2.

Example 5   Every positive real number has a real square root.
    Let t be a positive real number, and let

$$f: f(x) = x^2 - t.$$

Then $f(0) = -t,$

so $f(0) < 0,$

whereas $f(t + 1) = (t + 1)^2 - t = t^2 + t + 1,$

so $f(t + 1) > 0.$

Since Theorem 4.3.1 holds, and f is a polynomial function, there is a number c between 0 and $t + 1$ such that $f(c) = 0$, so c is a square root of t.
    Notice that the result of Example 5 is not true if the word *real* is replaced by the word *rational* because, for example, the positive rational number 2 does not have a rational square root. Again, since the rational number system satisfies the axioms of Section 1.2, those axioms must not be strong enough to imply even the result of Example 5, let alone Theorem 4.3.1.

    From our discussion preceding Theorem 4.3.1, it is clear that this theorem implies the following result.

THEOREM 4.3.2   If P is a polynomial function, and I is an interval that contains no zeros of P, then P has constant sign on I.

    Theorem 4.3.2 is a great aid in graphing polynomial functions whose zeros can be found and in solving inequalities.

Example 6   Sketch the graph of $p: p(x) = (x - 3)(x + 2)(x - \frac{1}{2})$.
    The zeros of p are -2, $\frac{1}{2}$ and 3. Hence, p is of constant sign on each of the intervals $(-\infty, -2)$, $(-2, \frac{1}{2})$, $(\frac{1}{2}, 3)$ and $(3, \infty)$. Evaluating p at a number in each of these intervals we find that $p(-4) < 0$, $p(-1) > 0$, $p(1) < 0$ and

$p(5) > 0$. Thus, for all x in $(-2, \frac{1}{2})$ or $(3, \infty)$, $p(x) > 0$, and for all x in $(-\infty, -2)$ or $(\frac{1}{2}, 3)$, $p(x) < 0$. Using these facts we obtain a rather rough sketch of the graph of p in Figure 5.

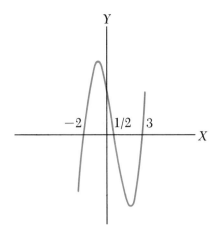

Figure 5

Example 7   Solve the inequality $2x^3 - 5x^2 + 3x > 0$.

Let $f: f(x) = 2x^3 - 5x^2 + 3x$. The solution set of the inequality is $\{x: f(x) > 0\}$. The zeros of f are 0, 3/2 and 1. Using the constant sign properties of f, the solution set is $\{x: 0 < x < 1 \text{ or } x > 3/2\}$. See the graph of f sketched in Figure 6.

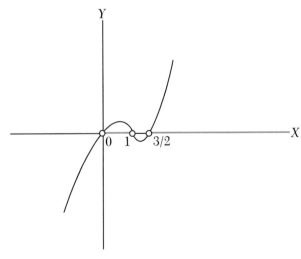

Figure 6

A final remark about the zeros of a polynomial function P must be made in connection with the graph of P. If the number c is a zero of P, then $D: D(x) = x - c$ is a factor of P, by Theorem 4.2.3. But D may be a "repeated" factor of P, and this will have an effect on how the graph of P looks near the point $(c, 0)$.

DEFINITION   Let P be a polynomial function and let c be a real number. Suppose there is a positive integer N and a polynomial function Q such that

(i) $P: P(x) = (x - c)^N Q(x)$,   and
(ii) $Q(c) \neq 0$.

Then c is said to be a **zero of order N** of the function P.

THEOREM 4.3.3   If c is a zero of order N of a polynomial function P, then the graph of P crosses the horizontal axis at $(c, 0)$ if N is odd, while if N is even, the graph intersects the horizontal axis at $(c, 0)$ without crossing it.

PROOF   From the hypothesis of the theorem, there must be a polynomial function Q such that

$$P: P(x) = (x - c)^N Q(x) \quad \text{and} \quad Q(c) \neq 0.$$

By the discussion in Example 3 of Section 4.2, Q has at most a finite number of zeros, and c is not a zero of Q, so there must be an open interval I containing the number c that contains no zeros of Q. Notice that Theorem 4.3.2 implies that Q has constant sign on I.

Now, let x_1 and x_2 be any two numbers in I such that $x_1 < c < x_2$. Then

$$
\begin{aligned}
P(x_1)P(x_2) &= (x_1 - c)^N Q(x_1) \cdot (x_2 - c)^N Q(x_2) \\
&= (-(c - x_1)^N) \cdot (x_2 - c)^N \cdot Q(x_1)Q(x_2) \\
&= (-1)^N (c - x_1)^N \cdot (x_2 - c)^N \cdot Q(x_1)Q(x_2)
\end{aligned}
$$

But $(c - x_1)^N$ and $(x_2 - c)^N$ will be positive no matter what N is, and $Q(x_1)Q(x_2) > 0$ since Q has constant sign on I. Hence, the number $P(x_1)P(x_2)$ has the same sign as $(-1)^N$.

Therefore, if N is odd, then $P(x_1)P(x_2) < 0$, so the graph of P crosses the horizontal axis at $(c, 0)$, while if N is even, then $P(x_1)P(x_2) > 0$, so the graph of P does not cross the horizontal axis at $(c, 0)$.

Theorem 4.3.3 gives a partial check on one's conclusions in graphing polynomial functions.

Example 8 Sketch the graph of

$$g: g(x) = (x+2)(x+1)(x-1)^2(x-3)^5.$$

Since the zeros of g are $-2, -1, 1$, and 3, we know that g has constant sign on each of

$$(-\infty, -2), \ (-2, -1), \ (-1, 1), \ (1, 3), \ (3, \infty).$$

If we check the sign of $g(x)$ for a particular number x in each of these intervals as in Example 6, we conclude that

$$\begin{aligned}
g(x) &< 0 \quad \text{if} \quad x \in (-\infty, -2) \\
g(x) &> 0 \quad \text{if} \quad x \in (-2, -1) \\
g(x) &< 0 \quad \text{if} \quad x \in (-1, 1) \\
g(x) &< 0 \quad \text{if} \quad x \in (1, 3) \\
g(x) &> 0 \quad \text{if} \quad x \in (3, \infty).
\end{aligned}$$

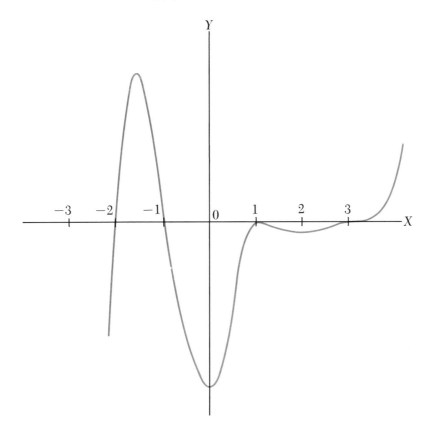

Figure 7

These results are consistent with Theorem 4.3.3 to the extent that $g(x)$ changes sign at -2, -1, and 3 since the factors $x + 2$, $x + 1$, and $x - 3$ each appear raised to odd powers, and $g(x)$ does not change sign at 1 since the factor $x - 1$ appears to an even power.

A rough sketch of the graph of g appears in Figure 7.

Perhaps the best way to remember what Theorem 4.3.3 says is to recall the functions f_N: $f_N(x) = x^N$ discussed in Example 5 of Section 4.1. The idea is that if c is a zero of order N of a polynomial function P, then the graph of P near the point $(c, 0)$ is going to behave very much as the graph of f_N does near the point $(0, 0)$. Incidentally, that is why the sketch of the graph of the function g that appears in Figure 7 has a "wiggle" near the point $(3, 0)$; the same thing happens to the graph of the function f_5 near the point $(0, 0)$.

It should be pointed out that the means we have at our disposal give only a general picture of what the graph of a polynomial function looks like. The accurate graphing of polynomial functions, especially those whose zeros cannot be computed, can be facilitated by more sophisticated techniques that are developed in calculus.

EXERCISES

1. Consider the functions whose graphs are given below. Which of these functions have the intermediate value property on the interval $[a, b]$? on the interval $[c, d]$? Find each function that has the intermediate value property on every interval contained in its domain.

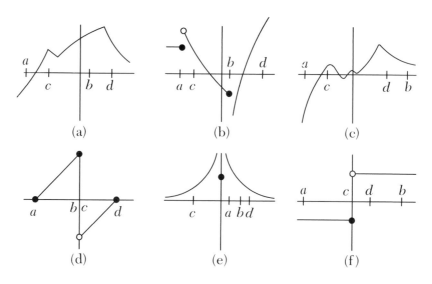

(a) (b) (c)

(d) (e) (f)

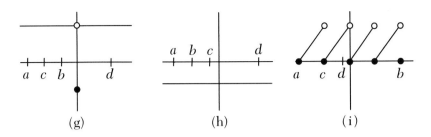

(g)   (h)   (i)

2. Sketch the graph of each of the following polynomial functions.
   (a) $P: P(x) = 2x^2 + 9x$
   (b) $Q: Q(x) = (x + 3)(x + 2) \cdot (x + 1)(x)(x - 1)(x - 2)(x - 3)$
   (c) $S: S(x) = x^4(2x - 1)^3$
   (d) $T: T(t) = 2t^3 + 3t^2 - t - 1$
   (e) $p: p(s) = (1 - s)(s - 1)^2 \cdot (s - 2)^3$
   (f) $x: x(y) = (y^2 - 1/4)^4$
   (g) $z: z(x) = (x^2 - 5x + 10) \cdot (2x^2 + x - 1)$

3. Solve each of the following inequalities.
   (a) $3x^2 \le x + 1 - 2x^3$
   (b) $2x^2 > 5x + 1$
   (c) $x^2 + 6x + 3 \ge 0$
   (d) $x > x^2 + 1$
   (e) $t(t + 1)^2(t - 3)^3 < 0$
   (f) $(s + 2)(s + 1)^2(s)^3(s - 1)^4 \cdot (s - 2)^5 \ge 0$
   (g) $\dfrac{1 + x}{x} > \dfrac{x}{1 + x}$

4. Which of the following functions have the intermediate value property on each interval contained in their domain?
   (a) $f: f(x) = 4x^{29} - 6x^{13} + 27x^7 - 5$
   (b) $g: g(t) = \dfrac{1}{t}$
   (c) $h: h(y) = [y] + y$
   (d) $p: p(x) = \dfrac{x^2 - 4}{x + 2}$

5. In each of (a) through (f) following appears a rough sketch of the graph of a polynomial function. In each case, find an algebraic description of a polynomial function whose graph has the indicated properties. (It will be useful to keep Theorem 4.3.3 in mind.)

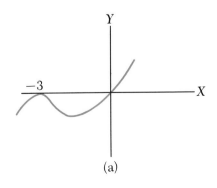

(a)

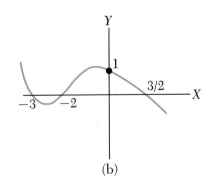

(b)

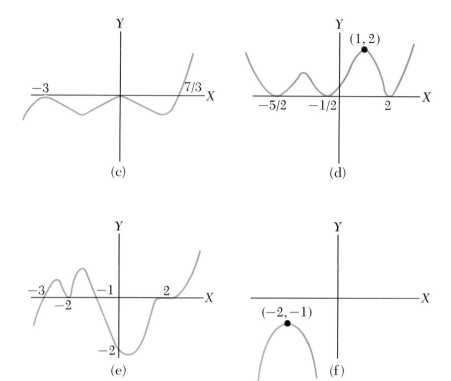

(c)

(d)

(e)

(f)

6. Let P be a polynomial function such that $P(a) > 0$ and $P(b) < 0$. By Theorem 4.3.1, there is a zero of P between a and b. Let c lie between a and b. If $P(c) > 0$, there is a zero of P between c and b. Pick a number d between c and b. If $P(d) < 0$, there is a zero of P between c and d. (See figure on page 155.)

Continuing in this manner we can find intervals as small as we like that contain a zero of P. That is, a zero of P can be approximated to any desired degree of accuracy.

Let $P: P(x) = x^4 + x^3 + x - 1$. Show that there is a zero of P between -2 and -1 and a zero of P between 0 and 1. Approximate

these zeros to the nearest hundredth. (Use the method of Exercises 6 and 7 of Section 4.2 and common sense in choosing the numbers at which you evaluate P.)

7. Approximate a zero of $f: f(x) = 2x^3 + x^2 + 4$ correct to the nearest tenth.

8. Work Exercise 7 if $h: h(x) = 2x^3 - 5x^2 + 3x - 7$.

9. Let $h: h(x) = x^2$ and let c be a real number. Define $S: S(x) = \dfrac{h(x) - h(c)}{x - c}$. Does S have the intermediate value property on each interval contained in its domain? Sketch the graph of S in case (i) $c = 0$, (ii) $c = 1$, (iii) $c = -2$. Give

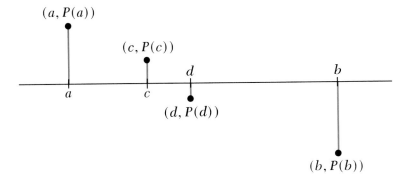

a geometric interpretation of S.

†10. Let m be a positive integer.
  (a) Use the idea underlying Example 1 to show that every positive real number has a positive mth root.
  (b) By Theorem 1.3.2, the function

$$g_m: g_m(x) = x^m, \; x > 0$$

is an increasing function. Use this fact together with the result of (a) to show that every positive real number has a *unique* positive mth root.

†11. In this exercise is outlined a proof of the fact that every cubic equation has a real root. The specific example in part (a) illustrates the more general attack in part (b).
  (a) Let $P: P(x) = x^3 - 3x^2 + 5x - 25$. We can show that P has a real zero as follows:
  (i) Write

$$P(x) = x^3\left(1 - \frac{3}{x} + \frac{5}{x^2} - \frac{25}{x^3}\right) \text{ for }$$

$x \neq 0.$
  (ii) Verify that if $|x| > 15$, then

$$\left|\frac{-3}{x}\right| < \frac{1}{5}, \left|\frac{5}{x^2}\right| < \frac{1}{5}, \text{ and}$$

$$\left|\frac{-25}{x^3}\right| < \frac{1}{5}$$

  (iii) Use (ii) to show that if $|x| > 15$, then

$$1 - \frac{3}{x} + \frac{5}{x^2} - \frac{25}{x^3} > \frac{2}{5}$$

  (iv) Use (iii) to show that $P(x) > 0$ if $x > 15$, and $P(x) < 0$ if $x < -15$.
  (v) Conclude that P has a zero that lies between -15 and 15.
  (b) Let $C: C(x) = x^3 + bx^2 + cx + d$. Show that C has a real zero as follows:
  (i) Write

$$C(x) = x^3\left(1 + \frac{b}{x} + \frac{c}{x^2} + \frac{d}{x^3}\right)$$

for $x \neq 0$.
  (ii) Verify that if t is the largest of the three numbers $5|b|$, $\sqrt{5}\sqrt{|c|}$, $\sqrt[3]{5}\sqrt[3]{|d|}$, and $|x| > t$, then

$$\left|\frac{b}{x}\right| < \frac{1}{5}, \left|\frac{c}{x^2}\right| < \frac{1}{5}, \text{ and } \left|\frac{d}{x^3}\right| < \frac{1}{5}.$$

  (iii) If t is chosen as in (ii), show that if $|x| > t$, then

$$1 + \frac{b}{x} + \frac{c}{x^2} + \frac{d}{x^3} > \frac{2}{5}.$$

  (iv) Use (iii) to show that $C(x) > 0$ if $x > t$ and $C(x) < 0$ if $x < -t$.
  (v) Conclude that C has a zero between $-t$ and t.
  (c) Prove that if a, b, c and d are real numbers with $a \neq 0$, and y_0 is any given real number, then the cubic equation

$$ax^3 + bx^2 + cx + d = y_0$$

has a real solution.

Exercises 12 and 13 lead to

the result that a polynomial function determines its coefficients uniquely. Exercises 14 and 15 use this fact to show why certain functions cannot be polynomial functions.

†12. Let $P: P(x) = a_0 + a_1 x + \cdots + a_n x^n$ be a polynomial function. If all the coefficients $a_0, a_1, \ldots, a_n$ are zero, then P is, of course, the zero polynomial. The question is, do all the coefficients *have* to be zero *if* P is the zero polynomial? Can we be sure that something such as

$$P: P(x) = 1 - 24x^3 + \pi x^{16} - x^{23} + \sqrt{2}\, x^{64}$$

isn't just a complicated description of the zero polynomial?

That the answer to this question is "yes" can be seen as follows.

(a) Assume that n is a positive integer and that $P: P(x) = a_0 + a_1 x + \cdots + a_n x^n$ is the zero polynomial. Prove that $a_0 = 0$.

(b) By part (a), $P: P(x) = a_1 x + \cdots + a_n x^n$, so that $P: P(x) = x\, Q(x)$, where $Q: Q(x) = a_1 + a_2 x + \cdots + a_n x^{n-1}$. Then Q is a polynomial function such that $Q(x) = 0$ whenever $x \neq 0$. Prove that also $Q(0) = 0$ by using Theorem 4.3.1. Hence, $a_1 = 0$.

(c) Use the idea suggested in parts (a) and (b) to prove by mathematical induction that the only way a polynomial function can be the zero polynomial is for all of its coefficients to be zero.

†13. A problem related to Exercise 12 is whether the concept of the degree of a polynomial function is given a legitimate definition in Section 4.1. The only problem is that we might be able to find two ways of describing the same poly-

nomial function so that if the "recipe" for finding the degree is applied to each description, two different answers would result. Fortunately, this is not the case; in fact, we can say more.

Let $P: P(x) = a_0 + a_1 x + \cdots + a_n x^n$ and $S: S(x) = b_0 + b_1 x + \cdots + b_m x^m$ be polynomial functions with $a_n \neq 0$ and $b_m \neq 0$. If $P = S$, then:

(i) $m = n$ and

(ii) For every integer k such that $0 \leq k \leq m = n$, we have $b_k = a_k$.

Thus, a polynomial function determines its coefficients uniquely.

Hint: If $P = S$, then $P - S$ is the zero polynomial. Apply Exercise 12.

†14. Consider the function $h: h(x) = 2 + x + 5x^{3/2}$ given in Example 1 of Section 4.1. We can use the results of Exercises 12 and 13 to show that h is not a polynomial function.

Suppose, to the contrary, that h is a polynomial function, and let $g: g(x) = h(x) - (2 + x)$. Then g must be a polynomial function. (Why?)

Now, let $f: f(x) = (g(x))^2$, so that f is also a polynomial function. (Why?)

But the results of Exercises 12 and 13 indicate that f can't possibly be a polynomial function, so our assumption that h is a polynomial function must be false.

Hint: Exercise 12 of Section 4.1 is useful here.

†15. Use the method of Exercise 14 to show that none of these functions are polynomial functions.

(a) $P: P(x) = x^{1/3}$

(b) $Q: Q(x) = x^2 - x^{1/3}$

(c) $f: f(x) = x^{-2}$

(d) $g: g(x) = 2 + \sqrt{x}$

(e) $h: h(x) = x^2/(x^2 + 1)$

(f) $S: S(x) = (x^2)^{1/2}$

■ 4.4 Rational Functions

Exercises 12 and 13 of Section 3.3 and Exercise 12 of Section 4.1 are examples of the following general question:

"Given a set of real functions, is it true that the sum, difference, product, quotient, or composite of any two members of the set is also a member of the set?"

In the case of the set of all polynomial functions, the answer to this question is that if P and Q are any two polynomial functions, then so are $P + Q, P - Q,$ $P \cdot Q$, and $P \circ Q$, but P/Q may not be. For this reason, special attention must be given to quotients of polynomial functions.

DEFINITION A real function f is a **rational function** if, and only if, there are polynomial functions P and Q such that $f = P/Q$.

Remember that if P and Q are polynomial functions, then $\mathscr{D}_P = R$ and $\mathscr{D}_Q = R$, so $\mathscr{D}_{P/Q} = \{x : Q(x) \neq 0\}$, and the quotient P/Q will not be defined when Q is the zero polynomial.

Example 1 Let $f : f(x) = (x^2 - 3x - 4)/(x + 1)$.

Then f is a rational function because if $P : P(x) = x^2 - 3x - 4$ and $Q : Q(x) = x + 1$, then P and Q are polynomial functions and $f = P/Q$. Notice that it is also true that $f : f(x) = x - 4$, $x \neq -1$. But f is *not* a polynomial function because $-1 \notin \mathscr{D}_f$.

Example 2 Let $f : f(x) = (x^4 - 1)/(x^2 + 1)$.

Again, f is a rational function. In fact, f is a polynomial function, because $\mathscr{D}_f = R$ and for each x in $\mathscr{D}_f$,

$$f(x) = (x^2 - 1)(x^2 + 1)/(x^2 + 1) = x^2 - 1.$$

Example 3 If $f : f(x) = (x + 1)^{1/2}/(x - 1)^{1/2}$, then f is not a rational function.

This doesn't follow from the fact that the given description of f doesn't *look* like the description of a rational function. (The function in Example 2 didn't look like a polynomial function at first glance, either.) The fact is that $\mathscr{D}_f = \{x : x + 1 \geq 0 \text{ and } x - 1 > 0\} = \{x : x > 1\}$. Now, suppose there *were* polynomial functions P and Q such that $f = P/Q$. By Example 3 of Section

4.2, the polynomial function Q has at most a finite number of zeros, and the only numbers which fail to belong to $\mathscr{D}_f$ are those zeroes. But this is impossible, since

$$\{x : x \in R \quad \text{and} \quad x \notin \mathscr{D}_f\} = \{x : x \le 1\},$$

and this set is certainly not a finite set of numbers.

EXERCISES

1. For each function, decide whether or not it is a rational function. If it is, write it in the form P/Q where P and Q are polynomial functions, and find the domain of the function.

(a) $f : f(x) = \dfrac{3x^2 - 2x + 1}{x^2 - 4}$

(b) $g : g(x) = \dfrac{x^6 - 4x^2 + 3x}{(x + 2)^2(x - 1)^2}$

(c) $h : h(x) = \dfrac{x^3 - 2x^2 + x}{(x - 1)^2}$

(d) $F : F(t) = \dfrac{(t - 1)^2}{t^3 - 2t^2 + t}$

(e) $G : G(x) = \dfrac{x + 1}{2x - 2}$

(f) $H : H(u) = (u^4 + 2u^2 + 1)^{1/2}$

(g) $f : f(t) = \dfrac{1}{3t^2 + 1}, \; t \ne 0$

(h) $g : g(t) = \left(\dfrac{t^4}{t^4 + 2t^2 + 1}\right)^{-1/2}$

2. Let $f : f(x) = \dfrac{x^2 + 1}{2x - 4}$, $g : g(u) = \dfrac{1}{u}$. Find each of the functions $f + g$, $f - g$, fg, f/g, and $f \circ g$. Remember to compute the domain of each of these functions.

3. Prove that if f and g are any two rational functions, then each of $f + g$, $f - g$, fg, f/g, and $f \circ g$ is a rational function.

■ 4.5 Graphing Rational Functions

In the analysis of the graph of a rational function, several of the same questions that were asked in connection with the graphing of a polynomial function will be asked again, namely, where the zeros of the function are, what symmetry properties the graph has, and on which intervals the function has constant sign. But we must also find out which numbers fail to belong to the domain of the function, and how the function behaves "near" such numbers.

DEFINITION   A **critical number** for a rational function f is a number c such that either c is a zero of f or else $c \notin \mathscr{D}_f$.

This means that if we write $f = P/Q$, where P and Q are polynomial functions, then the critical numbers for f are exactly those numbers c such that either $P(c) = 0$ or $Q(c) = 0$ (or both).

The following result summarizes those properties of the graph of a rational function f that are most closely related to properties of the graph of a polynomial function, and, in fact includes the special case where f is a polynomial function.

THEOREM 4.5.1   Let f be any rational function. Then
(i) f has at most a finite number of critical numbers.
(ii) If c and d are successive critical numbers for f, then f has constant sign on (c, d).
(iii) If m is the smallest critical number for f, and M is the largest critical number for f, then f has constant sign on each of the rays $(-\infty, m)$ and (M, ∞).

PROOF   Write $f = P/Q$ where P and Q are polynomial functions and Q is not the zero polynomial.

Part (i) follows directly from the discussion in Example 3 of Section 4.2, which implies that each of P and Q has at most a finite number of zeros. Notice that the case in which f has no critical numbers at all is included in the statement of (i).

To prove part (ii), observe first that if c and d are successive critical numbers for f, then for no x in (c, d) is $Q(x) = 0$, so $(c, d) \subset \mathscr{D}_f$. Moreover, the equation $P(x) = 0$ has no solutions in (c, d) either, so both P and Q have constant sign on (c, d) by Theorem 4.3.2. Hence, if x_1 and x_2 are any two numbers in (c, d), then $P(x_1)P(x_2) > 0$ and $Q(x_1)Q(x_2) > 0$, so $f(x_1) \cdot f(x_2) = P(x_1)P(x_2)/Q(x_1)Q(x_2)$ is the quotient of positive numbers and, therefore, must be positive.

Part (iii) follows by an argument similar to the proof of (ii).

The interested reader should work out an argument for the next theorem, based on the assumption that the statement of Theorem 4.3.1 is true. (Some hints are given in Exercise 4.)

THEOREM 4.5.2   Every rational function has the intermediate value property on every interval or ray that is contained in its domain.

The information in Theorem 4.5.1 is especially useful in the graphing of a rational function and in solving inequalities that involve rational functions.

Example 1   Let $f: f(x) = \dfrac{2x+1}{x-3}$.

The critical numbers of f are $-\frac{1}{2}$ and 3, so f has constant sign on each of the sets $(-\infty, -\frac{1}{2})$, $(-\frac{1}{2}, 3)$, and $(3, \infty)$. Since $f(-1) > 0$, $f(0) < 0$, and $f(4) > 0$, it follows that $f(x) > 0$ if $x < -\frac{1}{2}$ or $x > 3$, whereas $f(x) < 0$ if $-\frac{1}{2} < x < 3$. A sketch of the graph of f is given in Figure 1.

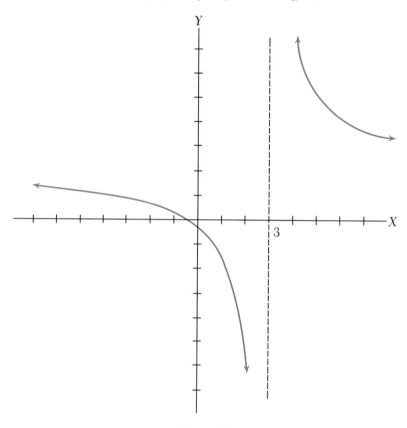

Figure 1

Example 2   Solve the inequality

$$\frac{(x-3)^3(x+2)^4}{(3x-2)^5} \geq 0.$$

Let
$$f: f(x) = \frac{(x-3)^3(x+2)^4}{(3x-2)^5}.$$

The critical numbers of f are -2, $2/3$, and 3, so f has constant sign on each of the sets $(-\infty, -2)$, $(-2, 2/3)$, $(2/3, 3)$, and $(3, \infty)$. Checking the value of

f at a point in each of these intervals, we find $f(-3) > 0, f(0) > 0, f(1) < 0$, and $f(4) > 0$. Thus, $f(x) > 0$ if, and only if, $x < -2$ or $-2 < x < 2/3$ or $3 < x$, and $f(x) = 0$ if, and only if, $x = -2$ or $x = 3$.

Hence, the solution set is

$$\left\{x : x < \frac{2}{3} \quad \text{or} \quad 3 \le x\right\}.$$

In order to proceed with the graphing of rational functions, we should have an orderly analysis of what happens to the graph near a critical number. Much of what will be said depends upon the result of Theorem 4.3.3.

THEOREM 4.5.3 Let $f = P/Q$ where P and Q are polynomial functions, and let c be a zero of f, so that for some positive integer N, c is a zero of order N of P, but $Q(c) \ne 0$.

Then the graph of f crosses the horizontal axis at $(c, 0)$ if N is odd, and does not if N is even.

If you have studied the proof of Theorem 4.3.3 carefully, you should be able to construct an argument for Theorem 4.5.3. The basic idea is to observe that Theorem 4.3.2 implies that Q must have constant sign in some open interval I containing c, because Q has only a finite number of zeros, and c is not one of them. Then, whether or not $f(x)$ changes sign at c depends only on whether or not $P(x)$ does, and that, in turn, depends on whether or not $(x - c)^N$ changes its sign at c.

Theorem 4.5.3 takes care of one sort of critical number that a rational function may have. Now we must look at the critical numbers that fail to be in the domain of the function.

Thus, suppose P and Q are polynomial functions with $f = P/Q$, and c is a number such that $Q(c) = 0$. There are two cases to consider.

CASE 1 $P(c) \ne 0$, i.e., the function $D : D(x) = x - c$ is not a factor of P.

Suppose N is the order of c as a zero of Q, so that there is a polynomial function Q_1 such that

$$Q : Q(x) = (x - c)^N Q_1(x),$$

and $$Q_1(c) \ne 0.$$

Then $$f : f(x) = \frac{P(x)}{(x - c)^N Q_1(x)}.$$

Notice that since c is not in the domain of f, there is no point that is on both the graph of f and the line $x = c$. In fact, as the distance from a number x to c gets smaller and smaller, the number

$$|f(x)| = \frac{1}{|x - c|^N} \cdot \frac{|P(x)|}{|Q_1(x)|}$$

is going to get larger and larger. This means that the line $x = c$ in the XY plane is a **vertical asymptote** of the graph of f. A precise statement of what this means will not be given here, since it involves the notion of limits. Let us agree, however, that the graph of f will have the appearance of one of (a), (b), (c), and (d) sketched in Figure 2.

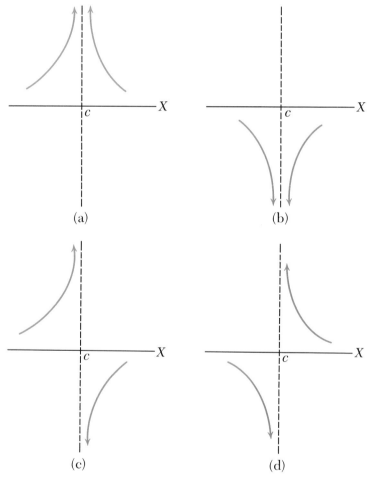

Figure 2

The reader should convince himself that (a) and (b) indicate what happens when the order N of c as a zero of Q is even, whereas (c) and (d) show the possibilities when N is odd.

It should not be inferred from these sketches that the graph of f is neces-sarily symmetric with respect to either the line $x = c$ or the point $(c, 0)$. Neither should it be assumed that when the concept of vertical asymptote is defined in calculus, the graph of *any* real function that has a vertical asymptote at $x = c$ must look like one of the graphs sketched in Figure 2.

CASE 2 $P(c) = 0$. Then there are positive integers r and s and polynomial functions P_1 and Q_1 such that $P_1(c) \neq 0$, $Q_1(c) \neq 0$, and for all real numbers x,

$$P(x) = (x - c)^r P_1(x), \quad Q(x) = (x - c)^s Q_1(x),$$

so that
$$f : f(x) = \frac{(x - c)^r}{(x - c)^s} \cdot \frac{P_1(x)}{Q_1(x)}.$$

If $r < s$,   then $f : f(x) = \dfrac{P_1(x)}{(x - c)^{s-r} Q_1(x)}$,   and

$P_1(c) \neq 0$, so the line $x = c$ is a vertical asymptote, by Case 1.

If $r = s$, then $f : f(x) = P_1(x)/Q_1(x)$, $x \neq c$, so the graph of f has a "hole" at the point $(c, P_1(c)/Q_1(c))$.

If $r > s$, then $f : f(x) = \dfrac{(x - c)^{r-s} P_1(x)}{Q_1(x)}$, $x \neq c$ so the graph of f has a "hole" at the point $(c, 0)$.

The graph of f for $r = s$ will look something like Figure 3(a), while Figures 3(b) and 3(c) indicate the cases where $r > s$ and $r - s$ is odd, and where $r > s$ and $r - s$ is even, respectively.

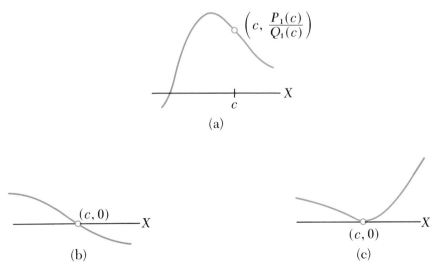

(a)

(b)   (c)

Figure 3

Example 3   Let $f: f(x) = x^2/(1-x^2)$.

Then f has the critical numbers -1, 0, 1, so f has constant sign on each of the sets $(-\infty, -1)$, $(-1, 0)$, $(0, 1)$, and $(1, \infty)$. The graph of f is symmetric with respect to the vertical axis, so we may concentrate on graphing f to the right of the vertical axis. Since $f(\frac{1}{2}) > 0$, $f(x) > 0$ for all x in $(0, 1)$; since $f(2) < 0$, $f(x) < 0$ for all x in $(1, \infty)$. Also, the lines $x = 1$ and $x = -1$ are vertical asymptotes. The graph of f is sketched in Figure 4.

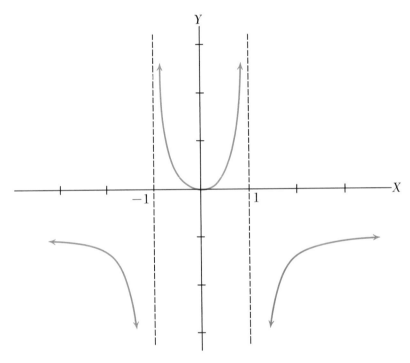

Figure 4

Example 4   Let

$$f: f(x) = \frac{(x^2 - 2x - 8)}{(x-4)^2(x-5)}$$

Then

$$f(x) = \frac{(x-4)(x+2)}{(x-4)^2(x-5)} = \frac{(x+2)}{(x-4)(x-5)},$$

so -2, 4, and 5 are the critical numbers for f. To determine the sign of f in $(-\infty, -2)$, note that $f(-3) < 0$, so $f(x) < 0$ for all x in $(-\infty, -2)$. Similarly,

$f(0) > 0$, so $f(x) > 0$ on $(-2, 4)$; $f(9/2) < 0$, so $f(x) < 0$ on $(4, 5)$; $f(6) > 0$, so $f(x) > 0$ for $x > 5$. The graph appears in Figure 5.

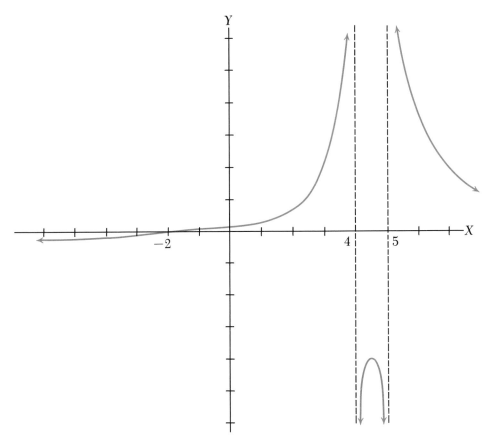

Figure 5

Example 5 Let $f\colon f(x) = (x^4 - x^3 + x^2)/(x^2 + x)$.

Then $f(x) = x^2(x^2 - x + 1)/x(x + 1)$,

so $f(x) = x(x^2 - x + 1)/(x + 1)$, $x \neq 0$.

Thus, the critical numbers of f are -1 and 0, but the number 0 is *not* a zero of f, and the graph will have a "hole" at $(0, 0)$. Since $x^2 - x + 1 > 0$ for all x, we have $f(x) > 0$ for $x > 0$ or $x < -1$, $f(x) < 0$ for $-1 < x < 0$. A sketch is given in Figure 6.

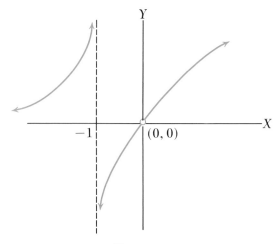

Figure 6

Example 6   Let $f \colon f(x) = \dfrac{(x-1)^5(x-3)(x+2)^4}{x^6(2x-8)^{15}}$

The critical numbers of f are -2, 0, 1, 3, and 4, so f has constant sign on each of the sets

$$(-\infty, -2),\ (-2, 0),\ (0, 1),\ (1, 3),\ (3, 4),\quad \text{and}\quad (4, \infty).$$

If f is evaluated at a number in each of these sets, it is found that

$$\begin{aligned}
f(x) &< 0 \quad\text{if}\quad x < -2; \\
f(x) &< 0 \quad\text{if}\quad -2 < x < 0; \\
f(x) &< 0 \quad\text{if}\quad 0 < x < 1; \\
f(x) &> 0 \quad\text{if}\quad 1 < x < 3; \\
f(x) &< 0 \quad\text{if}\quad 3 < x < 4; \\
f(x) &> 0 \quad\text{if}\quad 4 < x.
\end{aligned}$$

Also, the critical numbers -2, 1, and 3 are zeros of f, while the lines $x = 0$ and $x = 4$ in the XY plane are vertical asymptotes.

Notice that the graph of f sketched in Figure 7 is consistent with Theorem 4.5.3 and the remarks about vertical asymptotes that were made in connection with Figure 2. The graph of f crosses the horizontal axis at $(1, 0)$ and $(3, 0)$, because 1 and 3 are zeros of f of odd order, but the graph does not cross the horizontal axis at $(-2, 0)$ since -2 is an even-order zero of f. Also, the graph of f stays on the same side of the horizontal axis near the vertical asymptote $x = 0$, and does not near the line $x = 4$; this is because 0 is a zero of even order of $Q \colon Q(x) = x^6(2x-8)^{15}$, while 4 is a zero of odd order of Q.

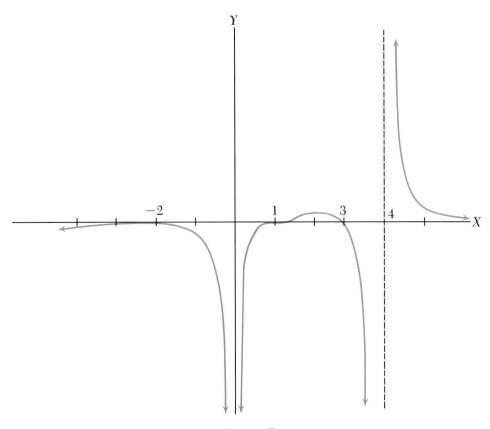

Figure 7

EXERCISES

1. Sketch the graph of each function.
   (a) $f: f(x) = (x - 1)/(x + 7)$
   (b) $g: g(x) = x^3/(x^2 - 4x + 3)$
   (c) $h: h(x) = (3x^2 - 4x - 4)/x^2$
   (d) $F: F(x)$
   $$= (x^2 - 5x + 6)/(x^2 + 1)$$
   (e) $G: G(x)$
   $$= (x - 2)^2(x - 3)^3(x + 4) \div$$
   $$x(x + 1)$$
   (f) $H: H(x)$
   $$= (2x + 1)^4(3x - 4)^3/(x + 5)^{12}$$
2. For each of (a), (b), (c), and (d) on page 168, find a rational function

f whose graph has the properties indicated in the sketch.
3. Solve the following inequalities.

   (a) $\dfrac{2x - 1}{x + 3} \leq 0$

   (b) $\dfrac{(x - 2)(x - 4)}{(3x + 1)} > 0$

   (c) $\dfrac{x^2 - 4x + 4}{x^2 + 5x + 6} \geq 0$

   (d) $\dfrac{x^3}{12x^2 + 5x - 2} < 0$

   (e) $\dfrac{2x - 3}{3x^2 + x + 1} > 0$

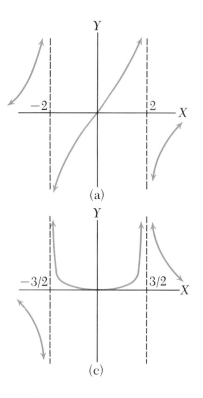

(a)

(b)

(c)

(d)

(f) $\dfrac{4x^2 + 2x - 8}{x^2} \le 1$

4. Prove Theorem 4.5.2. (*Hint:* First, establish that if *f* is a rational function and *a* and *b* are numbers such that $[a, b] \subset \mathcal{D}_f$ and $f(a)\,f(b) < 0$, then *f* has a zero between *a* and *b*. Then show how the general case can be reduced to this case.)

5. If *f* is a rational function, its graph may have a **horizontal asymptote**, that is, a line $y = d$ in the *XY* plane which the "tails" of the graph approach, as indicated in Figure 8. Roughly speaking, this means that the distance $|f(x) - d|$ can be made arbitrarily small by taking $|x|$ to be sufficiently large. For example, if $f\colon f(x) = 1/x$, then the line $y = 0$ is a horizontal asymptote, because

$$|f(x) - 0| = |1/x| = 1/|x|$$

can be made less than any given positive number *b* by taking *x* so that $|x| > 1/b$. Or, if $f\colon f(x) = \dfrac{2x}{x - 1}$, then the line $y = 2$ is a horizontal asymptote, since

$$|f(x) - 2| = \left| \frac{2x}{x - 1} - 2 \right| = \frac{2}{|x - 1|},$$

so $|f(x) - 2|$ can be made less than any given positive number *b* by taking *x* so that $|x| > \dfrac{2}{b} + 1$.

It turns out that there is a very simple test for horizontal asymptotes, as follows:

Let $f = P/Q$ with *P* and *Q* polynomial functions. Then:

(1) The horizontal axis is a hori-

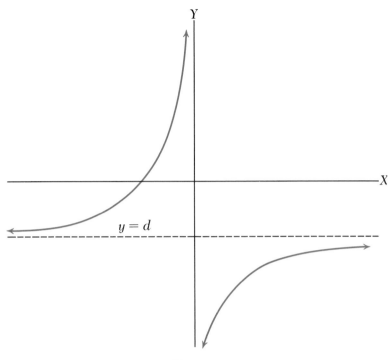

Figure 8

zontal asymptote if the degree of P is less than the degree of Q.

(2) If P and Q have the same degree with leading coefficients a_n and b_n, respectively, then the line $y = \dfrac{a_n}{b_n}$ in the XY plane is a horizontal asymptote.

(3) If the degree of P is greater than the degree of Q, then there is no horizontal asymptote.

Use this test to include a horizontal asymptote in each of your graphs found in Exercise 1, parts (a), (c), (d), and (f). Notice that the graph *may* intersect a horizontal asymptote, something that can't happen with a vertical asymptote.

6. For each of (a), (b), (c), and (d) on page 170, find a rational function whose graph has the properties indicated in the sketch.

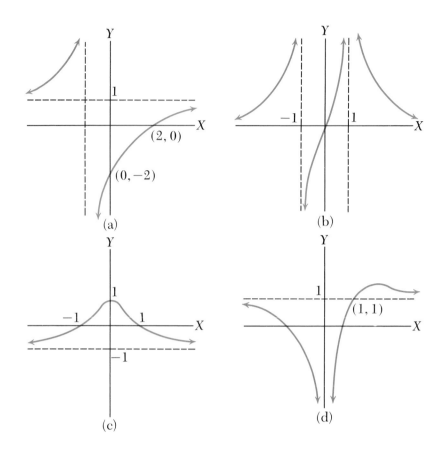

CHAPTER 5

CIRCULAR FUNCTIONS

■ 5.1 The Winding Function

Our examination of the class of real elementary functions continues in this chapter with the consideration of *circular functions*, which are probably better known to the reader as *trigonometric functions*. It is assumed that the reader has at least been exposed to angle trigonometry and some of its applications, a brief discussion of which is included in Appendix III. Before proceeding the reader may well ask, since he supposedly is acquainted with the trigonometric functions, why he should wade through another treatment of almost the same thing. A truly satisfactory answer would involve an examination of the historical development of trigonometry, and more generally, how the need to solve physical problems caused new mathematical theories to be invented and then refined so as to be more widely applicable. Although this would be a fascinating and enlightening thing to do it is not feasible here, so we will give only a token answer. It was discovered that many properties of trigonometric functions are present in physical systems in which no angles are involved. To utilize the results of trigonometry in such cases it was necessary to modify the definitions, or equivalently to invent new functions (circular functions) having the same properties as the trigonometric functions, but whose domains were number sets rather than sets of angles. A second, though perhaps less compelling answer, is that the fundamental concepts of calculus, for which this book is a preparation, are defined for *real* functions.

In this section we lay the groundwork for defining the basic circular functions in Section 5.2.

In defining the real circular functions, we will make use of several other functions whose domains and/or ranges are not subsets of R. Let C be the unit circle in a coordinate plane $\mathcal{P}$, that is, $C = \{(s, t) : s^2 + t^2 = 1\}$, and let L be a coordinate line such that the unit segments in $\mathcal{P}$ and L are congruent. (See Figure 1.)

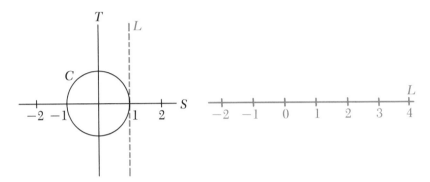

Figure 1

Suppose we take the line L and position it in the plane $\mathcal{P}$ so that the point 0 of L coincides with the point $P_0 = (1, 0)$ of $\mathcal{P}$ and then wind L around C as indicated in Figure 2. Then every point of L, and consequently every real

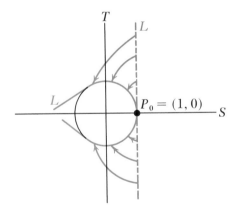

Figure 2

number, will be made to correspond to a point of C, namely, the point on which it falls in the winding process. Thus, to each real number x (point of L), there corresponds exactly one point P_x of C. The set $w = \{(x, P_x) : x \in R\}$ is then a function having domain R and range C.

Let us now use this geometric construction to define the function w a bit more precisely. Define $w(0) = (1, 0) = P_0$. For each positive real number x, define $w(x)$ to be the point P_x on C whose arc distance from P_0 along the circle in the counterclockwise direction is x. For each negative real number x, define $w(x)$ to be the point P_x on C whose distance from P_0 along the circle in the clockwise direction is $|x|$. The function

$$w = \{(x, P_x) : x \in R\}$$

is called the **winding function**.

It is easy to compute $w(x)$ for certain values of x. By definition $w(0) = (1, 0)$. Since the radius of C is 1, its circumference is 2π. Therefore, if we start at $P_0 = (1, 0)$ and measure a distance 2π along the circle in the counterclockwise direction, we end up back at the point $(1, 0)$. Hence, $w(2\pi) = P_{2\pi} = (1, 0)$. Similarly, proceeding a distance $2\pi = |-2\pi|$ from P_0 in the clockwise direction brings us back to $(1, 0)$, so $w(-2\pi) = P_{-2\pi} = (1, 0)$. Now, if n is any integer, moving around the circle from P_0 a distance $|2n\pi|$ in either direction will take us around the circle exactly $|n|$ times, bringing us back to $(1, 0)$. Hence, for each integer n,

$$w(2n\pi) = P_{2n\pi} = (1, 0).$$

Since the arc distance on C from $(1, 0)$ to $(-1, 0)$ is π in either direction, it is seen that

$$w(\pi) = w(-\pi) = (-1, 0).$$

The addition of an integral multiple of 2π to either π or $-\pi$ will simply put us at $(-1, 0)$ and then wind around the circle an integral number of times and hence, back to $(-1, 0)$. Therefore,

$$w(\pi + 2n\pi) = w(-\pi + 2n\pi) = (-1, 0)$$

for each integer n. We have therefore shown that the value of w at any even multiple of π is $(1, 0)$ and the value of w at any odd multiple of π is $(-1, 0)$.

Since we have observed that $w(0 + 2\pi) = w(0)$, $w(\pi + 2\pi) = w(\pi)$ and $w(-\pi + 2\pi) = w(-\pi)$, it is natural to ask whether $w(x + 2\pi) = w(x)$ for each real number x. If $w(x) = P_x$, then $w(x + 2\pi) = P_{x+2\pi}$ will be the point of C found by taking the arc distance $|x|$ from $(1, 0)$ in the appropriate direction, thus reaching P_x, and following this by one complete circuit of the circle in the counterclockwise direction, which brings us back to P_x. Therefore, $w(x + 2\pi) = w(x)$ for all $x \in R$. Similarly, for each integer n,

(#) $$w(x + 2n\pi) = w(x).$$

In the following theorem we will show that for each real number x there is a number z in the interval $[0, 2\pi)$ and an integer n such that $x = z + 2n\pi$. From equation (#) it follows that

$$w(x) = w(z + 2n\pi) = w(z).$$

This means that if the value of w is known at each number in the interval $[0, 2\pi)$, then its value at every real number is known.

THEOREM 5.1.1   Given any real number x, there exists a real number z, $0 \le z < 2\pi$, and an integer k such that

$$x = z + 2k\pi.$$

PROOF   To see this we make use of the greatest integer function that was introduced in Example 4 of Section 3.1. Recall that for any number a, the greatest integer in a, written $[a]$, is the largest integer m that is less than or equal to a. That is, $m = [a]$ means m is an integer and $m \le a < m + 1$.

Now, given x, let $k = \left[\dfrac{x}{2\pi}\right]$. Then $k \le \dfrac{x}{2\pi} < k + 1$, so that $2k\pi \le x < 2(k + 1)\pi$ and k is an integer. Setting $z = x - 2k\pi$, we have $0 \le z < 2\pi$ and $x = z + 2k\pi$, which completes the proof.

This leaves us in the pleasant situation where if we can compute $w(z)$ for each $z \in [0, 2\pi)$, then we can compute $w(x)$ for every real number x. There are many important functions for which essentially the same situation is true and it is convenient to have a descriptive name for them.

DEFINITION   A function f whose domain is a set of numbers is **periodic** if there is a positive number T such that

$$f(x + T) = f(x)$$

for every number x in the domain of f. The number T is called a **period** of f.

It is important to note that if f is a periodic function and T is a period of f, then the fact that $f(x + T) = f(x)$ for each $x \in \mathcal{D}_f$ implies that whenever x is in the domain of f, $x + T$ is also in the domain of f. This can be extended by mathematical induction. For, if k is any integer for which $x + kT \in \mathcal{D}_f$ then $x + (k + 1)T = (x + kT) + T$, which must also be in $\mathcal{D}_f$. Hence, if $x \in \mathcal{D}_f$ then $x + nT \in \mathcal{D}_f$ for every positive integer n.

The winding function is periodic, and 2π is a period of w. Notice, however, that there are other periods of w, namely, $4\pi, 6\pi, 8\pi, \dots$; that is, any positive integral integral multiple of 2π. This is the case for any periodic function. If f is a periodic function and T is a period of f, then for each $x \in \mathcal{D}_f$,

$$f(x + 2T) = f((x + T) + T) = f(x + T) = f(x),$$

so $2T$ is a period of f. This can be extended by mathematical induction to prove that if T is a period of f, then nT is a period of f for every positive integer n. (See Exercise 14.)

In the preceding discussion we proved the following theorem.

THEOREM 5.1.2   (Periodicity of w)   The winding function w is periodic and every positive integral multiple of 2π is a period of w. That is, for each positive integer n,

$$w(x + 2n\pi) = w(x)$$

for all $x \in R$.

Example 1   The evaluation of w at selected numbers:

(i)   Since $\pi/2$ is one fourth of the circumference of C, $w(\pi/2) = (0, 1)$ and $w(-\pi/2) = (0, -1)$.

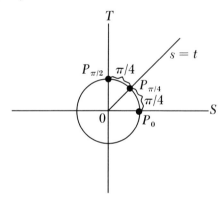

Figure 3

(ii)   To compute $w(\pi/4)$, let $w(\pi/4) = P_{\pi/4} = (s_0, t_0)$. Note that the arcs from P_0 to $P_{\pi/4}$ and from $P_{\pi/4}$ to $P_{\pi/2}$ have equal length. Hence, the angles $P_0 O P_{\pi/4}$ and $P_{\pi/4} O P_{\pi/2}$ are congruent, so the line through O and $P_{\pi/4}$ bisects the first quadrant and has equation $s = t$ in the ST plane. Thus, the coordinates of $P_{\pi/4}$ must satisfy this equation, so $s_0 = t_0$. But $P_{\pi/4}$ is also a point of the circle $s^2 + t^2 = 1$, so $s_0^2 + t_0^2 = 2s_0^2 = 1$. Since $P_{\pi/4}$ is in the first quadrant, $s_0 = t_0 = 1/\sqrt{2}$. Therefore, $w(\pi/4) = (1/\sqrt{2}, 1/\sqrt{2})$.

(iii)   Let $w(\pi/6) = P_{\pi/6} = (s_1, t_1)$. Since $\pi/6 = (1/3)(\pi/2)$, the length of the arc from $P_{\pi/6}$ to $P_{\pi/2}$ in the counterclockwise direction is twice the length of the arc from P_0 to $P_{\pi/6}$ in the counterclockwise direction. Hence, angle $P_0OP_{\pi/6}$ is one third of a right angle. If Q is the point of intersection of the horizontal axis and the vertical line through $P_{\pi/6}$, then the triangle $OQP_{\pi/6}$ is a 30–60 right triangle, so

$$|QP_{\pi/6}| = \frac{1}{2}|OP_{\pi/6}| = \frac{1}{2}.$$

That is $t_1 = 1/2$. Since (s_1, t_1) is on the circle $s^2 + t^2 = 1$, we obtain $s_1 = \sqrt{3}/2$. Therefore, $w(\pi/6) = (\sqrt{3}/2, 1/2)$. (See Figure 4.)

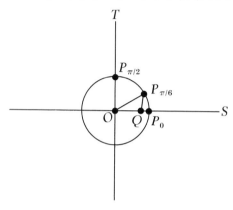

Figure 4

If we apply Theorem 5.1.2 to the facts obtained in (i)–(iii) we obtain the following results.

(iv) For each positive integer n,

$$w([4n + 1]\pi/2) = w(\pi/2 + 2n\pi) = w(\pi/2) = (0, 1)$$

and

$$w([4n - 1]\pi/2) = w(-\pi/2 + 2n\pi) = w(-\pi/2) = (0, -1).$$

(v) For each positive integer n,

$$w([8n + 1]\pi/4) = w(\pi/4 + 2n\pi) = w(\pi/4) = (1/\sqrt{2}, 1/\sqrt{2}).$$

(vi) For each positive integer n,

$$w(\pi/6 + 2n\pi) = w(\pi/6) = (\sqrt{3}/2, 1/2).$$

To illustrate how (iv), (v), and (vi) can be used we compute $w(25\pi/6)$. Since $25\pi/6 = \pi/6 + 4\pi$, an application of (vi) gives $w(25\pi/6) = w(\pi/6 + 4\pi) = w(\pi/6) = (\sqrt{3}/2, 1/2)$.

Given the value of w at one number, Theorem 5.1.2 enables us to compute its value at many other numbers. There are several other relationships that are useful in the same way, and we turn to them now before computing $w(x)$ for other values of x.

THEOREM 5.1.3   For each real number x, if $w(x) = (a, b)$ then $w(-x) = (a, -b)$. Geometrically this means that for each number x, the points $w(x)$ and $w(-x)$ are symmetric with respect to the horizontal axis.

PROOF   The proof is divided into two cases.

CASE 1. $0 \le x < 2\pi$.

The length of the arc from P_0 to P_x in the direction determined by x is $|x| = x$, since $x \ge 0$, and the length of the arc from P_0 to P_{-x} in the direction determined by $-x$ is $|-x| = x$. Since these arcs are equal in length, the central angles $P_0 O P_x$ and $P_0 O P_{-x}$ are congruent, as are the angles $P_x O Q$ and $P_{-x} O Q$. (See Figure 5.) Then the triangles $O P_x Q$ and $O P_{-x} Q$ are congruent, and hence the horizontal axis is the perpendicular bisector of $P_x P_{-x}$. This means that P_x and P_{-x} are symmetric with respect to the horizontal axis, so if $P_x = (a, b)$ then $P_{-x} = (a, -b)$.

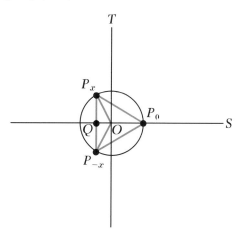

Figure 5

CASE 2. $x \notin [0, 2\pi)$.

By Theorem 5.1.1 there exist a number z with $0 \le z < 2\pi$ and an integer k such that $x = z + 2k\pi$. From Theorem 5.1.2, $w(x) = w(z)$ and similarly $w(-x) = w(-z + 2(-k)\pi) = w(-z)$. We conclude by Case 1, therefore, that if $w(x) = (a, b) = w(z)$ then $w(-x) = w(-z) = (a, -b)$ and the result is proved.

THEOREM 5.1.4 If $w(x) = (a, b)$ then

(i) $w(x + \pi) = w(x - \pi) = (-a, -b)$
(ii) $w(\pi - x) = (-a, b)$
(iii) $w(\pi/2 + x) = (-b, a)$
(iv) $w(\pi/2 - x) = (b, a)$.

PROOF   (i) Simply note that the segment $w(x)w(x \pm \pi)$ is a diameter of C, so $w(x \pm \pi)$ is the reflection of $w(x)$ in the origin.

(ii) $$w(\pi - x) = w(-(x - \pi))$$

$$w(x - \pi) = (-a, -b), \qquad \text{from (i)}$$

Hence, $$w(\pi - x) = (-a, b), \qquad \text{by Theorem 5.1.3.}$$

The reader should supply a proof of (iii) by referring to Figure 6, and of (iv) by applying (iii) to $w(-x)$.

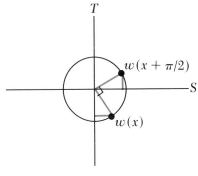

Figure 6

Parts (i), (ii), and (iv) have obvious interpretations in terms of symmetry. (What are they?) Can (iii) be described in this way?

Example 2   Let us use Theorems 5.1.2, 5.1.3, and 5.1.4 to evaluate w at several more numbers.

(a) Since $3\pi/4 = \pi/4 + \pi/2$ and $w(\pi/4) = (1/\sqrt{2}, 1/\sqrt{2})$, an application of (iii) of Theorem 5.1.4 gives $w(3\pi/4) = (-1/\sqrt{2}, 1/\sqrt{2})$.
(b) Since $5\pi/6 = \pi - \pi/6$ and $w(\pi/6) = (\sqrt{3}/2, 1/2)$, an application of (ii) of Theorem 5.1.4 gives $w(5\pi/6) = (-\sqrt{3}/2, 1/2)$.

(c) Since $39\pi/4 = -\pi/4 + 2(5)\pi$, $w(39\pi/4) = w(-\pi/4)$ by Theorem 5.1.2. But by Theorem 5.1.3 and the fact that $w(\pi/4) = (1/\sqrt{2}, 1/\sqrt{2})$ we have $w(39\pi/4) = w(-\pi/4) = (1/\sqrt{2}, -1/\sqrt{2})$.

(d) Since $\pi/3 = \pi/2 - \pi/6$ and $w(\pi/6) = (\sqrt{3}/2, 1/2)$, an application of (iv) of Theorem 5.1.4 gives $w(\pi/3) = (1/2, \sqrt{3}/2)$.

Before closing this section, let us examine the connection between the winding function and trigonometric angles. If at any stage the reader feels uncertain about angles and angle measurement, he should review the material in the first section of Appendix III.

Recall that to obtain a trigonometric angle in standard position having radian measure θ, we start with a ray r_1 coinciding with the positive horizontal axis and the point P of this ray one unit from the origin. (See Figure 7.)

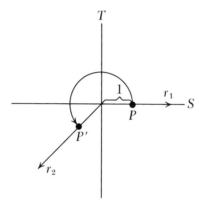

Figure 7

The ray r_1 is then rotated about the origin (in the counterclockwise sense if $\theta > 0$, the clockwise sense if $\theta < 0$) until the point P has traversed the distance $|\theta|$. If r_2 is the terminal position of r_1 after this rotation, the ordered pair of rays (r_1, r_2) with the rotation is an angle whose measure is θ radians.

Now, in the rotation, the point P moves along the unit circle a distance $|\theta|$ in the appropriate direction. Let P' be the terminal position of P after the rotation. Then it is clear from the way the winding function w is defined that $P' = w(\theta)$. That is, for any real number θ, $w(\theta)$ is the point of intersection of the unit circle with the terminal side of the angle in standard position whose measure is θ radians.

EXERCISES

1. For each of the following numbers x, find a number z, $0 \le z < 2\pi$, and an integer k such that $x = z + 2k\pi$.

(a) $x = 3\pi$ (e) $x = -81\pi$

(b) $x = \dfrac{7\pi}{2}$ (f) $x = -\dfrac{65\pi}{3}$

(c) $x = -\dfrac{7\pi}{2}$ (g) $x = \dfrac{19\pi}{6}$

(d) $x = \dfrac{\pi}{6}$ (h) $x = 2\pi$

2. Compute $w(x)$ for each number x in Exercise 1.

3. Use the various properties of the winding function w that have been proved or stated to compute $w(2\pi/3)$, $w(4\pi/3)$, $w(5\pi/3)$, $w(47\pi/3)$, $w(-5\pi/3)$, $w(-5\pi/6)$, $w(5\pi/2)$, $w(-7\pi/4)$, $w(14\pi)$, $w(-15\pi/6)$, $w(21\pi)$, $w(3\pi/2)$, $w(-3\pi/2)$.

4. Locate as closely as possible each of the points listed below on the unit circle C.
$w(\pi/12)$, $w(1/2)$, $w(\pi/6)$, $w(\pi/4)$, $w(1)$, $w(\pi/3)$, $w(\pi/2)$, $w(2)$, $w(2\pi/3)$, $w(\pi)$, $w(5\pi/4)$, $w(3\pi/2)$, $w(3)$, $w(2\pi)$.

5. (a) Wherever possible in Theorem 5.1.4, interpret the results in terms of symmetry.
   (b) Supply proofs for parts (iii) and (iv) of that theorem.
   (c) Now, without referring to the text, derive properties (i) and (ii).

6. (a) Compute the distances $|w(0)w(\pi/3)|$ and $|w(\pi/3)w(2\pi/3)|$.
   (b) You should have found that these distances are the same. Draw a picture and give a geometric reason why they are equal.
   (c) Without computing the distances, explain why the distances $|w(0)w(4\pi/3)|$ and $|w(\pi/3)w(5\pi/3)|$ are equal.

*7. Let x_1 and x_2 be numbers such that $0 \le x_1 \le x_2 < 2\pi$.
   (a) What is the length of the arc on C from $w(x_1)$ to $w(x_2)$ in the counterclockwise direction?
   (b) Show that $0 \le x_2 - x_1 < 2\pi$.

(c) What is the length of the arc from $w(0)$ to $w(x_2 - x_1)$ in the counterclockwise direction?

*8. Your answers to parts (a) and (c) of Exercise 7 should have been the same, namely $x_2 - x_1$. Use this to show that the distances $|w(x_1)w(x_2)|$ and $|w(0)w(x_2 - x_1)|$ are the same.

*9. Under the same assumptions about x_1 and x_2 as in Exercise 7:
   (a) Give a geometric argument to show that $|w(0)w(x_1 - x_2)| = |w(0)w(x_2 - x_1)|$.
   (b) Give an algebraic argument to show that $|w(0)w(x_1 - x_2)| = |w(0)w(x_2 - x_1)|$. (Theorem 5.1.3 may be useful in both (a) and (b).)
   (c) Combine the above result with the result of Exercise 7 to conclude that if z_1 and z_2 are any two numbers in the interval $[0, 2\pi)$, then $|w(z_1)w(z_2)| = |w(0)w(z_2 - z_1)|$.

*10. With the help of Theorem 5.1.1 and Exercise 9(c) show that for any numbers x_1 and x_2, $|w(x_1)w(x_2)| = |w(0)w(x_2 - x_1)|$.

*11. Let $w(x_1) = (s_1, t_1)$, $w(x_2) = (s_2, t_2)$, and $w(x_2 - x_1) = (c, d)$.
   (a) Show that $|w(x_1)w(x_2)| = \sqrt{2 - 2(s_1 s_2 + t_1 t_2)}$ (Remember that $w(x_1)$ and $w(x_2)$ are points on the unit circle C.)
   (b) Show that $|w(0)w(x_2 - x_1)| = \sqrt{2 - 2c}$.
   (c) Use parts (a) and (b) and Exercise 10 to show that $c = s_1 s_2 + t_1 t_2$.
   (d) Justify each of the following statements.
   (i) $w(-x_1) = (s_1, -t_1)$.
   (ii) $w(\pi/2 - x_2) = (t_2, s_2)$.
   (iii) $w(\pi/2 - (x_2 - x_1)) = (d, s_1 s_2 + t_1 t_2)$.
   (iv) $|w(\pi/2 - x_2)w(-x_1)| = |w(0)w(\pi/2 - (x_2 - x_1))|$.
   (v) $\sqrt{2 - 2(s_1 t_2 - t_1 s_2)} = \sqrt{2 - 2d}$.

(vi) $d = s_1 t_2 - t_1 s_2$.
(vii) $w(x_2 - x_1)$
$\quad = (s_1 s_2 + t_1 t_2,\ s_1 t_2 - s_2 t_1)$.
(viii) $w(x_1 - x_2)$
$\quad = (s_1 s_2 + t_1 t_2,\ t_1 s_2 - s_1 t_2)$.
(ix) $w(x_1 + x_2)$
$\quad = (s_1 s_2 - t_1 t_2,\ t_1 s_2 + s_1 t_2)$.

12. Compute.
  (a) $w(\pi/12)$
      (*Hint:* $\pi/12 = \pi/3 - \pi/4$)
  (b) $w(7\pi/12)$
  (c) $w(-5\pi/12)$
  (d) $w(\pi/8)$
      Hint: Let
      $$w(\pi/8) = (s, t).$$
      Then
      $$w(\pi/4) = w(\pi/8 + \pi/8),$$
      but
      $$w(\pi/4) = (1/\sqrt{2},\ 1/\sqrt{2}).$$
      You will also want to observe that $w(\pi/8)$ is in the first quadrant.

13. Examples of periodic functions.
  (a) Show that if g is a real constant function, say $g: g(x) = c$, then g is periodic and every positive number T is a period of g.
  (b) Let $h: h(x) = 2$, x not an integer. Show that 1 is a period of h. Show that each positive integer n is a period of h. Show that $\frac{1}{2}$ is not a period of h. Sketch the graph of h.
  (c) Let $F: F(x) = x - [x]$. Show that F is periodic and has 1 as a period. (*Hint:* For any number x, there is an integer n such that $x \in [n, n + 1)$.) Sketch the graph of F.

14. Let F be a periodic function having T as a period. Use mathematical induction to prove that nT is a period of F for each positive integer n.

*15. Let each of f and g be periodic functions having T as a period. Show that $f + g$, $f - g$, $f \cdot g$, and f/g are periodic and have T as a period. If h is any function for which $h \circ f$ exists, show that $h \circ f$ is periodic and has T as a period.

16. The number 2π is the smallest period of w. If f is a periodic function and has a smallest period T_0, T_0 is called the **fundamental period** of f. Constant functions do not have a fundamental period since every positive number is a period.
  (a) Show that if f has a fundamental period T_0, and $\mathscr{D}_f = R$, then every period of f is an integral multiple of T_0.
  (b) Show that the function
      $$G: G(x) = \begin{cases} 1 & \text{for } x \text{ rational} \\ 0 & \text{for } x \text{ irrational} \end{cases}$$
      is periodic but does not have a fundamental period.
  (c) Show that if H is a periodic function having every positive real number as a period, then H is a constant function.

17. Let f be a periodic function having 1 as a fundamental period, $\mathscr{D}_f = R$, and let $g: g(x) = 2x$. If $h = f \circ g$, show that h is periodic and has $1/2$ as a fundamental period.

18. Let f be a periodic function with $\mathscr{D}_f = R$ and let $g: g(x) = mx + b$ where m and b are constants. Let $h = f \circ g$.
  (a) Show that h is periodic.
  (b) If f has T_0 as a fundamental period, does h necessarily have a fundamental period?
  (c) Find the fundamental period of h when it exists.

■ 5.2 The Sine and Cosine Functions

For each real number x, $w(x)$ is a point on the unit circle in a coordinate plane, and therefore an ordered pair of real numbers. The first coordinate of $w(x)$ is called the **cosine** of x and the second coordinate of $w(x)$ is called the **sine** of x. Thus, we define two new real functions.

DEFINITION The function whose value at any real number x is the first coordinate of $w(x)$ is called the **cosine function** and is abbreviated **cos**. The function whose value at any real number x is the second coordinate of $w(x)$ is called the **sine function** and is abbreviated **sin**.

For each real number x,

$$w(x) = (\cos(x), \sin(x)).$$

Thus, every statement concerning w is also a statement about the sine and cosine functions. For example, since $w(0) = (1, 0)$ and $w(0) = (\cos(0), \sin(0))$, we have $\cos(0) = 1$ and $\sin(0) = 0$. Similarly, since $w(\pi/6) = (\sqrt{3}/2, 1/2) = (\cos(\pi/6), \sin(\pi/6))$, it follows that $\cos(\pi/6) = \sqrt{3}/2$ and $\sin(\pi/6) = 1/2$. Since $w(\pi/2) = (0, 1) = (\cos(\pi/2), \sin(\pi/2))$, we have $\cos(\pi/2) = 0$ and $\sin(\pi/2) = 1$. Also, $w(\pi/4) = (1/\sqrt{2}, 1/\sqrt{2}) = (\cos(\pi/4), \sin(\pi/4))$, so $\cos(\pi/4) = 1/\sqrt{2}$ and $\sin(\pi/4) = 1/\sqrt{2}$.

It is customary to omit the parentheses when writing the value of the sine or cosine function at a number x. Thus, we write $\sin x$ for $\sin(x)$ and $\cos x$ for $\cos(x)$. Rewriting a few of the above results we have $\sin 0 = 0$, $\cos \pi/6 = \sqrt{3}/2$, $\sin \pi/2 = 1$, and so on.

We now find ourselves in a most pleasant situation. Most of the properties of the sine and cosine functions in which we will be interested are immediate corollaries of results already obtained about the winding function.

THEOREM 5.2.1 The sine and cosine functions are periodic functions having 2π as a period.

PROOF   Since 2π is a period of w, for each $x \in R$

$$(\cos(x + 2\pi), \sin(x + 2\pi)) = w(x + 2\pi) = w(x) = (\cos x, \sin x).$$

Hence, $\cos(x + 2\pi) = \cos x$ and $\sin(x + 2\pi) = \sin x$.

THEOREM 5.2.2   For each real number x,

(i) $\cos(-x) = \cos x$,   and
(ii) $\sin(-x) = -\sin x$.

PROOF   Since $w(x) = (\cos x, \sin x)$, Theorem 5.1.3 implies that $w(-x) = (\cos x, -\sin x)$. But $w(-x) = (\cos(-x), \sin(-x))$. Hence, $\cos(-x) = \cos x$ and $\sin(-x) = -\sin x$.

Geometrically, Theorem 5.2.2 states that the graph of the cosine function is symmetric with respect to the vertical axis and the graph of the sine function is symmetric with respect to the origin.

THEOREM 5.2.3   For each real number x,

(i) $\cos(\pi/2 - x) = \sin x$,   and
(ii) $\sin(\pi/2 - x) = \cos x$.

PROOF   By part (iv) of Theorem 5.1.4 and the fact that $w(x) = (\cos x, \sin x)$, we have

$$w(\pi/2 - x) = (\cos(\pi/2 - x), \sin(\pi/2 - x)) = (\sin x, \cos x),$$

from which the desired results follow.

Example 1   Evaluation of the sine and cosine functions at some special numbers.

(i)   Since $\pi/3 = \pi/2 - \pi/6$, an application of Theorem 5.2.3 gives

$$\sin \pi/3 = \sqrt{3}/2$$

and $$\cos \pi/3 = 1/2.$$

(ii)   If we note that $17\pi/4 = \pi/4 + 2(2\pi)$, an application of Theorem 5.2.1 gives

$$\sin 17\pi/4 = \sin \pi/4 = 1/\sqrt{2}$$

and $$\cos 17\pi/4 = \cos \pi/4 = 1/\sqrt{2}.$$

(iii)   From Theorems 5.2.1 and 5.2.2,

$$\sin 11\pi/2 = \sin(-\pi/2 + 6\pi) = \sin(-\pi/2) = -\sin \pi/2 = -1$$

and $\cos 11\pi/2 = \cos(-\pi/2) = \cos \pi/2 = 0$.

THEOREM 5.2.4   For each pair of real numbers x_1 and x_2,

(i) $\qquad \cos(x_1 - x_2) = \cos x_1 \cos x_2 + \sin x_1 \sin x_2$
(ii) $\qquad \cos(x_1 + x_2) = \cos x_1 \cos x_2 - \sin x_1 \sin x_2$
(iii) $\qquad \sin(x_1 - x_2) = \sin x_1 \cos x_2 - \cos x_1 \sin x_2$
(iv) $\qquad \sin(x_1 + x_2) = \sin x_1 \cos x_2 + \cos x_1 \sin x_2$.

PROOF   In Exercise 11 of Section 5.1 we saw that if

$$w(x_1) = (s_1, t_1),\ w(x_2) = (s_2, t_2) \quad \text{and} \quad w(x_2 - x_1) = (c, d)$$

then $w(x_1 - x_2) = (c, -d)$ and $c = t_1 t_2 + s_1 s_2$. By definition, $w(x_1) = (\cos x_1, \sin x_1)$, $w(x_2) = (\cos x_2, \sin x_2)$, and $w(x_1 - x_2) = (\cos(x_1 - x_2), \sin(x_1 - x_2))$.

Hence, $\qquad \cos(x_1 - x_2) = \cos x_1 \cos x_2 + \sin x_1 \sin x_2$.

To prove (ii) we note that

$$\begin{aligned}
\cos(x_1 + x_2) &= \cos(x_1 - (-x_2)) \\
&= \cos x_1 \cos(-x_2) + \sin x_1 \sin(-x_2), \qquad \text{by (i)}, \\
&= \cos x_1 \cos x_2 - \sin x_1 \sin x_2, \qquad \text{by Theorem 5.2.2}.
\end{aligned}$$

For part (iii),

$$\begin{aligned}
\sin(x_1 - x_2) &= \cos(\pi/2 - (x_1 - x_2)), \qquad \text{by Theorem 5.2.3}, \\
&= \cos((\pi/2 - x_1) + x_2) \\
&= \cos(\pi/2 - x_1)\cos x_2 - \sin(\pi/2 - x_1)\sin x_2, \qquad \text{by (ii)}, \\
&= \sin x_1 \cos x_2 - \cos x_1 \sin x_2, \qquad \text{by Theorem 5.2.3}.
\end{aligned}$$

Part (iv) follows from (iii) in the same way that (ii) followed from (i).

The four equations in Theorem 5.2.4 are called **addition formulas** and have many applications.

Example 2   Find $\sin 7\pi/12$ and $\cos 7\pi/12$.

$$\begin{aligned}
\sin 7\pi/12 &= \sin(\pi/4 + \pi/3) = \sin \pi/4 \cos \pi/3 + \cos \pi/4 \sin \pi/3 \\
&= \sqrt{2}/2 \cdot 1/2 + \sqrt{2}/2 \cdot \sqrt{3}/2 = (\sqrt{2} + \sqrt{6})/4. \\
\cos 7\pi/12 &= \cos(\pi/4 + \pi/3) = \cos \pi/4 \cos \pi/3 - \sin \pi/4 \sin \pi/3 \\
&= \sqrt{2}/2 \cdot 1/2 - \sqrt{2}/2 \cdot \sqrt{3}/2 = (\sqrt{2} - \sqrt{6})/4.
\end{aligned}$$

Example 3   Find $\sin(-13\pi/3)$ and $\cos 5\pi/6$.

$$\begin{aligned}
\sin(-13\pi/3) &= \sin(-\pi/3 - 4\pi) = \sin(-\pi/3), \quad \text{by Theorem 5.2.1}, \\
&= -\sin \pi/3, \quad \text{by Theorem 5.2.2},
\end{aligned}$$

$$= -\sqrt{3}/2.$$

$$\cos 5\pi/6 = \cos(\pi - \pi/6)$$
$$= \cos \pi \cos \pi/6 + \sin \pi \sin \pi/6, \quad \text{by Theorem 5.2.4,}$$
$$= (-1) \cdot \sqrt{3}/2 + 0 \cdot 1/2$$
$$= -\sqrt{3}/2.$$

So far we have evaluated the sine and cosine functions only at very special numbers. If we want to talk about the value of the sine function at the number 2 we would write $\sin 2$, since this is the only way we have of denoting this number exactly. In dealing with physical problems we will use approximations to the actual values of the sine and cosine functions. Methods for approximating $\sin x$ and $\cos x$ to any desired degree of accuracy are developed in calculus and are discussed briefly in Exercise 17.

The practical procedure that is usually followed is to compile a table listing approximate values of $\sin x$ and $\cos x$ for a limited set of values of x. With the theorems of this section we can show that if we can compute $\sin z$ and $\cos z$ for $0 \le z \le \pi/4$, then we can compute $\sin x$ and $\cos x$ for every real number x. (See Exercise 10.)

Let us now turn the problem around and ask for the numbers at which the sine or cosine function has a given value. It is clear first that if an equation $\sin x = a$ or $\cos x = a$ has a solution for a given number a, then it has infinitely many solutions. For, if x_0 is a solution, then so is $x_0 + 2n\pi$ for any integer n. We will see that if we can find one particular solution, then all the other solutions are known.

Example 4   Solve the equation $\cos x = -1/2$.

$\cos x = -1/2$ if and only if the first coordinate of $w(x)$ is $-1/2$. That is, $w(x)$ is a point of intersection of the unit circle $s^2 + t^2 = 1$ and the line $s = -1/2$ in the ST plane. It should be clear from Figure 1 that there is exactly

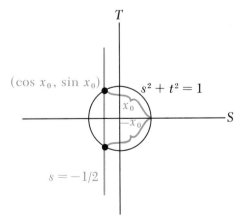

Figure 1

one number x_0 between 0 and π for which the first coordinate of $w(x_0)$ is $-1/2$, and by symmetry the first coordinate of $w(-x_0)$ is also $-1/2$. Also, any number z for which the first coordinate of $w(z)$ is $-1/2$ must be either x_0 plus an integral multiple of 2π or $-x_0$ plus an integral multiple of 2π. That is, the solution set will be

$$\{x: x = x_0 + 2n\pi \quad \text{or} \quad x = -x_0 + 2n\pi,\ n \text{ an integer}\},$$
where x_0 is the number between 0 and π such that $\cos x_0 = -1/2$.

Now, if we note that $\cos \pi/3 = 1/2$ and for any number z, $\cos (\pi - z) = -\cos z$, we see that $2\pi/3 = \pi - \pi/3$ is the number between 0 and π such that $\cos 2\pi/3 = -1/2$. Hence, the solution is

$$\{x: x = 2\pi/3 + 2n\pi \quad \text{or} \quad x = -2\pi/3 + 2n\pi,\ n \text{ an integer}\}.$$

Example 5   Solve the equation $\cos x = 1/\sqrt{2}$.
   We note that $0 \le \pi/4 \le \pi$ and $\cos \pi/4 = 1/\sqrt{2}$.
Hence, the solution is

$$\{x: x = \pm\pi/4 + 2n\pi,\ n \text{ an integer}\}.$$

Example 6   Solve the equation $\cos x = 2$.
   If x_0 is a solution, then $w(x_0)$ is a point of intersection of the unit circle $s^2 + t^2 = 1$ and the line $s = 2$ in the ST plane. But this line does not intersect the unit circle. Therefore, there are no solutions, or more precisely, the solution set is the empty set.

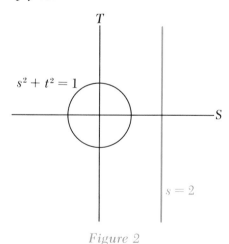

Figure 2

For a given number c, in order that there be a solution of the equation $\cos x = c$, the number c must be in the range of the cosine function, or equivalently, c must be in the horizontal extent of the unit circle. Hence, $-1 \le c \le 1$.

If c is in the range of cos, there is a unique number x_0, $0 \le x_0 \le \pi$, such that $\cos x_0 = c$, and the solution of the equation $\cos x = c$ is

$$\{x: x = x_0 + 2n\pi \quad \text{or} \quad x = -x_0 + 2n\pi, \ n \text{ an integer}\}.$$

Similarly, if $-1 \le d \le 1$, there is a unique number x_0, $-\pi/2 \le x_0 \le \pi/2$, such that $\sin x_0 = d$ and the solution of the equation $\sin x = d$ is

$$\{x: x = x_0 + 2n\pi \quad \text{or} \quad x = (\pi - x_0) + 2n\pi, \ n \text{ an integer}\}.$$

The justification of this fact is left to the reader (Exercise 11).

Example 7   Solve the equation $\sin x = -1/\sqrt{2}$.
   We note first that $\sin(-\pi/4) = -1/\sqrt{2}$ and $-\pi/2 \le -\pi/4 \le \pi/2$. Therefore, the solution is

$$\{x: x = -\pi/4 + 2n\pi \quad \text{or} \quad x = 5\pi/4 + 2n\pi, \ n \text{ an integer}\}.$$

Example 8   Solve the equation $\sin 3x = 1/2$.
   Since $\sin \pi/6 = 1/2$, the solution set can be written as

$$\{x: 3x = \pi/6 + 2n\pi \quad \text{or} \quad 3x = 5\pi/6 + 2n\pi, \ n \text{ an integer}\}$$

or more clearly as

$$\{x: x = \pi/18 + 2n\pi/3 \quad \text{or} \quad x = 5\pi/18 + 2n\pi/3, \ n \text{ an integer}\}.$$

It was pointed out in Section 5.1 that for any real number θ, $w(\theta) = (\cos\theta, \sin\theta)$ is on the terminal side of the angle in standard position whose measure is θ radians. Recall that the trigonometric sine of an angle in standard position is the ratio of the vertical coordinate of a point on the terminal side to the distance between that point and the origin and the trigonometric cosine is the ratio of the horizontal coordinate to the distance from the origin. Since $w(\theta)$ is 1 unit from the origin,

$$\sin(\theta \text{ rad}) = \frac{\sin\theta}{1} = \sin\theta$$

and

$$\cos(\theta \text{ rad}) = \frac{\cos\theta}{1} = \cos\theta.$$

Similar equations hold for the other corresponding trigonometric and circular functions. Hence, for any real number x, $\sin x = \sin(x \text{ rad})$, $\cos x = \cos(x \text{ rad})$, and so on.

This connection between circular and trigonometric functions gives us a wider scope for interpreting results obtained with them. The symbol $\sin x$ can be thought of as standing for the circular sine of the real number x or the trigonometric sine of an angle whose radian measure is x.

EXERCISES

1. Define the functions sine and cosine.
2. Compute the values of the winding, sine, and cosine functions at each of the following numbers: $0,\ \pi/6,\ \pi/4,\ \pi/3,\ \pi/2,\ 2\pi/3,\ 3\pi/4,$ $5\pi/6,\ \pi, 7\pi/6, 5\pi/4, 4\pi/3, 3\pi/2, 5\pi/3,$ $7\pi/4,\ 11\pi/6,\ 2\pi,\ -\pi/6,\ -\pi/4,\ -\pi/3,$ $-\pi/2,\ -\pi,\ -3\pi/2, -2\pi.$
3. Compute the values of the functions sin and cos at each of the following numbers: $\pi/12,\quad 5\pi/12,$ $-7\pi/12,\ 82\pi/3,\ -41\pi/2,\ -61\pi/12,$ $287\pi/2,\ 435\pi,\ -16\pi/3,\ 15\pi/4.$
4. Find explicitly the numbers in each of the following sets.
$$Z_1 = \{x: \sin x = 0\}$$
$$P_1 = \{x: \sin x > 0\}$$
$$N_1 = \{x: \sin x < 0\}$$
$$Z_2 = \{x: \cos x = 0\}$$
$$P_2 = \{x: \cos x > 0\}$$
$$N_2 = \{x: \cos x < 0\}$$
*5. Justify each of the following for each real number x.
   (a) $\cos (x + \pi) = \cos (x - \pi)$
   $$= -\cos x$$
   (b) $\sin (x + \pi) = \sin (x - \pi)$
   $$= -\sin x$$
   (c) $\cos (\pi - x) = -\cos x$
   (d) $\sin (\pi - x) = \sin x$
   (e) $\cos (\pi/2 + x) = -\sin x$
   (f) $\sin (\pi/2 + x) = \cos x$
*6. Show that $(\sin x)^2 + (\cos x)^2 = 1$ for all $x \in R.$
7. Use the result of Exercise 6 to compute
   (a) $\cos x$, if $\sin x = 1/3$ and $\cos x < 0.$
   (b) $\sin x$, if $\cos x = -6/7$ and $\sin x > 0.$
   (c) $\sin x$, if $\cos x = -1/\sqrt{3}$ and

$w(x)$ is in the second quadrant.
   (d) $\cos x$, if $\sin x = 3/5$ and $4\pi \le x \le 9\pi/2.$
8. Show that these statements are true for each real number x.
   (a) $\sin 2x = 2 \sin x \cos x$
   (b) $\cos 2x = (\cos x)^2 - (\sin x)^2$
   (c) $\cos 2x = 2(\cos x)^2 - 1$
   $$= 1 - 2(\sin x)^2$$
   Hint: Use part (b) and Exercise 6.
9. Compute $\sin \pi/8$ and $\cos \pi/8.$
   Hint: Use the fact that $2 \cdot \pi/8 = \pi/4$, Exercise 8(c), and the fact that $w(\pi/8)$ is in the first quadrant.
10. Show that if the values of $\sin x$ and $\cos x$ are known for $0 \le x \le \pi/4$, they can be determined for all x.
   (a) First show that $\sin x$ and $\cos x$ can be determined for $0 \le x \le \pi/2$ by means of Theorem 5.2.3.
   (b) Extend this to all real numbers x by means of Theorems 5.2.4, 5.1.1 and 5.2.1.
11. Let d be a fixed real number.
   (a) Show that the solution set of the equation $\sin x = d$ is non-empty if and only if $|d| \le 1.$
   (b) If $|d| \le 1$, show that there is exactly one number $x_0, -\pi/2 \le x_0 \le \pi/2$, such that $\sin x_0 = d.$
   (c) For $|d| \le 1$, let x_0 be the unique number in the interval $[-\pi/2, \pi/2]$ such that $\sin x_0 = d.$ Show that $\{x: \sin x = d\} = \{x: x = x_0 + 2n\pi$ or $x = (\pi - x_0) + 2n\pi,$ n an integer$\}.$
12. Let $f = \{(d, x): |d| \le 1$ and x is a number in $[-\pi/2, \pi/2]$ such that $\sin x = d\}.$

(a) Show that f is a function.
(b) What are $\mathcal{D}_f$ and $\mathcal{R}_f$?
(c) Show that f is a one-to-one function.
(d) Compute $f(1)$, $f(-1)$, $f(1/2)$, $f(-\sqrt{3}/2)$, $f(1/\sqrt{2})$, $f(0)$.
(e) Compute $\sin f(d)$ for $d \in \mathcal{D}_f$.
(f) Compute $f(\sin \pi/4)$, $f(\sin \pi/2)$, $f(\sin 3\pi/4)$, $f(\sin 7\pi/6)$.
(g) Compute $f(\sin x)$ if $3\pi/2 \le x \le 5\pi/2$.
(h) Compute $f(\cos x)$ if $0 \le x \le \pi/2$.
(i) Compute $f(\cos x)$ if $\pi/2 \le x \le \pi$.

13. Let $g = \{(c, x) : |c| \le 1,$ $0 \le x \le \pi$ and $\cos x = c\}$.
(a) Show that g is a function.
(b) What are $\mathcal{D}_g$ and $\mathcal{R}_g$?
(c) Show that g is a one-to-one function.
(d) Compute: $g(1)$, $g(-1)$, $g(-1/2)$, $g(\sqrt{3}/2)$, $g(1/\sqrt{2})$, $g(0)$.
(e) Compute $\cos g(c)$ for $c \in \mathcal{D}_g$.
(f) Compute $g(\cos \pi/6)$, $g(\cos \pi)$, $g(\cos (-\pi/4))$.
(g) Compute $g(\cos x)$ if $-\pi \le x \le 0$.
(h) Compute $g(\sin x)$ if $0 \le x \le \pi/2$.

14. Solve each of the following equations.
(a) $\cos x = \sqrt{3}/2$
(b) $\cos x = 0$
(c) $\cos x = 1$
(d) $\cos x = -1$
(e) $\cos x/2 = 1/2$

15. Solve each of the following equations.
(a) $\sin x = -1/2$
(b) $\sin x = \sqrt{3}/2$
(c) $\sin x = 0$
(d) $\sin x = 1$

(e) $\sin x = -1$
(f) $\sin 2x = 1/\sqrt{2}$
(g) $\sin x = 3/2$

16. Solve the equation $\sin x = \cos x$. *Hint:* x_0 is a solution if and only if $w(x_0)$ is a point of intersection of the unit circle $s^2 + t^2 = 1$ and the line $s = t$ in the ST plane.

17. It will be shown in calculus that for each real number x,

$$\sin x = x - \frac{x^3}{3!} + \frac{x^5}{5!}$$

(approximately),

and

$$\cos x = 1 - \frac{x^2}{2!} + \frac{x^4}{4!} - \frac{x^6}{6!}$$

(approximately).

Moreover, the error in the approximation for $\sin x$ is less than $|x^7/7!|$ and the error in the approximation for $\cos x$ is less than $|x^8/8!|$. Use these approximation formulas to complete the following table so that each entry is correct to three decimal places.

x	$\sin x$	$\cos x$
0		
.1		
.2		
.3		
.4		
.5		
.6		
.7		
.8		
.9		
1		

Note: A desk calculator is a great convenience here.

■ 5.3 Other Circular Functions

The functions sine and cosine are called *circular functions* since their values are defined in terms of coordinates of points on the unit circle. In this section we consider some other circular functions defined in terms of sine and cosine.

DEFINITION The functions **tangent**, **cotangent**, **secant**, and **cosecant**, abbreviated **tan, cot, sec,** and **csc** respectively, are defined by

(i)   tan = sin/cos
(ii)   cot = cos/sin
(iii) sec = 1/cos
(iv)   csc = 1/sin.

Unlike the sine and cosine functions, these functions are not defined for all real numbers. From the results of Section 3.3,

$$\mathscr{D}_{\tan} = \{x : x \in \mathscr{D}_{\sin} \text{ and } x \in \mathscr{D}_{\cos} \text{ and } \cos x \neq 0\}$$
$$= \{x : \cos x \neq 0\}.$$

Now, $\cos x = 0$ if and only if $w(x)$ is a point of the vertical axis; *i.e.*, $w(x) = (0, 1)$ or $w(x) = (0, -1)$, in which case x is an odd multiple of $\pi/2$. Thus,

$$\mathscr{D}_{\tan} = \{x : x \neq (2n + 1)\pi/2, \ n \text{ an integer}\}.$$

Likewise,

$$\mathscr{D}_{\sec} = \{x : x \in \mathscr{D}_{\cos} \text{ and } \cos x \neq 0\}$$
$$= \{x : x \neq (2n + 1)\pi/2, \ n \text{ an integer}\}.$$

A similar argument yields

$$\mathscr{D}_{\cot} = \mathscr{D}_{\csc} = \{x : x \neq n\pi, \ n \text{ an integer}\}$$
$$= \{x : x \text{ is not a multiple of } \pi\}.$$

From the definition it is clear that we can evaluate these new functions whenever we can evaluate sin and cos.

Example 1   tan 0 = sin 0/cos 0 = 0/1 = 0.
                                 sec 0 = 1/cos 0 = 1.

The functions cot and csc are not defined at 0 since $0 \notin \mathscr{D}_{\cot}$ and $0 \notin \mathscr{D}_{\csc}$.

$$\tan \pi/6 = \frac{\sin \pi/6}{\cos \pi/6} = \frac{1/2}{\sqrt{3}/2} = \frac{1}{\sqrt{3}}$$

$$\sec \pi/6 = \frac{1}{\cos \pi/6} = \frac{1}{\sqrt{3}/2} = \frac{2}{\sqrt{3}}$$

$$\cot \pi/6 = \frac{\cos \pi/6}{\sin \pi/6} = \frac{\sqrt{3}/2}{1/2} = \sqrt{3}$$

$$\csc \pi/6 = \frac{1}{\sin \pi/6} = \frac{1}{1/2} = 2$$

THEOREM 5.3.1 Each of the functions tan, cot, sec, and csc is periodic and

(i)   tan and cot have π as a period,
(ii) sec and csc have 2π as a period.

PROOF From Exercise 15 of Section 5.1 and Theorem 5.2.1, each of these functions is periodic and has 2π as a period, so the only thing left to show is (i).

An application of parts (a) and (b) of Exercise 5 in Section 5.2 gives for each $x \in \mathscr{D}_{\tan}$,

$$\tan (x + \pi) = \frac{\sin (x + \pi)}{\cos (x + \pi)} = \frac{-\sin x}{-\cos x} = \frac{\sin x}{\cos x} = \tan x,$$

and for each $x \in \mathscr{D}_{\cot}$,

$$\cot (x + \pi) = \frac{\cos (x + \pi)}{\sin (x + \pi)} = \frac{-\cos x}{-\sin x} = \frac{\cos x}{\sin x} = \cot x.$$

THEOREM 5.3.2

(i)   For each number $x \in \mathscr{D}_{\tan} = \mathscr{D}_{\sec}$

$$\tan (-x) = -\tan x \quad \text{and}$$

$$\sec (-x) = \sec x.$$

(ii) For each number $x \in \mathscr{D}_{\cot} = \mathscr{D}_{\csc}$

$$\cot (-x) = -\cot x \quad \text{and}$$

$$\csc (-x) = -\csc x.$$

PROOF   The proof follows directly from Theorem 5.2.2.

Example 2

(i)
$$\tan(-5\pi/4) = -\tan 5\pi/4 = -\tan(\pi/4 + \pi)$$
$$= -\tan \pi/4 = \frac{-\sin \pi/4}{\cos \pi/4} = \frac{-1/\sqrt{2}}{1/\sqrt{2}} = -1.$$

(ii)
$$\cot 17\pi/4 = \cot(\pi/4 + 4\pi) = \cot \pi/4 = \frac{\cos \pi/4}{\sin \pi/4} = 1.$$

(iii)
$$\sec(-\pi/3) = \sec \pi/3 = \frac{1}{\cos \pi/3} = \frac{1}{1/2} = 2.$$

(iv)
$$\csc 11\pi/2 = \csc(-\pi/2 + 6\pi) = \csc(-\pi/2)$$
$$= -\csc \pi/2 = \frac{-1}{\sin \pi/2} = -1.$$

Example 3   Let a be a fixed real number, and consider the problem of trying to solve the equation $\tan x = a$. The line L determined by the points $(1, a)$ and $(0, 0)$ will intersect the unit circle in two points, one in the right half-plane and one in the left half-plane. (See Figure 1.) The point in the right

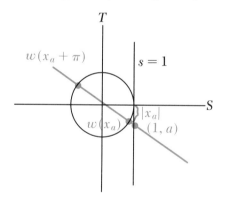

Figure 1

half-plane will be $w(x_a)$ for some number x_a between $-\pi/2$ and $\pi/2$. Since $w(x_a) = (\cos x_a, \sin x_a)$, the slope of L is

$$\frac{\sin x_a - 0}{\cos x_a - 0} = \tan x_a$$

and an equation of L in the ST plane is

$$t = (\tan x_a) \cdot s.$$

The point $(1, a)$ is on L so

$$a = \tan x_a.$$

Now, if z is any number between $-\pi/2$ and $\pi/2$ different from x_a, the line through $(0,0)$ and $w(z)$ will intersect the line $s = 1$ in the point $(1, \tan z) \neq (1, a)$ so $\tan z \neq a$. Therefore, the equation $\tan x = a$ has exactly one solution x_a in the open interval $(-\pi/2, \pi/2)$. Any other solution will be $x_a + n\pi$ for some integer n. That is, the solution set of the equation $\tan x = a$ is

$$\{x: x = x_a + n\pi, \ n \text{ an integer}\}$$

where x_a is the unique solution between $-\pi/2$ and $\pi/2$.

Example 4   Solve the equation $\tan x = \sqrt{3}$.
   We note that

$$\tan \pi/3 = \frac{\sin \pi/3}{\cos \pi/3} = \frac{\sqrt{3}/2}{1/2} = \sqrt{3} \quad \text{and} \quad -\pi/2 < \pi/3 < \pi/2.$$

Therefore, the solution set is

$$\{x: x = \pi/3 + n\pi, \ n \text{ an integer}\}.$$

Example 5   Solve the equation $\sec x = \sqrt{2}$.
   From the definition of sec, $\sec x = \sqrt{2}$ if and only if $1/\cos x = \sqrt{2}$, that is $\cos x = 1/\sqrt{2}$. Since $\cos \pi/4 = 1/\sqrt{2}$, the solution is

$$\{x: x = \pi/4 + 2n\pi \quad \text{or} \quad x = -\pi/4 + 2n\pi, \ n \text{ an integer}\}.$$

Example 6   Solve $\tan x = \cot x$.
   A number x is a solution of this equation if and only if $\tan x = 1/\tan x$, or equivalently $(\tan x)^2 = 1$ and x is not an integral multiple of $\pi/2$ (*i.e.*, x is in $\mathscr{D}_{\tan}$ and $\mathscr{D}_{\cot}$). Hence, x is a solution if and only if $\tan x = 1$ or $\tan x = -1$. We note that $\pi/4$ and $-\pi/4$ are in the interval $(-\pi/2, \pi/2)$, $\tan \pi/4 = 1$ and $\tan (-\pi/4) = -1$. Therefore, the solution is

$$\{x: x = \pi/4 + n\pi \quad \text{or} \quad x = -\pi/4 + n\pi, \ n \text{ an integer}\},$$

or equivalently

$$\{x: x = \pi/4 + n\pi/2, \ n \text{ an integer}\}.$$

EXERCISES

1. Define each of the functions w, sine, cosine, tangent, cotangent, secant, and cosecant. What is the domain of each of these functions?

2. Without referring to your work in previous sections, complete the following table.

x	$w(x)$	$\sin x$	$\cos x$	$\tan x$	$\cot x$	$\sec x$	$\csc x$
0	$(1,0)$	0	1	0	undefined	1	undefined
$\pi/6$	$(\sqrt{3}/2, 1/2)$	$1/2$	$\sqrt{3}/2$	$1/\sqrt{3}$	$\sqrt{3}$	$2/\sqrt{3}$	2
$\pi/4$							
$\pi/3$							
$\pi/2$	$(0,1)$	1	0				
$2\pi/3$							
$3\pi/4$							
$5\pi/6$							
π							
$3\pi/2$				undefined			
$-\pi/6$							
$-\pi/4$			$1/\sqrt{2}$		-1		
$-\pi/3$							
$-\pi/2$							
$-2\pi/3$							
$-\pi$			-1				
2π							
$13\pi/3$						2	
$-47\pi/2$							
$\pi/12$							
$-5\pi/12$							

3. (a) For each number x that is in both $\mathscr{D}_{\tan}$ and $\mathscr{D}_{\cot}$, show that $\cot x \cdot \tan x = 1$.

   (b) Give an explicit description of the set of numbers x such that $\cot x \cdot \tan x = 1$.

   (c) In light of your result to part (b) explain why it is not reasonable to define the cotangent function by $\cot = 1/\tan$.

4. (a) Find the solution set of the equation

$$(\tan x)^2 + 1 = (\sec x)^2.$$

   Hint: Recall Exercise 6 of Section 5.2.

   (b) Find the solution set of the equation

$$1 + (\cot x)^2 = (\csc x)^2.$$

5. Show that if x is any number for which each member of the equa-

tion makes sense, then each of the following statements is true.

   (a) $\tan (\pi/2 - x) = \cot x$

   (b) $\cot (\pi/2 - x) = \tan x$

   (c) $\sec (\pi/2 - x) = \csc x$

   (d) $\csc (\pi/2 - x) = \sec x$

   (e) $\tan (\pi - x) = -\tan x$

   (f) $\csc (\pi - x) = \csc x$

6. (a) Show as in Example 3 that the line through the origin and the point $w(x)$ intersects the line $s = 1$ in the ST plane at the point $(1, \tan x)$ for each number $x \in \mathscr{D}_{\tan}$.

   (b) Locate the point $(\cot x, 1)$ for each $x \in \mathscr{D}_{\cot}$.

   (c) Locate the point $(0, \sec x)$. (Recall Exercise 4.)

   (d) Locate the point $(\csc x, 0)$.

7. (a) Use the construction of the point $(1, \tan x)$ in Example 3 to argue that the range of the

tangent function is the set of all real numbers.

(b) Use the construction of Exercise 6(b) to argue that $\mathcal{R}_{\cot} = R$.

(c) Use Exercise 6 to argue that $\mathcal{R}_{\sec} = \mathcal{R}_{\csc} = \{r : |r| \geq 1\}$.

8. Let ρ be the ray in the ST plane with vertex $(0,0)$, through the point $w(x)$.

(a) Show that the intersection of ρ with the circle $s^2 + t^2 = r^2$ is $(r \cdot \cos x, r \cdot \sin x)$.

(b) Use part (a) to show that every point in the plane can be expressed as $(r \cos \theta, r \sin \theta)$ for some numbers r and θ. Give a geometric interpretation of the numbers r and θ.

9. Solve each of the following equations.

(a) $\tan x = 1$

(b) $\cot x = -1$

(c) $\sec x = 2/\sqrt{3}$

(d) $\csc x = 2/\sqrt{3}$

(e) $\tan x = 0$

(f) $\cot x = 0$

10. Solve each of the following equations.

(a) $\sin x = \tan x$

(b) $\sec x + \csc x = 0$

(c) $\cot 2x = \sqrt{3}$

(d) $\csc x = 0$

(e) $\tan \dfrac{2x - 1}{5} = 1/\sqrt{3}$

11. Solve each of the following inequalities.

(a) $\tan x > 0$

(b) $\cot x > 0$

(c) $\sec x > 0$

(d) $\csc x > 0$

12. Solve each of the following inequalities.

(a) $\tan x > \cot x$

(b) $\sec x < \csc x$

(c) $\sec x \leq \cos x$

(d) $|\tan x/2| < 1$

(e) $\cot x > \sqrt{3}$

13. Let $h = \{(e, x) : x \in (-\pi/2, \pi/2)$ and $\tan x = e\}$.

(a) Explain why h is a function.

(b) What are $\mathcal{D}_h$ and $\mathcal{R}_h$?

(c) Show that h is a one-to-one function.

(d) Compute: $h(1)$, $h(-1)$, $h(-\sqrt{3})$, $h(-1/\sqrt{3})$, $h(0)$.

(e) Compute $\tan h(e)$ for $e \in R$.

(f) Compute: $h(\tan \pi/4)$, $h(\tan -\pi/5)$, $h(\tan \pi)$.

(g) Compute $h(\tan x)$ if $-3\pi/2 < x < -\pi/2$.

(h) Compute $\sin h(e)$ if $0 \leq e < \pi/2$.

(i) Compute $\cos h(e)$ if $0 \leq e < \pi/2$.

14. For $x \in [0, \pi/2)$, show that $\sec x > \tan x$.

◾ 5.4 Graphs of the Basic Circular Functions

Virtually all the qualitative properties of a real function, and many quantitative properties as well, can easily be determined from the graph of the function. Thus, a knowledge of the graph of a function can be a potent tool for recalling its properties. In this section we will determine the graphs of the six basic circular functions that should become firmly implanted in the reader's memory.

The graphing of circular functions is greatly facilitated by the fact that they are periodic. Let f be a periodic function having T as a period. Then the graph of f on any semiopen interval $[x_0, x_0 + T)$ completely determines the graph since every number in $\mathcal{D}_f$ is in an interval of the form $[x_0 + nT,$

$x_0 + (n + 1)T)$ where n is an integer. If $x \in [x_0 + nT, x_0 + (n + 1)T)$, then $f(x) = f(x - nT)$. But $x - nT$ is an element of $[x_0, x_0 + T)$ where the graph is known. Thus, the graph of f on $[x_0 + nT, x_0 + (n + 1)T)$ is a copy of the graph of f on $[x_0, x_0 + T)$. To graph f then, we simply determine the graph on a semiopen interval $[x_0, x_0 + T)$ of length T and repeat it on every interval $[x_0 + nT, x_0 + (n + 1)T)$ that contains elements of $\mathscr{D}_f$.

For example, if f is periodic with period 2, $\mathscr{D}_f = R$ and its graph on $[-1/2, 3/2)$ is found to be that in Figure 1(a), then the completion of its graph is indicated in Figure 1(b).

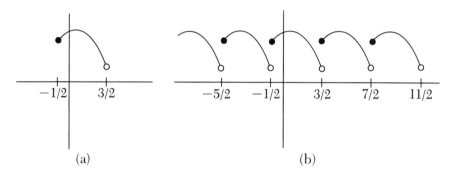

(a)   (b)

Figure 1

For the sine function we need only determine its graph in the interval $[0, 2\pi)$. To find the graph in the XY plane, place an ST coordinate system to the left of the Y-axis so that the horizontal axes of the two systems coincide and they have congruent unit segments.

Let C be the unit circle in the ST plane. For any number $x_1 \in [0, 2\pi)$, find the point $w(x_1)$ on C. Its vertical coordinate is $\sin x_1$, which is the vertical coordinate of the point $(x_1, \sin x_1)$ on the graph of sin. Thus, by traversing C in the counterclockwise direction one time, we can generate the graph of sin on the interval $[0, 2\pi)$ as indicated in Figure 2.

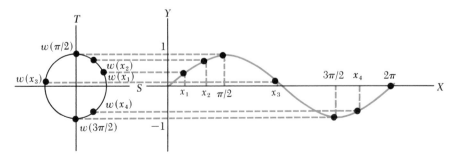

Figure 2

The graph of sin is then completed in Figure 3 by using the fact that 2π is a period of sin.

Notice that the graph obtained in this manner displays many of the properties discovered in Section 5.2. It is symmetric with respect to the origin, its vertical extent is $[-1, 1]$, and so on. Notice also that from the graph it is obvious where the sine function is positive, negative, increasing, decreasing, and where it has a high point or low point. As your familiarity and experience with this graph increase, you will be able to use it to recall many other properties of the sine function as well.

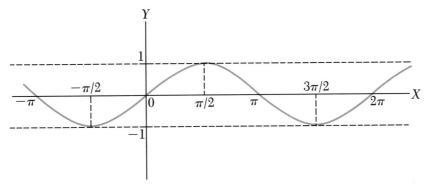

Figure 3

To find the graph of the cosine function in the XY plane, recall from Section 5.2 that for all $x \in R$, $\cos x = \sin (x + \pi/2)$. Thus, if we let the UV plane be a translation of the XY plane determined by $(0, 0)_{UV} = (-\pi/2, 0)_{XY}$, so that $u = x + \pi/2$ and $v = y$, the graph of cos in the XY plane will be the graph of the sine function in the UV plane. (See Figure 4.) The graph of the cosine function in the XY plane appears in Figure 5.

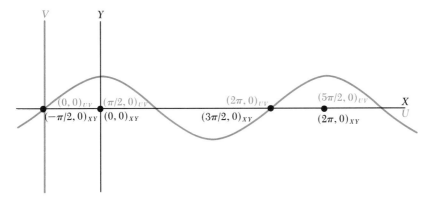

Figure 4

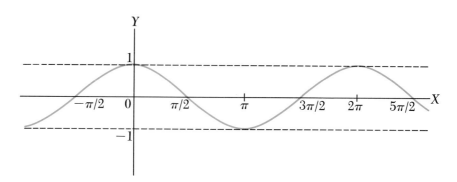

Figure 5

To graph the tangent function, we make use of the geometric construction of Example 3 in Section 5.3. In the ST plane, we take the point $w(x) = (\cos x, \sin x)$ on the unit circle C for each $x \in [0, \pi/2)$. The line through the origin and the point $w(x)$ has

$$t = (\tan x)\ s$$

as an equation and the point of intersection of this line with the line $s = 1$ is $(1, \tan x)$. Hence, we can use a construction like that used for the sine function to sketch the graph of tan on $[0, \pi/2)$. (See Figure 6.)

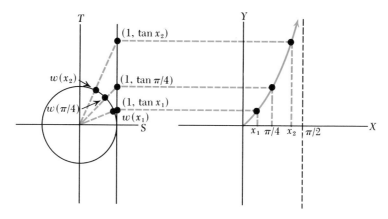

Figure 6

By Theorem 5.3.2 (i) we know that the graph of the tangent function is symmetric with respect to the origin, so we obtain the graph on the interval $(-\pi/2, \pi/2)$. (See Figure 7.) Finally, by Theorem 5.3.1, the tangent function

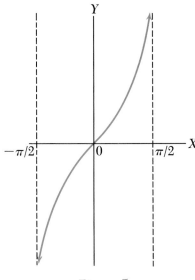

Figure 7

has period π and hence its graph can be completed by periodicity. (See Figure 8.)

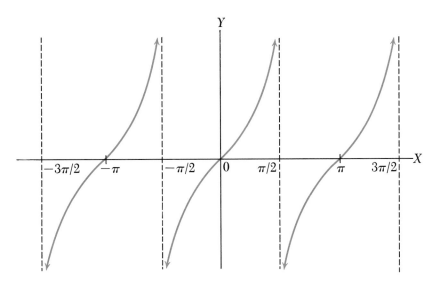

Figure 8

Notice that each of the lines $x = (2n + 1)\pi/2$, n an integer, is a vertical asymptote of the graph as discussed in Section 4.5.

The graphs of cot, sec, and csc are given in Figures 9, 10, and 11 respectively. Methods for constructing these graphs are given in the exercises.

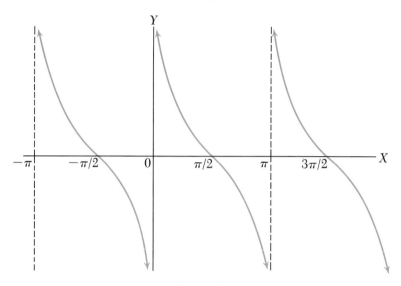

Figure 9

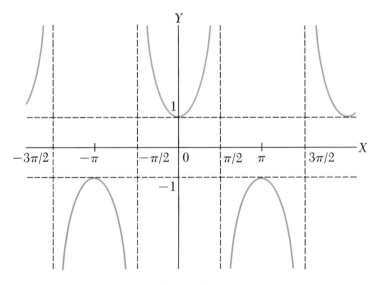

Figure 10

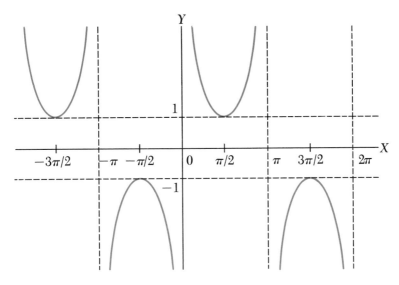

Figure 11

EXERCISES

1. Without referring to the text, reproduce the construction of the graph of the sine function. Do the same for the graphs of the cosine and tangent functions. (If you cannot do this, study the text again carefully, and return to this problem later.)

2. Sketch the graph of the sine function in the XY plane by plotting points for $x \in [0, \pi]$ and then using symmetry and periodicity. Do the same for the cosine function.

3. Sketch the graphs of the tangent, cotangent, secant, and cosecant functions by first plotting points and then using symmetry and periodicity.

4. Devise a method of constructing the graph of the cotangent function similar to that given in the text

for the tangent function. Recall Exercise 6 of Section 5.3.

5. (a) Show that the point Q in Figure 12 on page 202 has coordinates $(0, \sec x)$.
(b) Use the result of (a) to sketch the graph of the secant function in the XY plane for $0 \le x < \pi/2$.
(c) Find a similar construction to graph the secant function for $\pi/2 < x \le \pi$.

6. Devise a method similar to that of Exercise 5 for graphing the cosecant function.

7. For each of the basic circular functions, using only its graph determine
(a) its domain.
(b) its range.
(c) where it is positive.
(d) where it is negative.

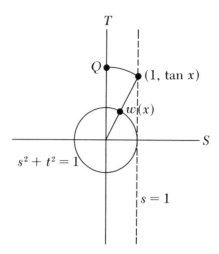

Figure 12

(e) where it is increasing.

(f) where it is decreasing.

(g) the high points of its graph.

(h) the low points of its graph.

8. Sketch the graph of each function.

    (a) $g: g(x) = -\sin x$

    (b) $h: h(x) = -\cos x$

    (c) $G: G(x) = \sin(-x)$

    (d) $H: H(x) = \cos(-x)$

9. How could you recall from the graphs of sin and cos that

    (a) $\sin(x + \pi) = -\sin x$ for all $x \in R$?

    (b) $\cos(x + \pi) = -\cos x$ for all $x \in R$?

    (c) $\sin(x + \pi/2) = \cos x$ for all $x \in R$?

    (d) $\cos(x + \pi/2) = -\sin x$ for all $x \in R$?

10. Use your knowledge of the graphs of the sine and cosine functions and an appropriate translation to sketch the graph of each function.

    (a) $f: f(x) = \sin(x - \pi/4)$

    (b) $g: g(x) = \cos(x + \pi/4)$

    (c) $F: F(x) = \sin(x + \pi/3)$

    (d) $G: G(x) = \cos(x - \pi/6)$

11. (a) Show that the function

$f: f(x) = \sin 2x$ is periodic and has period π.

    (b) Use the method used in the text for graphing the sine function to sketch the graph of f.

    (c) Sketch the graph of $g: g(x) = \cos 2x$.

    (d) Sketch the graph of $h: h(x) = \sin 3x$.

    (e) Sketch the graph of $F: F(x) = \sin x/2$.

12. Sketch the graph of each function f.

    (a) $f: f(x) = 2 \sin x$

    (b) $f: f(x) = 3 \sin x$

    (c) $f: f(x) = \tfrac{1}{2} \sin x$

    (d) $f: f(x) = 2 \sin 3x$

    (e) $f: f(x) = 3 \cos 2x$

†13. (a) Show that if $0 < x < \pi/2$, then $\sin x < x < \tan x$.   (Consider Figure 13.)

    (b) Show that if $0 < x < \pi/2$, then
$$\cos x < \frac{\sin x}{x} < 1.$$

    (c) Show that if $0 < x < \pi/2$, then $1 - x^2/2 < \cos x$.

    (d) Parts (b) and (c) yield
$$1 - x^2/2 < \frac{\sin x}{x} < 1 \text{ for}$$

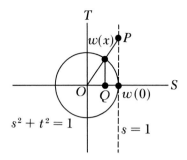

Figure 13

0 < x < π/2.   Show that this inequality also holds if −π/2 < x < 0.

(e) Sketch the graph of f: f(x) = $\frac{\sin x}{x}$, 0 < |x| < π/2.

(f) Compare the graph of f with the graphs of

g: g(x) = 1 − x²/2,
                    0 < |x| < π/2

and

h: h(x) = 1,   0 < |x| < π/2.

■ 5.5 Relationships Between the Basic Circular Functions

In this section we take a systematic look at the amazing wealth of interrelationships that exist among the basic circular functions. The relationships to be considered are usually called *identities*.

DEFINITION   An equation is called an **identity on a set D** provided the equation becomes a true statement when any values from D are assigned to the nonconstant terms.

Thus, the equation

(#)
$$x + 2 = \frac{x^2 - 4}{x - 2}$$

is an identity on the set D = {x: x ∈ R and x ≠ 2}, since if x is replaced by any real number except 2 (for which the right side is undefined) the equation becomes a true statement. It should be clear to the reader that an equation may be an identity on one set without necessarily being an identity on another set and that if an equation is an identity on a set D, then it is also an identity on every subset of D. The statement that equation (#) is an identity on the set $D = \{x : x \in R \text{ and } x \neq 2\}$ can be written more briefly by the statement

$$x + 2 = \frac{x^2 - 4}{x - 2} \quad \text{for} \quad x \neq 2.$$

meaning that the equation is true for all real numbers except 2. In any case it will be necessary to specify the numbers for which the equation is and/or is not true.

The most basic identities among the circular functions are found in the *definition* of tan, cot, sec, and csc. Thus,

(i) $\qquad\qquad \tan x = \dfrac{\sin x}{\cos x} \ $ for $x \neq (2n+1)\pi/2$, n an integer;

(ii) $\qquad\qquad \cot x = \dfrac{\cos x}{\sin x} \ $ for $x \neq n\pi$, n an integer;

(iii) $\qquad\qquad \sec x = \dfrac{1}{\cos x} \ $ for $x \neq (2n+1)\pi/2$, n an integer;

(iv) $\qquad\qquad \csc x = \dfrac{1}{\sin x} \ $ for $x \neq n\pi$, n an integer.

Like all definitions, these must be remembered exactly.

Before stating the first theorem we make the following convention. Let f be a real function and define f^2 to be the function $f \cdot f$. That is,

$$f^2 : f^2(x) = (f \cdot f)(x) = f(x)f(x) = [f(x)]^2.$$

Thus, instead of writing $(\sin x)^2$ we write $\sin^2 x$. Similarly, we define $f^3 = f^2 \cdot f$, $f^4 = f^3 \cdot f$, and so on.

THEOREM 5.5.1 (Pythagorean Identities)

(1) $\sin^2 x + \cos^2 x = 1$, for all $x \in R$.
(2) $\tan^2 x + 1 = \sec^2 x$, for $x \neq (2n+1)\pi/2$, n an integer.
(3) $1 + \cot^2 x = \csc^2 x$, for $x \neq n\pi$, n an integer.

PROOF If $x \in R$ then $w(x) = (\cos x, \sin x)$. Since $w(x) \in \{(s, t) : s^2 + t^2 = 1\}$, we have

(1) $\qquad\qquad \cos^2 x + \sin^2 x = 1 \quad$ for all x.

If x is any real number other than an odd multiple of $\pi/2$ then $\cos x \neq 0$, so we divide each side of equation (1) by $\cos^2 x$ to obtain

$$\left(\frac{\sin x}{\cos x}\right)^2 + \left(\frac{\cos x}{\cos x}\right)^2 = \left(\frac{1}{\cos x}\right)^2.$$

But $\dfrac{\sin x}{\cos x} = \tan x$ and $\dfrac{1}{\cos x} = \sec x$, so

(2) $\tan^2 x + 1 = \sec^2 x$ for $x \neq (2n+1)\pi/2$, n an integer.

Similarly, if $x \neq n\pi$, n an integer, then $\sin x \neq 0$ and dividing through equation (1) by $\sin^2 x$ gives

(3) $1 + \cot^2 x = \csc^2 x$ for $x \neq n\pi$, n an integer.

The definition of the basic circular functions and Theorem 5.5.1 are fundamental in establishing other useful relationships.

Example 1 $\sec^2 x \csc^2 x = \sec^2 x + \csc^2 x$ for $x \neq n\pi/2$, n an integer.
For $x \neq n\pi/2$,

$$\begin{aligned}
\sec x^2 + \csc^2 x &= \frac{1}{\cos^2 x} + \frac{1}{\sin^2 x} \\
&= \frac{\sin^2 x + \cos^2 x}{\cos^2 x \ \sin^2 x} \\
&= \frac{1}{\cos^2 x \ \sin^2 x} \\
&= \left(\frac{1}{\cos x}\right)^2 \left(\frac{1}{\sin x}\right)^2 \\
&= \sec^2 x \ \csc^2 x.
\end{aligned}$$

Example 2 $\dfrac{\sec^2 x}{1 + \sin x} = \dfrac{\sec^2 x - \sec x \ \tan x}{\cos^2 x}$

for all numbers x for which each side of the equation is defined.
The left side is defined whenever $\sec x$ is defined and $1 + \sin x \neq 0$. The number $\sec x$ is defined if $x \neq (2n+1)\pi/2$ and $\sin x \neq -1$ provided $x \neq -\pi/2 + 2n\pi = (4n-1)\pi/2$. Hence, the left side is defined if x is not an odd multiple of $\pi/2$. The right side is also defined if $x \neq (2n+1)\pi/2$.
If $x \neq (2n+1)\pi/2$, n an integer, then

$$\begin{aligned}
\frac{\sec^2 x}{1 + \sin x} &= \frac{\sec^2 x}{1 + \sin x} \cdot \frac{1 - \sin x}{1 - \sin x} \\
&= \frac{\sec^2 x - \sec^2 x \ \sin x}{1 - \sin^2 x}
\end{aligned}$$

$$= \frac{\sec^2 x - \sec x \cdot \dfrac{\sin x}{\cos x}}{\cos^2 x}, \quad \text{(Equation (1) and definition of sec)}$$

$$= \frac{\sec^2 x - \sec x \ \tan x}{\cos^2 x}. \quad \text{(Definition of tan)}$$

Many important identities involve circular functions evaluated at the sum, difference, or product of numbers. These are all consequences of the addition formulas derived in Theorem 5.2.4, which we list here again for reference.

ADDITION FORMULAS For all real numbers x_1 and x_2,

(4) $\cos (x_1 - x_2) = \cos x_1 \ \cos x_2 + \sin x_1 \ \sin x_2$
(5) $\cos (x_1 + x_2) = \cos x_1 \ \cos x_2 - \sin x_1 \ \sin x_2$
(6) $\sin (x_1 - x_2) = \sin x_1 \ \cos x_2 - \cos x_1 \ \sin x_2$
(7) $\sin (x_1 + x_2) = \sin x_1 \ \cos x_2 + \cos x_1 \ \sin x_2.$

Example 3 If x_1 and x_2 are any real numbers in $\mathscr{D}_{\tan}$ for which $x_1 + x_2$ is also in $\mathscr{D}_{\tan}$, then

$$\tan (x_1 + x_2) = \frac{\tan x_1 + \tan x_2}{1 - \tan x_1 \ \tan x_2}.$$

If $x_1 \in \mathscr{D}_{\tan}$, $x_2 \in \mathscr{D}_{\tan}$ and $x_1 + x_2 \in \mathscr{D}_{\tan}$, then each of $\cos x_1$, $\cos x_2$ and $\cos (x_1 + x_2)$ is different from zero. Hence,

$$\tan (x_1 + x_2) = \frac{\sin (x_1 + x_2)}{\cos (x_1 + x_2)} = \frac{\sin x_1 \ \cos x_2 + \cos x_1 \ \sin x_2}{\cos x_1 \ \cos x_2 - \sin x_1 \ \sin x_2}$$

$$= \frac{\dfrac{\sin x_1}{\cos x_1} \cdot \dfrac{\cos x_2}{\cos x_2} + \dfrac{\cos x_1}{\cos x_1} \cdot \dfrac{\sin x_2}{\sin x_2}}{\dfrac{\cos x_1}{\cos x_1} \cdot \dfrac{\cos x_2}{\cos x_2} - \dfrac{\sin x_1}{\cos x_1} \cdot \dfrac{\sin x_2}{\cos x_2}} = \frac{\tan x_1 + \tan x_2}{1 - \tan x_1 \ \tan x_2}$$

Because of its importance, the following is stated as a theorem, although it is a simple corollary of the Addition Formulas.

THEOREM 5.5.2 For each real number x,

(8) $\sin 2x = 2 \sin x \ \cos x$
(9) $\cos 2x = \cos^2 x - \sin^2 x$
(10) $\cos 2x = 2 \cos^2 x - 1$
(11) $\cos 2x = 1 - 2 \sin^2 x.$

PROOF   From the Addition Formulas, for each $x \in R$,

$$\begin{aligned} \sin 2x &= \sin x \, \cos x + \sin x \, \cos x \\ &= 2 \sin x \, \cos x. \end{aligned}$$

$$\begin{aligned} \cos 2x &= \cos (x + x) \\ &= \cos x \, \cos x - \sin x \, \sin x \\ &= \cos^2 x - \sin^2 x. \end{aligned}$$

To obtain (10), we use equation (1) in the form

$$\sin^2 x = 1 - \cos^2 x \quad \text{for all } x.$$

From (9)

$$\begin{aligned} \cos 2x &= \cos^2 x - \sin^2 x \\ &= \cos^2 x - (1 - \cos^2 x) \\ &= 2 \cos^2 x - 1 \quad \text{for all } x. \end{aligned}$$

(11) follows from (9) and (1) in a similar way.

COROLLARY   For each real number x,

(12)
$$\sin^2 \frac{x}{2} = \frac{1 - \cos x}{2}$$

(13)
$$\cos^2 \frac{x}{2} = \frac{1 + \cos x}{2}.$$

PROOF   (12) follows from (11) and (13) follows from (10) by replacing x by $\frac{x}{2}$.

Example 4   Find $\sin \pi/8$ and $\cos \pi/8$.
From the corollary,

$$\sin^2 \frac{\pi}{8} = \frac{1 - \cos \pi/4}{2} = \frac{1 - \sqrt{2}/2}{2} = \frac{2 - \sqrt{2}}{4} \quad \text{and}$$

$$\cos^2 \frac{\pi}{8} = \frac{1 + \cos \pi/4}{2} = \frac{1 + \sqrt{2}/2}{2} = \frac{2 + \sqrt{2}}{4}.$$

Since $w(\pi/8) = (\cos \pi/8, \sin \pi/8)$ is in the first quadrant, each of $\cos \pi/8$ and $\sin \pi/8$ must be positive. Therefore,

$$\sin\frac{\pi}{8} = \frac{\sqrt{2 - \sqrt{2}}}{2} \quad \text{and} \quad \cos\frac{\pi}{8} = \frac{\sqrt{2 + \sqrt{2}}}{2}.$$

Example 5   Show that $\cos^4\frac{x}{2} - \sin^4\frac{x}{2} = \cos x$ for all $x \in R$.
For each $x \in R$,

$$\cos^4\frac{x}{2} - \sin^4\frac{x}{2} = \left(\cos^2\frac{x}{2} + \sin^2\frac{x}{2}\right)\left(\cos^2\frac{x}{2} - \sin^2\frac{x}{2}\right)$$

$$= \cos^2\frac{x}{2} - \sin^2\frac{x}{2}, \quad \text{from (1),}$$

$$= \cos 2 \cdot \frac{x}{2}, \quad \text{from (9),}$$

$$= \cos x.$$

A few general remarks of a practical nature are in order. A significant portion of the reader's future experience with circular functions will involve rewriting an expression involving circular functions in an equivalent form that is easier to work with in a given problem, or from which geometric or physical interpretations can be readily made. This, of course, means being able to use and derive identities. In practice you will not be asked to prove that a given equation is an identity on some set; rather, you will have to find a useful identity yourself. To do this requires that you remember a basic core of identities and be able to derive more from them.

For a start take the basic core to be the definitions and the numbered equations in this section. The reader may discover some common-sense memory devices with which he can reduce the basic core he needs.

One final remark: although it is possible to show that a given equation is an identity on a set D by showing that each side of the equation is equivalent to a third expression on D, the reader should avoid this whenever possible because in practice he will be finding identities, not verifying them.

EXERCISES

1. By means of the definitions, express each of the following in terms of $\sin x$ and $\cos x$ only. In each case find the set on which the resulting equation is an identity.
   (a) $\tan x + \sec x$
   (b) $\cos x \, \tan x + \sec x$
   (c) $\sec^2 x + \cot^2 x$
   (d) $\cot^2 x - \sin x \tan x$
   (e) $\dfrac{\csc x}{\csc x + \cot x}$
   (f) $\tan^2 x + 1/\sec^2 x$
   (g) $\tan x + \cot x$
   (h) $(\csc x - \cot x)^2$
   (i) $\sin 3x$
   (j) $\cos 3x$
   (k) $\tan 3x$
   (l) $\csc 3x$

2. Express each part of Exercise 1 in terms of $\sin$ only, if
   (i) $x \in (0, \pi/2)$
   (ii) $x \in (\pi/2, \pi)$

(iii) $x \in (\pi, 3\pi/2)$
(iv) $x \in (-\pi/2, 0)$

3. Show that the following equations are identities on the set of all numbers for which each side is defined.

(a) $\dfrac{\sin^2 x + \cos^2 x}{\cos^2 x} = \sec^2 x$

(b) $\dfrac{\sec^2 y - \tan^2 y}{\sin^2 y} = \csc^2 y$

(c) $\dfrac{\sin^2 \alpha}{\cos^4 \alpha + \cos^2 \alpha \, \sin^2 \alpha} = \tan^2 \alpha$

(d) $\cot x \cos x = \csc x - \sin x$

(e) $\dfrac{1 + \tan t}{\sec t} = \sin t + \cos t$

(f) $\dfrac{\tan s - 1}{\tan s + 1} = \dfrac{1 - \cot s}{1 + \cot s}$

(g) $\dfrac{\sin x - \cos x}{\sin x + \cos x} = \dfrac{\tan x - 1}{\tan x + 1}$

(h) $\sin^2 x \sec^2 x + 1 = \sec^2 x$

(i) $\dfrac{\sec x + \csc x}{1 + \tan x} = \csc x$

(j) $\dfrac{1}{\sin \beta + 1} = \sec^2 \beta - \sec \beta \tan \beta.$

(k) $\dfrac{1}{\cos \rho - 1}$

$\qquad = -\csc \rho \, \cot \rho - \csc^2 \rho$

4. Evaluate each of the six basic circular functions at each of the following numbers for which they are defined.
(a) $5\pi/12$ (d) $\pi/16$
(b) $3\pi/8$ (e) $-11\pi/12$
(c) $-15\pi/8$

5. (a) Derive a formula for $\tan (x_1 - x_2)$ in terms of $\tan x_1$ and $\tan x_2$. State the set on which the formula is an identity.

(b) Do the same for $\cot (x_1 + x_2)$ and $\cot (x_1 - x_2)$.

6. Show that the following equations are identities on the set for which both sides are defined.

(a) $(\sin x \cos y + \sin y \cos x)^2 + (\cos x \cos y - \sin x \sin y)^2 = 1$

(b) $\sec (x - y) = \dfrac{\sec x \, \sec y}{1 + \tan x \, \tan y}$

(c) $\sin^2 x \cos^2 x = \dfrac{1 - \cos 4x}{8}$

(d) $\sin 2\theta = \dfrac{2 \tan \theta}{1 + \tan^2 \theta}$

(e) $\cos 2x = \dfrac{1 - \tan^2 x}{1 + \tan^2 x}$

(f) $\tan x = \dfrac{\sin 2x}{1 + \cos 2x}$

(g) $\tan x = \dfrac{1 - \cos 2x}{\sin 2x}$

(h) $\sin 4x = 8 \cos^3 x \, \sin x - 4 \cos x \, \sin x$

(i) $\tan \dfrac{x}{2} = \dfrac{\sin x}{1 + \cos x}$

7. Use the Addition Formulas to prove each statement.
(a) $\sin (x + y) + \sin (x - y) = 2 \sin x \cos y$
(b) $\sin (x + y) - \sin (x - y) = 2 \cos x \sin y$
(c) $\cos (x + y) + \cos (x - y) = 2 \cos x \cos y$
(d) $\cos (x + y) - \cos (x - y) = -2 \sin x \sin y$

8. Use the results of Exercise 7 to show that for all α, β,
(a) $\sin \alpha + \sin \beta = 2 \sin \dfrac{\alpha + \beta}{2} \cos \dfrac{\alpha - \beta}{2}$

(b) $\sin \alpha - \sin \beta = 2 \cos \dfrac{\alpha + \beta}{2} \sin \dfrac{\alpha - \beta}{2}$

(c) $\cos \alpha + \cos \beta = 2 \cos \dfrac{\alpha + \beta}{2} \cos \dfrac{\alpha - \beta}{2}$

(d) $\cos \alpha - \cos \beta = -2 \sin \dfrac{\alpha + \beta}{2} \sin \dfrac{\alpha - \beta}{2}$

Hint: Let $x = \dfrac{\alpha + \beta}{2}$ and $y = \dfrac{\alpha - \beta}{2}.$

9. Use Exercises 7 and/or 8 to prove each statement.

(a) $\sin 2x \cos 3x = \dfrac{1}{2} \sin 5x - \dfrac{1}{2} \sin x$

(b) $\cos 8x + \cos 4x = 2 \cos 6x \cos 2x$
(c) $\cos 7x = 2 \cos 6x \cos x - \cos 5x$
(d) $\sin 3x - \sin 2x + \sin x = 4 \cos \dfrac{3}{2} x \cos x \sin \dfrac{x}{2}$

■ 5.6 Sine Waves

In this section we consider the graphs of functions of the form $f: f(x) = A \sin(kx + B)$, where A, B and k are constants with $A > 0$ and $k > 0$. The graph of any function of this type is called a **sine wave**.

Example 1 Sketch the graph of $f: f(x) = 2 \sin x$.
   It is clear that the graph of f can be obtained from the graph of sin by doubling the vertical coordinate of each point on the graph of sin. (See Figure 1.)

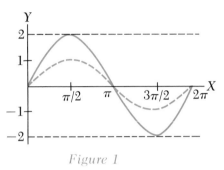

Figure 1

Example 2 Sketch the graph of $g_A: g_A(x) = A \sin x$, $A > 0$. As before, the graph of g_A can be obtained from the graph of sin by multiplying the vertical coordinate of each point on the graph of sin by A. If $A > 1$, this amounts to stretching the graph of sin away from the horizontal axis by a factor of A. If $A < 1$, it amounts to compressing the graph of sin toward the horizontal axis by a factor of A. The graphs of $g_{1/2}$, g_1, g_2, and g_3 appear in Figure 2.

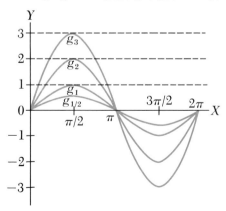

Figure 2

Notice that g_A is a periodic function having 2π as a period and its range is $[-A, A]$. The largest value of g_A is A and its smallest value is $-A$. The number A is called the **amplitude** of g_A and is a measure of the largest deviation of g_A from 0.

Example 3   Sketch the graph of F: $F(x) = \sin 2x$.
The graph can be obtained by the same construction used in Section 5.3 for graphing sin. The difference is that $w(2x)$ will make one complete circuit of the unit circle as x increases π units, so the period of F is π. (See Figure 3.)

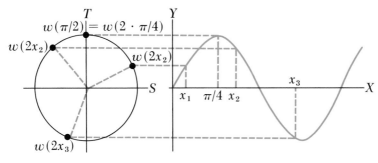

Figure 3

Example 4   Sketch the graph of h_k: $h_k(x) = \sin kx$, $k > 0$.
If we let x start at 0 and increase, then $w(kx)$ will have made one circuit of the unit circle when $kx = 2\pi$; *i.e.*, when $x = 2\pi/k$. Hence, $2\pi/k$ will be the fundamental period of h_k. The graphs of $h_{1/2}$, h_1, and h_3 are given in Figure 4. Notice that the period of $h_{1/2}$ is $2\pi/(1/2) = 4\pi$, and the period of h_3 is $2\pi/3$.

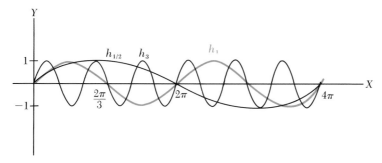

Figure 4

Example 5   Sketch the graph of q: $q(x) = 2 \sin \pi x$.
The graph of q is a sine wave with amplitude 2 and period $k = 2\pi/\pi = 2$. The graph is shown in Figure 5.

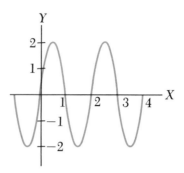

Figure 5

Example 6   Sketch the graph of $f: f(x) = A \sin (kx + B)$, $A > 0$, $k > 0$.
The graph of f in the XY plane is the graph of the equation

$$y = A \sin (kx + B)$$

or equivalently, $$y = A \sin k\left(x + \frac{B}{k}\right).$$

If we let the UV plane be a translation of the XY plane determined by $(0, 0)_{UV} = (-(B/k), 0)_{XY}$ so that

$$u = x + \frac{B}{k} \quad \text{and} \quad v = y,$$

then the graph of f in the XY plane is the graph of $F: F(u) = A \sin ku$ in the UV plane. (See Figure 6.)

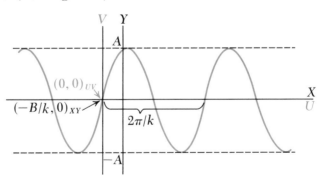

Figure 6

That is, we can sketch the graph of f by drawing a sine wave with amplitude A and period $2\pi/k$, where the wave "starts" at the point $(-B/k, 0)$. The number B/k is called the **phase displacement** of f.

Example 7   Sketch the graph of $f: f(x) = \frac{3}{2} \sin\left(\frac{1}{2}x - \frac{\pi}{3}\right)$ in the XY plane. plane.

The graph is a sine wave with amplitude $3/2$, period $2\pi/(1/2) = 4\pi$, and phase displacement $-(2\pi/3)$. The graph "starts" at $(2\pi/3, 0)$. (See Figure 7.)

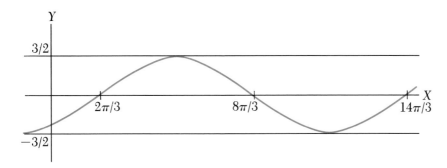

Figure 7

Although the method of graphing a sine wave used in Example 7 is very quick and efficient, it requires that we remember the formulas for period and phase displacement. Unless a person uses these formulas frequently, he tends to forget their exact form. Hence, a more common-sense approach to the graphing of sine waves is useful.

To graph a function $f: f(x) = A \sin(kx + B)$, we recognize that the graph will be some sort of sine wave with amplitude A. But the graph "starts" when $kx + B = 0$ and completes one period when $kx + B = 2\pi$. Thus, the graph "starts" at $x = -B/k$, and completes one period when $x = 2\pi/k - B/k$, so the graph has period $2\pi/k$.

The results we obtain using this approach agree with those established before and have the advantage that they do not depend on the memorization of any formulas.

Example 8   Sketch the graph of $f: f(x) = \frac{3}{2} \sin\left(\frac{1}{2}x - \frac{\pi}{3}\right)$ in the XY plane. plane.

The graph is a sine wave with amplitude $3/2$ which "starts" when $x/2 - \pi/3 = 0$, and completes one period when $x/2 - \pi/3 = 2\pi$, that is, a sine wave with amplitude $3/2$ that starts when $x = 2\pi/3$ and completes one period when $x = 14\pi/3$. Thus, we need only sketch one period of a sine wave with amplitude $3/2$ over the interval $[2\pi/3, 14\pi/3)$ and extend the graph by periodicity as in Figure 8. This, of course, agrees with the results of Example 7.

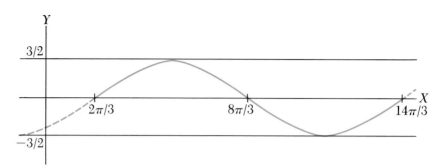

Figure 8

Example 9 Sketch the graph of $f: f(x) = 2 \sin (3x + 1)$ in the XY plane.
The graph is a sine wave with amplitude 2 that "starts" when $3x + 1 = 0$ and completes one period when $3x + 1 = 2\pi$. That is, it starts at $-\frac{1}{3}$ and completes one period at $2\pi/3 - 1/3$. The graph is sketched in Figure 9.

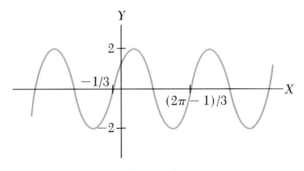

Figure 9

Example 10 Sketch the graph of $f: f(x) = 2 \cos (2x - \pi/4)$ in the XY plane.
For all x,

$$2 \cos (2x - \pi/4) = 2 \sin [(2x - \pi/4) + \pi/2]$$
$$= 2 \sin (2x + \pi/4).$$

Hence, the graph is a sine wave with amplitude 2, which starts when $x = -\pi/8$ and completes one period when $x = 7\pi/8$. That is, the graph is a sine wave with amplitude 2, period π and phase displacement $\pi/8$. (See Figure 10.)

Example 11 Sketch the graph of $g: g(x) = \sin x + \sqrt{3} \cos x$ in the XY plane.

Note that
$$g(x) = 2\left(\sin x \cdot \frac{1}{2} + \frac{\sqrt{3}}{2} \cos x\right)$$

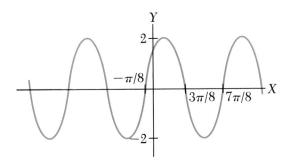

Figure 10

and
$$\frac{1}{2} = \cos\frac{\pi}{3}, \quad \frac{\sqrt{3}}{2} = \sin\frac{\pi}{3}.$$

Hence,
$$g(x) = 2\left(\sin x \,\cos\frac{\pi}{3} + \sin\frac{\pi}{3}\,\cos x\right)$$
$$= 2\,\sin\left(x + \frac{\pi}{3}\right)$$

by the Addition Formula (7) of Section 5.5. Hence, the graph of g is a sine wave with amplitude 2, period 2π and phase displacement $\pi/3$. (See Figure 11.)

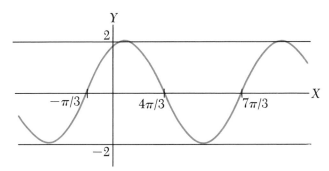

Figure 11

Example 12   The method used in Example 11 is always applicable when graphing functions of the form

$$h\colon h(x) = A_1\,\sin kx + A_2\,\cos kx.$$

For, if we factor out $\sqrt{A_1^2 + A_2^2}$, we have

$$h(x) = \sqrt{A_1^2 + A_2^2}\ (B_1\,\sin kx + B_2\,\cos kx)$$

where $$B_1 = \frac{A_1}{\sqrt{A_1^2 + A_2^2}}, \quad B_2 = \frac{A_2}{\sqrt{A_1^2 + A_2^2}}.$$

But $B_1^2 + B_2^2 = 1$, so the point (B_1, B_2) is on the unit circle. Hence, there is· a number θ such that $w(\theta) = (B_1, B_2)$; that is, $\cos \theta = B_1$ and $\sin \theta = B_2$. Therefore,

$$h(x) = \sqrt{A_1^2 + A_2^2} \ (\sin kx \cos \theta + \sin \theta \cos kx)$$
$$= \sqrt{A_1^2 + A_2^2} \ \sin (kx + \theta).$$

Then the graph of h is a sine wave with amplitude $\sqrt{A_1^2 + A_2^2}$, period $2\pi/k$ and phase displacement θ/k.

EXERCISES

1. For each of the following functions, find its amplitude, period, and phase displacement, and sketch its graph.

   (a) $f: f(x) = \sin\left(\frac{1}{3}x + \frac{\pi}{6}\right)$

   (b) $g: g(x) = \frac{3}{4} \sin\left(\frac{3}{2}x - \frac{\pi}{3}\right)$

   (c) $h: h(x) = 2 \sin \pi x$

   (d) $F: F(x) = \pi \sin(x + \pi)$

   (e) $G: G(x) = \frac{1}{4} \sin\left(\frac{\pi}{3}x + \frac{\pi}{3}\right)$

   (f) $H: H(x) = \sqrt{2} \sin 2\pi x$

2. Show that the graph of each of the following functions is a sine wave, find its amplitude, period, and phase displacement, and sketch its graph.

   (a) $f: f(x) = \cos(2x - \pi/6)$

   (b) $g: g(x) = -\cos(3x + \pi/4)$

   (c) $h: h(x) = \frac{1}{\sqrt{2}} (\sin x + \cos x)$

   (d) $F: F(x) = -3 \sin 4x + \sqrt{3} \cos 4x$

   (e) $G: G(x) = \cos x - \sin x$

   (f) $H: H(x) = \sin(-2x)$

   (g) $q: q(x) = -3 \sin(2x - 1)$

3. Show that the graph of the func-
   tion $f: f(x) = A \sin(kx + B)$, $A \neq 0$, $k \neq 0$, is a sine wave. Find the amplitude, period, and phase displacement. Note that the conditions $A > 0$, $k > 0$ in the definition have been relaxed here.

4. (a) Show that the graph of the function

   $$g: g(x) = A_0 \sin(kx + B_0) + A_1 \cos(kx + B_1)$$

   is a sine wave.

   (b) Find the amplitude, period, and phase displacement of

   $$h: h(x) = 3 \sin(2x + \pi/6) - \cos(2x - \pi/3).$$

5. In considering the graph of $f: f(x) = A \sin kx$, $A > 0$, $k > 0$ in the XY plane, let the UV plane be a similarity of the XY plane determined by $(1,0)_{UV} = (1/k, 0)_{XY}$. (Refer to Exercise 8 of Section 2.6.) Show that the graph of f in the XY plane is the graph of $v = kA \sin u$ in the UV plane. Use this to conclude that the graph of f has amplitude A and period $2\pi/k$.

CHAPTER 6

INVERTIBLE FUNCTIONS

■ 6.1 Algebra of One-to-One Functions

Recall from Section 3.2 that to show that a function f is one-to-one is to show that the statement

$$(\#) \qquad\qquad f(x_1) = f(x_2) \quad \text{implies} \quad x_1 = x_2$$

is true. It is interesting to return to the definition given in Section 3.1 of what it means to be a function and interpret the statement $(\#)$ in that context. For,

$$f = \{(x, y) : y = f(x)\},$$

so $(\#)$ means that

$$\text{if} \quad (x_1, y) \in f \quad \text{and} \quad (x_2, y) \in f, \quad \text{then} \quad x_1 = x_2.$$

Then, to say $(\#)$ is true amounts to saying that if

$$g = \{(y, x) : (x, y) \in f\}.$$

then g is a function.

THEOREM 6.1.1 If f is a function, then f is one-to-one if, and only if, $\{(y, x) : (x, y) \in f\}$ is a function.

Although we have indicated why this theorem is true, it would be good practice in handling "if, and only if" statements for the reader to start from scratch, *i.e.*, from the definitions of *function* and *one-to-one function*, and write out in complete detail a proof of the theorem.

DEFINITION   If f is a one-to-one function, then the function

$$\{(y, x) : (x, y) \in f\}$$

is called the **inverse** of f, and is denoted f^{-1}.

Given this terminology, it is reasonable to call a one-to-one function an **invertible** function.

Our definition of the inverse of a one-to-one function has the advantage that it is quite compact, and that it will be easy to see how the graph of the inverse of an invertible *real* function f is related to the graph of f. This relationship will be examined in Section 6.2.

But the definition doesn't spell out how to go about computing f^{-1} explicitly, that is, finding its domain and, it is to be hoped, a formula for calculating the values of f^{-1}. The next theorem takes care of this problem.

THEOREM 6.1.2

(i)   A function f is invertible if, and only if, for every element y in $\mathscr{R}_f$, there is a *unique* element x in $\mathscr{D}_f$ such that $f(x) = y$.
(ii)   If f is invertible, then $\mathscr{D}_{f^{-1}} = \mathscr{R}_f$, and for each y in $\mathscr{D}_{f^{-1}}$, $f^{-1}(y)$ is the unique solution x of the equation $f(x) = y$.

Before we give a formal proof of the theorem, notice how the theorem solves the problem of computing f^{-1}. Part (i) implies that, instead of first verifying that a given function f is one-to-one by using the definition, we can instead show that the equation $f(x) = y$ has a unique solution x for each y in $\mathscr{R}_f$. In doing this, it will be almost automatic that we will have discovered what $\mathscr{R}_f$ is (for which values of y does $f(x) = y$ have a solution at all?), and for a given y, what the unique solution x of $f(x) = y$ is. Part (ii) says that x must actually be $f^{-1}(y)$.

PROOF   (i)   "Only if" part: Assume f is invertible. Given y in $\mathscr{R}_f$, there is at least one x in $\mathscr{D}_f$ such that $f(x) = y$. But if there were an element x' in $\mathscr{D}_f$ such that $f(x') = y$ and $x' \neq x$, then we would have $f(x') = f(x)$ and $x' \neq x$, which contradicts the assumption that f is invertible. Hence, there is one and only one x in $\mathscr{D}_f$ such that $f(x) = y$.

"If" part: Assume that for every y in $\mathscr{R}_f$, there is a unique x in $\mathscr{D}_f$ such that $f(x) = y$. Now, to show f is invertible, suppose x_1 and x_2 are in $\mathscr{D}_f$ with $f(x_1) = f(x_2)$. Let $y = f(x_1)$. Then $y \in \mathscr{R}_f$, and each of x_1 and x_2 is a solution of $f(x) = y$, so $x_1 = x_2$. Therefore, f is one-to-one, *i.e.*, f is invertible.

(ii)   Suppose $y \in \mathscr{D}_{f^{-1}}$ and let $x = f^{-1}(y)$. By the definition of *function*, this means that $(y, x) \in f^{-1}$. But then $(x, y) \in f$, by definition of f^{-1}, so $f(x) = y$.

This shows that $\mathscr{D}_{f^{-1}} \subset \mathscr{R}_f$, and that for y in $\mathscr{D}_{f^{-1}}$, $f^{-1}(y) = x$ is a solution of $f(x) = y$; so, by part (i), x is in fact the unique solution of this equation.

The proof that $\mathscr{R}_f \subset \mathscr{D}_{f^{-1}}$ is left to the reader. This, together with $\mathscr{D}_{f^{-1}} \subset \mathscr{R}_f$, gives that $\mathscr{D}_{f^{-1}} = \mathscr{R}_f$.

Example 1 $f: f(x) = 3x - 4$.

The plan prescribed by Theorem 6.1.2 indicates that we first set up the equation

$$y = f(x) = 3x - 4$$

and attempt to solve the equation for x.

Clearly, the equation has the unique solution

$$x = \frac{1}{3}(y + 4),$$

valid for any real number y.

Thus, we have established by (i) of Theorem 6.1.2 that f is invertible. We also have that $\mathscr{R}_f = R$, so $\mathscr{D}_f^{-1} = \mathscr{R}_f = R$, and for each y in R,

$$f^{-1}(y) = \frac{1}{3}(y + 4),$$

by (ii) of Theorem 6.1.2.

Therefore, $$f^{-1}: f^{-1}(y) = \frac{1}{3}(y + 4).$$

Example 2 $$f: f(t) = \frac{t}{t + 1}.$$

The equation $s = f(t)$ is equivalent to

(*) $$s = \frac{t}{t + 1},$$

and we are trying to solve (*) for t.

Equivalently, $$s(t + 1) = t \qquad \text{(Why?)}$$
$$st + s = t$$
$$t(1 - s) = s.$$

This last equation can be solved for t if $s \neq 1$, namely,

$$t = \frac{s}{1-s}.$$

Now, for $s = 1$, (*) has no solution t at all, else there would be a number t such that

$$1 = \frac{t}{t+1},$$

so $$t + 1 = t$$

and $$1 = 0,$$

which is impossible.

Thus, $$\mathscr{R}_f = \{s : s \in R \quad \text{and} \quad s \neq 1\},$$

and for each s in $\mathscr{R}_f$, there is a unique solution

$$t = \frac{s}{1-s}$$

of the equation $$s = f(t).$$

Therefore, f is invertible, and

$$f^{-1} : f^{-1}(s) = \frac{s}{1-s}.$$

Example 3 $$g : g(z) = \sqrt{\frac{z+1}{z^2}}, \quad z > 0.$$

Suppose $w \in \mathscr{R}_g$, so that $w = g(z)$ for some z in $\mathscr{D}_g$. This implies that

(*) $$w = \sqrt{\frac{z+1}{z^2}},$$

which is equivalent to

$$w^2 = \frac{z+1}{z^2} \quad \text{and} \quad w \geq 0. \qquad \text{(Why?)}$$

Hence, $$w^2 z^2 = z + 1 \quad \text{and} \quad w \geq 0,$$

$$w^2 z^2 - z - 1 = 0 \quad \text{and} \quad w \geq 0,$$

so $$z = \frac{1 \pm \sqrt{1 + 4w^2}}{2w^2} \quad \text{if} \quad w > 0,$$

and $$z = -1 \quad \text{if} \quad w = 0.$$

It appears that if $w > 0$, then (*) has two solutions,

$$\text{(a)} \quad z = \frac{1 + \sqrt{1 + 4w^2}}{2w^2} \quad \text{and} \quad \text{(b)} \quad z = \frac{1 - \sqrt{1 + 4w^2}}{2w^2}.$$

But this is really not the case, because a solution z of (*) must be in $\mathcal{D}_g$, and

$$\mathcal{D}_g = \{z : z > 0 \quad \text{and} \quad z + 1 \geq 0\} = \{z : z > 0\}.$$

Now, if

$$z = \frac{1 - \sqrt{1 + 4w^2}}{2w^2},$$

then

$$z \leq 0$$

because

$$\sqrt{1 + 4w^2} \geq \sqrt{1} = 1,$$

so the solution (b) is eliminated. So is the possibility that $w = 0$, since $z = -1 \notin \mathcal{D}_g$.

Our conclusion, then, is that the equation $w = g(z)$ is equivalent to

$$z = \frac{1 + \sqrt{1 + 4w^2}}{2w^2}, \quad w > 0.$$

Hence, f is invertible with $\mathcal{D}_{f^{-1}} = \mathcal{R}_f = \{w : w > 0\}$, and

$$f^{-1}: f^{-1}(w) = \frac{1 + \sqrt{1 + 4w^2}}{2w^2}, \quad w > 0.$$

There are two other critical algebraic relationships between a one-to-one function and its inverse that follow directly from Theorem 6.1.2.

THEOREM 6.1.3 Let f be a one-to-one function.

(i)   For every x in $\mathcal{D}_f$, $f^{-1}(f(x)) = x$.
(ii) For every y in $\mathcal{D}_{f^{-1}}$, $f(f^{-1}(y)) = y$.

PROOF (i) Suppose $x \in \mathcal{D}_f$ and $y = f(x)$. Then $y \in \mathcal{R}_f = \mathcal{D}_{f^{-1}}$, so let $t = f^{-1}(y)$. By (ii) of Theorem 6.1.2, t is the unique element of $\mathcal{D}_f$ such that $f(t) = y$. But already $f(x) = y$, so it must be that $t = x$. Putting all this together gives

$$x = f^{-1}(y) = f^{-1}(f(x)).$$

(ii) Suppose $y \in \mathcal{D}_{f^{-1}}$ and $x = f^{-1}(y)$. By (ii) of Theorem 6.1.2 again, $x \in \mathcal{D}_f$ and $f(x) = y$, i.e.,

$$y = f(x) = f(f^{-1}(y)).$$

Example 4   Let f: $f(t) = \dfrac{t}{t+1}$, as in Example 2.

It was found that f^{-1}: $f^{-1}(s) = \dfrac{s}{1-s}$, and we can check directly that

(i) $f^{-1}(f(t)) = \dfrac{f(t)}{1-f(t)} = \dfrac{t/(t+1)}{1-t/(t+1)} = \dfrac{t}{t+1-t} = t, \quad t \neq -1;$

(ii) $f(f^{-1}(s)) = \dfrac{f^{-1}(s)}{f^{-1}(s)+1} = \dfrac{s/(1-s)}{s/(1-s)+1} = \dfrac{s}{s+1-s} = s, \quad s \neq 1.$

The two parts of Theorem 6.1.3 are often useful in simplifying expressions that involve the inverse of a function, as will be seen in Section 6.3. The reader has probably noticed that the theorem is really saying something about the composite functions $f^{-1} \circ f$ and $f \circ f^{-1}$. Part (i) says that the composite $f^{-1} \circ f$ "acting" on an element of $\mathscr{D}_f$ has essentially no effect on that element, in the sense that $(f^{-1} \circ f)(x) = x$ for every x in $\mathscr{D}_f$. Part (ii) says that $f \circ f^{-1}$ has the same sort of neutral action on $\mathscr{D}_{f^{-1}}$. These statements about $f^{-1} \circ f$ and $f \circ f^{-1}$ can be neatly summarized if we introduce the following concept.

DEFINITION   If A is any nonempty set, then

$$I_A = \{(x,y): x \in A \quad \text{and} \quad y = x\}.$$

Thus, I_A is the function whose domain is A and for each x in A, $I_A(x) = x$. For this reason, I_A is called the **identity function on A.**

Parts (i) and (ii) of Theorem 6.1.3 can be put as follows:

(i′) $f^{-1} \circ f = I_A, \quad \text{where } A = \mathscr{D}_f.$

(ii′) $f \circ f^{-1} = I_B, \quad \text{where } B = \mathscr{D}_{f^{-1}} = \mathscr{R}_f.$

It would not be surprising if the reader felt that it was hardly worth the effort to take the results of Theorem 6.1.3, which are stated there in a nice "computational" form, and write them as we have just done. The point is that you are going to have to cope more and more with statements like (i′) and (ii′). They express a relationship between functions in terms of operations on functions (in this case, the operation of composition) just as many important relations between numbers are expressed in terms of the basic operations of addition, subtraction, multiplication, and division. There are several examples in the exercises of this "abstract" point of view, and you are encouraged to do as much as you can with them.

EXERCISES

1. Compute the inverse of each of the following functions. Also, in each case verify directly the result of Theorem 6.1.3.

   (a) $f: f(x) = \frac{1}{2}x + 10$

   (b) $g: g(x) = mx + b$, where $m \neq 0$

   (c) $f: f(t) = \dfrac{2t}{3t + 1}$

   (d) $h: h(u) = \sqrt{\dfrac{u}{u - 1}}$

   (e) $f: f(v) = \sqrt{v}$

   (f) $F: F(x) = x^2,\ x \geq 0$

   (g) $G: G(v) = \dfrac{av + b}{cv + d}$, where $ad - bc \neq 0$

   (h) $H: H(x) = \dfrac{x^2}{1 + x},\ x \geq 0$

   (i) $g: g(y) = \dfrac{y}{1 - y^2},\ y \geq 0$

   (j) $f: f(x) = x + [x]$

°2. One result of Exercise 6 of Section 3.2 is that any monotone function is invertible. Now, show that if f is an increasing function, so is f^{-1}, and if f is a decreasing function, so is f^{-1}. *Hint:* Use Theorem 6.1.3 part (ii), and trichotomy.

†3. You should also have found in working Exercise 9 of Section 3.2 that there are invertible real functions that are not monotone. But the following result holds.

   Let f be an invertible real function whose domain is an interval J, and suppose f has the intermediate value property on J. Then f is monotone. (*Hint:* Assume, to the contrary, that f is not monotone, *i.e.*, f is neither an increasing function nor a decreasing function. There are several cases to consider, each of which leads to a contradiction.)

4. Let f be a function with domain A, and suppose that there is a function g such that $g \circ f = I_A$. Prove that f is invertible, but that it is not necessarily the case that $g = f^{-1}$.

†5. Here is a sort of converse of Theorem 6.1.3. Let f be a function whose domain is a set A and whose range is a set B. Suppose there is a function g whose domain is B such that

$$g \circ f = I_A \quad \text{and} \quad f \circ g = I_B.$$

   Then f is invertible, and $g = f^{-1}$.

†6. Use the result of Exercise 5 to establish each of the following:

   (a) If a function F is invertible, then so is F^{-1}, and $(F^{-1})^{-1} = F$.

   (b) If F and G are invertible and the composite function $F \circ G$ is defined, then it is also invertible, and

$$(F \circ G)^{-1} = G^{-1} \circ F^{-1}.$$

7. Illustrate the result of Exercise 6(b) with $F: F(x) = \sqrt{x}$, $G: G(u) = \dfrac{u}{u - 1}$. You have already computed $(F \circ G)^{-1}$ in Exercise 1(d). Now, compute F^{-1} and G^{-1} separately to see that $(F \circ G)^{-1} = G^{-1} \circ F^{-1}$.

■ 6.2 Graphing Invertible Functions

The definition of the inverse of an invertible function f makes it easy to see how the graph of f^{-1} compares with the graph of f in case f is a real function. For, $f^{-1} = \{(y, x) : (x, y) \in f\}$, so we can imagine that when f is a real function, f and f^{-1} can be identified with their corresponding graphs in a natural coordinate plane $\mathscr{P}$. But, if L is the line which bisects the first and third quadrants of $\mathscr{P}$, then a point $P = (y, x)$ is on the graph of f^{-1} if, and only if, its reflection $Q = (x, y)$ in the line L is on the graph of f, as in Figure 1.

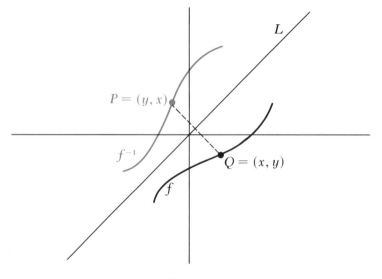

Figure 1

THEOREM 6.2.1   Let S be the graph of a invertible real function f in the XY plane. Then the graph of f^{-1} in the XY plane is the reflection of S in the line $y = x$.

Figure 2 shows several general examples that illustrate this relationship between the graph of f and the graph of f^{-1}.

Another general property that is useful in graphing many of the important invertible real functions is found in Exercise 2 of Section 6.1. We found there that the inverse of an increasing function is also an increasing function, and that the inverse of a decreasing function is a decreasing function. Here is a graphical interpretation of these results.

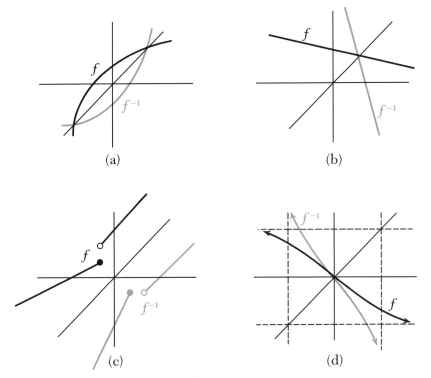

Figure 2

THEOREM 6.2.2 Let f be an invertible real function.

(i)   If the graph of f is always rising from left to right, so is the graph of f^{-1}.
(ii) If the graph of f is always falling from left to right, so is the graph of f^{-1}.

So far, we have talked about some general relationships between the graph of an invertible real function and the graph of its inverse. When it comes down to graphing a specific example, there is one source of difficulty that is induced by the notation used in Section 6.1. For example, suppose f is an invertible function that is described in the form

(1) $f : f(x) = \ldots .$

where the letter x has been used to stand for an arbitrary element of $\mathscr{D}_f$. Then, to compute f^{-1}, the equation $f(x) = y$ is solved for x in terms of y and $\mathscr{D}_{f^{-1}}$ is found, resulting in a description for f^{-1} of the form

(2) $$f^{-1}: f^{-1}(y) = \ldots.$$

using the letter y to represent an arbitrary element of $\mathcal{D}_{f^{-1}}$. This is sound practice if it is the algebraic connection between f and f^{-1} on which we are concentrating. But if we want to draw the graphs of both f and f^{-1} in the XY plane, confusion will reign supreme if we stick to the description (2) of f^{-1}. For the graph of f^{-1} in the XY plane will not, in general, be the graph of the equation $f^{-1}(y) = x$ in that plane. It *will* be the graph of the equation $f^{-1}(x) = y$ in the XY plane, just as with any other real function.

Therefore, if we want the graph of f^{-1} in the XY plane, we should replace each appearance of the letter y in formula (2) by the letter x, arriving at

(2′) $$f^{-1}: f^{-1}(x) = \ldots.$$

In Section 6.3, we will return to some algebraic problems involving an invertible function and its inverse, and there we will want to use the scheme suggested by (1) and (2), that is, using different letters to stand for the domain "variables" for f and f^{-1}. But, we will also want to make some graphical interpretations of what is happening, so you should be prepared to suddenly switch to the notation (2′), using the same letter to stand for the domain "variables" for f and f^{-1}.

Example 1 $f: f(x) = 4x - 1$

The equation $f(x) = y$ has the unique solution $x = \frac{1}{4}(y + 1)$, for all real numbers y, so $f^{-1}: f^{-1}(y) = \frac{1}{4}(y + 1)$. To draw the graphs of f and f^{-1} in the XY plane, we rewrite f^{-1} as

$$f^{-1}: f^{-1}(x) = \tfrac{1}{4}(x + 1),$$

so the graphs of f and f^{-1} are the graphs in the XY plane of the equations

$$y = f(x) = 4x - 1,$$
$$y = f^{-1}(x) = \tfrac{1}{4}x + \tfrac{1}{4}.$$

(See Figure 3.)

Example 2 $g: g(x) = -\frac{1}{2}x + 1$.

The equation $g(x) = y$ has the unique solution $x = -2y + 2$, for all real numbers y, so $g^{-1}: g^{-1}(y) = -2y + 2$. Hence, we can also describe g^{-1} by $g^{-1}: g^{-1}(x) = -2x + 2$. Then the graphs of g and g^{-1} in the XY plane are the graphs of

$$y = g(x) = -\tfrac{1}{2}x + 1,$$
$$y = g^{-1}(x) = -2x + 2.$$

(See Figure 4.)

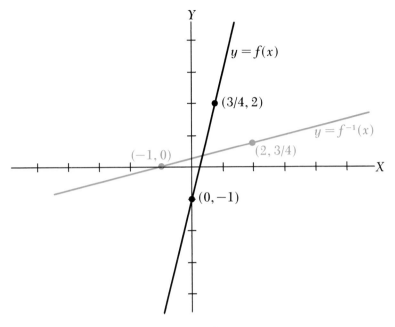

Figure 3

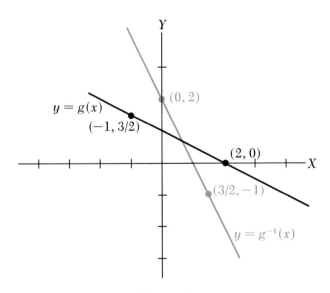

Figure 4

Example 3 $h: h(u) = u^2, u \leq 0.$

The equation $h(u) = v$ is equivalent to $u = -\sqrt{v}$, so $h^{-1}: h^{-1}(v) = -\sqrt{v}$. To draw the graphs of h and h^{-1} in the UV plane, we first write $h^{-1}: h^{-1}(u) = -\sqrt{u}$, and then draw the graphs of

$$v = u^2, \ u \leq 0$$

and

$$v = -\sqrt{u}.$$

(See Figure 5.)

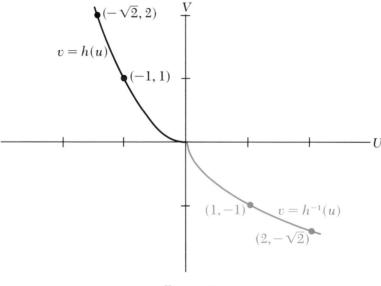

Figure 5

Example 4 $f: f(t) = \dfrac{t}{t+1}.$

In Example 2 of Section 6.1, we found that

$$f^{-1}: f^{-1}(s) = \frac{s}{1-s}.$$

To graph both f and f^{-1} in the TS plane, we describe f^{-1} by $f^{-1}: f^{-1}(t) = \dfrac{t}{1-t}$, and then graph the equations

$$s = f(t) = \frac{t}{t+1},$$

$$s = f^{-1}(t) = \frac{t}{1-t}$$

in the TS plane, as in Figure 6.

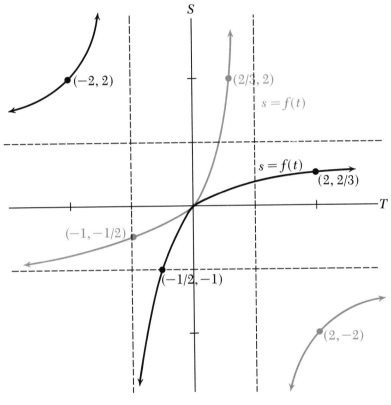

Figure 6

EXERCISES

1. In each of (a), (b), (c), and (d) on page 230 is sketched the graph of an invertible function. Make a tracing of the sketch on your own paper, and then sketch the graph of the inverse of the function.

2. Find the inverse of each function, and then sketch the graph of both the function and its inverse in the indicated coordinate plane.
   (a) $f\colon f(x) = \tfrac{1}{3}x + 2$.
      Graph in the XY plane.
   (b) $g\colon g(s) = -2s$.
      Graph in the ST plane.

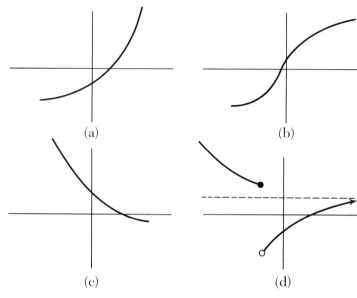

(a)   (b)

(c)   (d)

(c) $h: h(u) = u^2$, $u \geq 0$.
     Graph in the UV plane.
(d) $f: f(w) = w^3$.
     Graph in the WZ plane.
(e) $F: F(t) = (2t + 1)/(t - 3)$.
     Graph in the TS plane.
(f) $G: G(x) = x + [x]$.
     Graph in the XY plane.
3. Having worked several examples,
   you might find the following con-
   jecture to be attractive:
       "If the graphs of f and f^{-1} are
   drawn in the XY plane, then the
   only points common to the graph
   of f and f^{-1} lie on the line $y = x$."
       Show that this conjecture is false.
4. Suppose you draw the graph of the
   equation $f^{-1}(y) = x$ in the XY
   plane. What does the graph of this
   equation have to do with the graph
   of f in the XY plane?

5. One example of a real function
   that is its own inverse is the identity function I_R on R, that is, if

   $$I_R: I_R(x) = x, \ x \in R, \quad \text{then}$$
   $$I_R^{-1} = I_R.$$

       Find some other real functions f
   such that $f^{-1} = f$. It is suggested
   that you first try to draw the graph
   of such a function, keeping Theorem 6.2.1 in mind. Then, try for
   an algebraic description of the
   function.
6. Let f be an invertible real function.
   Let A and B denote the horizontal
   and vertical extents, respectively,
   of the graph of f. Show that A is the
   vertical extent and B is the *horizontal* extent of the graph of f^{-1}.
   (Remember that A and B are sets
   of *numbers*.)

■ 6.3 The Principal Circular Functions

In Exercise 9 of Section 5.3, we considered problems of the following sort:
    "Find the solutions of the equation $\tan x = 1$." In this case, the solution
set is

$$\{x: x = \pi/4 + n\pi \quad \text{for some integer } n\}.$$

This problem is an example of the more general problem:

"Given a number y_0 in the range of the tangent function, solve the equation $\tan x = y_0$." The idea is to find a particular solution x_0 of the equation $\tan x = y_0$, for we can then write the solution set S as

$$S = \{x: x = x_0 + n\pi \quad \text{for some integer } n\}.$$

It is clear that the particular solution x_0 we choose is not uniquely determined by the equation, because we can pick any number x_1 in the set S, and it will be true that x_1 is a particular solution of our equation.

What is needed is an orderly way of choosing a particular solution x_0 of the equation. One way to do this is to find an interval J of numbers such that the tangent function assumes each of its values once, and only once, in the interval J. If such an interval J could be found, then the function

$$f: f(x) = \tan x, \ x \in J$$

would be an invertible function whose range is R, the range of the tangent function. Then, given any real number y_0, we could choose as a particular solution x_0 of the equation $\tan x = y_0$ the number $x_0 = f^{-1}(y_0)$.

An inspection of the graph of the tangent function indicates that there are many possible choices for the interval J. Just this much of the graph of tan

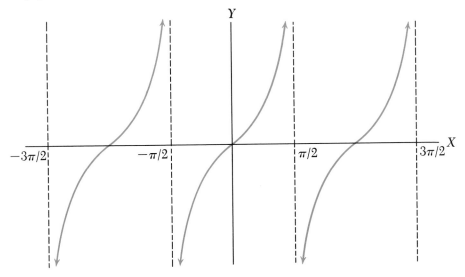

Figure 1

suggests that any one of the intervals $(-3\pi/2, -\pi/2)$, $(-\pi/2, \pi/2)$, or $(\pi/2, 3\pi/2)$ would have the property that each value of the tangent function is assumed exactly once in the interval. The choice that is universally agreed upon, however, is the interval $(-\pi/2, \pi/2)$.

DEFINITION   The **principal tangent function,** denoted **Tan,** is the function

$$\text{Tan}: \text{Tan } x = \tan x, \ x \in (-\pi/2, \ \pi/2).$$

Thus, the principal tangent of a number x is the ordinary tangent of x, but it is only defined when $-\pi/2 < x < \pi/2$.

We do not have all the machinery available to give a truly rigorous argument for the fact that Tan is a function that has the properties we are after. But, if we consider how the graph of Tan can be constructed by the procedure in Section 5.4, it is certainly plausible that Tan is invertible (in fact, it is an increasing function), that Tan has range R and, of course, for each number x in $\mathscr{D}_{\text{Tan}}$, Tan $x = \tan x$. Figure 2 indicates the graph of Tan.

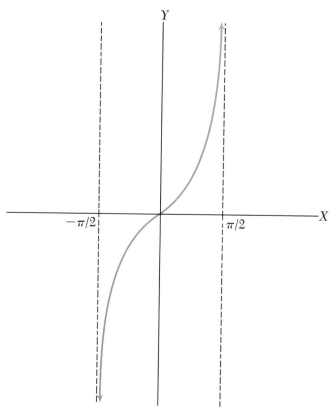

Figure 2

The inverse of Tan is called the **arctangent function,** and is denoted either **Tan**$^{-1}$ or **Arctan.** Its domain is R and its range is the open interval $(-\pi/2, \pi/2)$. Since Tan is an increasing function, so is Tan^{-1}, by Exercise 2 of Section 6.1. The graph of Tan^{-1} is sketched in Figure 3.

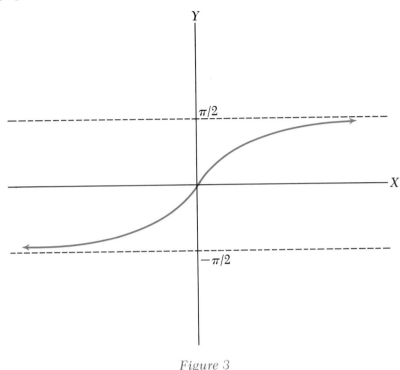

Figure 3

Example 1 For the purpose of performing algebraic manipulations with Tan and Tan^{-1}, it is best to keep in mind that if a and b are real numbers, then the following statements are equivalent:

$$b = \text{Tan}^{-1} a$$
$$a = \text{Tan } b$$
$$a = \tan b \quad \text{and} \quad -\pi/2 < b < \pi/2$$

For instance, if $b = \text{Tan}^{-1} 1$, then b is the number that satisfies $\tan b = 1$ *and* $-\pi/2 < b < \pi/2$, so $b = \pi/4$; if $b = \text{Tan}^{-1}(-\sqrt{3})$, then $\tan b = -\sqrt{3}$ *and* $-\pi/2 < b < \pi/2$, so $b = -\pi/3$.

Example 2 The equivalence of the statements in Example 1 can help to keep the following facts straight:

(1) For every real number a, tan Tan$^{-1}\,a = a$.

(2) For $-\pi/2 < b < \pi/2$, Tan^{-1} tan $b = b$.

The first statement holds because if $a \in R$, then Tan$^{-1}\,a$ is defined, and if $b = $ Tan$^{-1}\,a$, then $b \in (-\pi/2, \pi/2)$. So, not only is tan b defined, it is actually the same as Tan b. Thus, for any a in R,

$$\text{tan Tan}^{-1}\,a = \text{Tan Tan}^{-1}\,a = a,$$

by Theorem 6.1.3. The second statement holds for much the same reason, because tan $b = $ Tan b if $-\pi/2 < b < \pi/2$, so Tan^{-1} tan $b = $ Tan^{-1} Tan $b = b$ if $b \in (-\pi/2, \pi/2)$. Notice that it is necessary to have the hypothesis $-\pi/2 < b < \pi/2$ in (2); for example, if $b = 9\pi/4 = \pi/4 + 2\pi$, then Tan^{-1} tan $b = $ Tan^{-1} tan $(\pi/4 + 2\pi) = $ Tan^{-1} tan $\pi/4 = \pi/4$,   since $-\pi/2 < \pi/4 < \pi/2$,   but Tan^{-1} tan $b = b$ does not hold. Exercise 9 elaborates on this situation.

We now turn our attention to the other basic circular functions. In the case of the sine function, what we are looking for is an interval J of numbers so that if

$$f\!: f(x) = \sin x, \ x \in J,$$

then f will be an invertible function such that $\mathscr{R}_f = [-1, 1]$, the range of the sine function. An inspection of the graph of sin indicates a wealth of possible choices for J:

$$[-3\pi/2, -\pi/2], \ [-\pi/2, \pi/2], \ [\pi/2, 3\pi/2], \quad \text{and so on.}$$

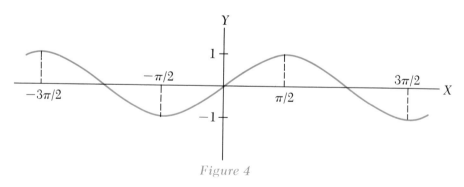

Figure 4

The universal choice made for J is $[-\pi/2, \pi/2]$.

DEFINITION   The **principal sine function**, denoted **Sin**, is the function

$$\text{Sin}\!: \text{Sin}\,x = \sin x, \ x \in [-\pi/2, \pi/2].$$

The graph of Sin is shown in Figure 5, and if we look at the construction given in Section 5.4 for the graph of the sine function, we are led to believe that Sin is an increasing function whose range is that of sin, and we have $\text{Sin } x = \sin x$ whenever $x \in \mathscr{D}_{\text{Sin}} = [-\pi/2, \pi/2]$.

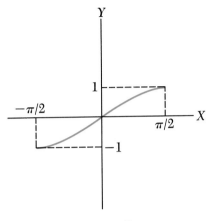

Figure 5

Since Sin is increasing, it is invertible, and its inverse is called the **arcsine function,** denoted either **Sin^{-1}** or **Arcsin.** Its domain is $[-1, 1]$ ($=$ the range of Sin) and its range is $[-\pi/2, \pi/2]$ ($=$ the domain of Sin). It will also be an increasing function and its graph in the XY plane must, of course, be the reflection in the line $y = x$ of the graph of Sin, by Theorem 6.2.1. (See Figure 6.)

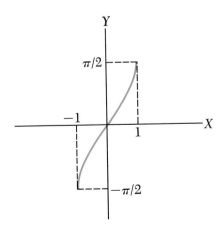

Figure 6

Example 3   It is important in dealing with Sin and Sin^{-1} to realize that for real numbers a and b, the following are equivalent:

$$b = \text{Sin}^{-1} a$$
$$a = \text{Sin } b$$
$$a = \sin b \quad \text{and} \quad -\pi/2 \le b \le \pi/2$$

Then, to compute $\text{Sin}^{-1} 1/2$, we let $b = \text{Sin}^{-1} 1/2$. This means that $\frac{1}{2} = \sin b$ and $-\pi/2 \le b \le \pi/2$, so $b = \pi/6$. To find $\text{Sin}^{-1}\left(-\dfrac{\sqrt{2}}{2}\right)$, we find the number b such that

$$-\sqrt{2}/2 = \sin b \quad \text{and} \quad -\pi/2 \le b \le \pi/2, \quad \text{so}$$

$b = \text{Sin}^{-1} (-\sqrt{2}/2) = -\pi/4$.

Example 4   The results for sin and Sin^{-1} which correspond to those given in Example 2 for tan and Tan^{-1} are:

(1)   If $-1 \le a \le 1$, then $\sin \text{Sin}^{-1} a = a$.
(2)   If $-\pi/2 \le b \le \pi/2$, then $\text{Sin}^{-1} \sin b = b$.

(1) holds because $\sin \text{Sin}^{-1} a = \text{Sin } \text{Sin}^{-1} a = a$ for $-1 \le a \le 1$, and (2) holds because $\text{Sin}^{-1} \sin b = \text{Sin}^{-1} \text{Sin } b = b$ for $-\pi/2 \le b \le \pi/2$. Notice that the condition $-\pi/2 \le b \le \pi/2$ is important in (2), since $\text{Sin}^{-1} \sin b = b$ cannot be true if $b \notin [-\pi/2, \pi/2]$. (Why not?)

Example 5   It should be pointed out that solving the equation $\sin x = y_0$, where $y_0 \in \mathscr{R}_{\sin}$, is not quite as straightforward as is the case for tan. We can't just take $x_0 = \text{Sin}^{-1} y_0$ for a particular solution and then claim that

$$S_1 = \{x : x = x_0 + 2n\pi \quad \text{for some integer } n\}$$

is the solution set of $\sin x = y_0$. The reason is that, given $\sin x_0 = y_0$, then also $\sin (\pi - x_0) = \sin x_0 = y_0$, but the number $\pi - x_0$ is not a member of S_1 unless we have the special case where x_0 is an odd multiple of $\pi/2$. So, if we let

$$S_2 = \{x : x = (\pi - x_0) + 2m\pi \quad \text{for some integer } m\},$$

then the solution set of $\sin x = y_0$ is

$$S = \{x : x \in S_1 \quad \text{or} \quad x \in S_2\}.$$

The situations with regard to cos and cot are handled in a similar fashion, as follows.

DEFINITION The **principal cosine function**, denoted **Cos**, is the function

$$\text{Cos}: \text{Cos } x = \cos x, \ 0 \le x \le \pi.$$

The **principal cotangent function**, denoted **Cot**, is the function

$$\text{Cot}: \text{Cot } x = \cot x, \ 0 < x < \pi.$$

The function Cos is a decreasing function with domain $[0, \pi]$ and range $[-1, 1]$. Its inverse is called the **arccosine function**, denoted by **Cos⁻¹** or **Arccos**. Cos⁻¹ will be a decreasing function (Exercise 2 of Section 6.1) whose domain is $[-1, 1]$ and whose range is $[0, \pi]$. The graph of Cos is sketched in Figure 7 (a), and that of Cos⁻¹ in Figure 7 (b).

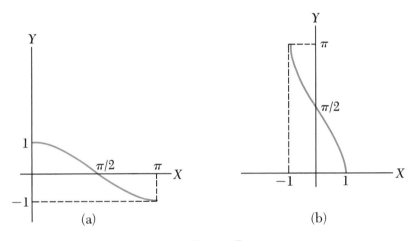

Figure 7

It is also the case that Cot is a decreasing function, and its domain is $(0, \pi)$ while its range is R. Its inverse, denoted **Cot⁻¹** or **Arccot**, is called the **arccotangent function**, and will be a decreasing function whose domain is R and whose range is $(0, \pi)$. The graphs of Cot and Cot⁻¹ are given in Figures 8(a) and 8(b), respectively on page 238.

The reason we have gone over the definitions of these functions rather quickly is found in the next two examples.

Example 6 $\text{Cos } x = \text{Sin } (\pi/2 - x)$ for $0 \le x \le \pi$.

This holds because it is known that for *any* number x, $\cos x = \sin (\pi/2 - x)$. (See Theorem 5.2.3, part (ii).) Now, a number x satisfies $0 \le x \le \pi$ (*i.e.,*

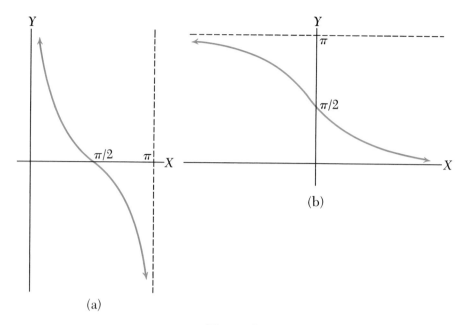

$x \in \mathscr{D}_{\text{Cos}}$) if, and only if, $-\pi/2 \le \pi/2 - x \le \pi/2$ (*i.e.*, $\pi/2 - x \in \mathscr{D}_{\text{Sin}}$). So, for $0 \le x \le \pi$, $\text{Cos}\, x = \cos x = \sin(\pi/2 - x) = \text{Sin}(\pi/2 - x)$.

What this implies is that we could just as well have *defined* Cos in terms of Sin. It also implies a very simple formula that expresses Cos^{-1} in terms of Sin^{-1}. (You might try to figure out what the formula is—it is given in Exercise 11.)

Example 7 $\text{Cot}\, x = \text{Tan}(\pi/2 - x)$ for $0 < x < \pi$.

The reasoning employed to show this result is similar to that in Example 6, and the details are left to the reader. Again, the result implies that nothing can be said about Cot that can't be said in terms of Tan.

Before discussing the situation regarding sec and csc, we will look at some samples of a type of simplification problem that comes up in calculus. There are certain important formulas that contain monstrosities like "$\sec \text{Sin}^{-1} x$" and "$\cos^2 \text{Tan}^{-1} x$." Fortunately, these expressions can be simplified greatly, but doing so requires one to be very certain of the basic properties of the principal circular functions and their inverses.

Example 8   Let $F = \sec \circ \text{Sin}^{-1}$. Find a simple description of F.

To have a number x be in $\mathscr{D}_F$ is to have $x \in \mathscr{D}_{\text{Sin}^{-1}}$ and $\text{Sin}^{-1} x \in \mathscr{D}_{\text{sec}}$. This means that $-1 \le x \le 1$ and $\text{Sin}^{-1} x$ is neither $-\pi/2$ nor $\pi/2$, at which sec is not defined. Hence, $\mathscr{D}_F = \{x: -1 < x < 1\} = (-1, 1)$.

Now, for $-1 < x < 1$, the trick in simplifying the expression $F(x) = \sec \text{Sin}^{-1} x$ is to use the relation

$$\cos^2 u + \sin^2 u = 1,$$

valid for all numbers u. In particular, it is valid when $u = \text{Sin}^{-1} x$.

Hence,
$$1 = \cos^2 \text{Sin}^{-1} x + \sin^2 \text{Sin}^{-1} x$$
$$= (\cos \text{Sin}^{-1} x)^2 + (\sin \text{Sin}^{-1} x)^2$$
$$= \left(\frac{1}{\sec \text{Sin}^{-1} x} \right)^2 + x^2. \quad \text{(Recall Example 4.)}$$

Therefore,
$$(\sec \text{Sin}^{-1} x)^2 = \frac{1}{1 - x^2} \quad \text{for } -1 < x < 1.$$

Finally, if $u = \text{Sin}^{-1} x$ and $-1 < x < 1$, then $-\pi/2 < u < \pi/2$, so $\sec u > 0$.

Hence,
$$\sec \text{Sin}^{-1} x = \sqrt{\frac{1}{1 - x^2}} \quad \text{for } -1 < x < 1,$$

and
$$F: F(x) = \sqrt{\frac{1}{1 - x^2}}.$$

Example 9   Let $G = \sin \circ \text{Tan}^{-1}$. Find a simple description of G.

Since both Tan^{-1} and $\sin$ have R as their domain, it follows that $\mathscr{D}_G = R$. To simplify the expression $G(x) = \sin \text{Tan}^{-1} x$, we use the relation

$$\tan^2 u + 1 = \sec^2 u,$$

valid whenever u is not an odd multiple of $\pi/2$. In particular, if $u = \text{Tan}^{-1} x$, then $-\pi/2 < u < \pi/2$, and we have

$$\tan^2 \text{Tan}^{-1} x + 1 = \sec^2 \text{Tan}^{-1} x,$$
$$(\tan \text{Tan}^{-1} x)^2 + 1 = (\sec \text{Tan}^{-1} x)^2,$$
$$x^2 + 1 = (\sec \text{Tan}^{-1} x)^2, \quad \text{by Example 2,}$$

so
$$(\cos \text{Tan}^{-1} x)^2 = \frac{1}{x^2 + 1}.$$

But
$$(\sin \text{Tan}^{-1} x)^2 = 1 - (\cos \text{Tan}^{-1} x)^2$$
$$= 1 - \frac{1}{x^2 + 1} = \frac{x^2}{x^2 + 1}.$$

Now, we have a problem because $\sin u$ is not positive for all u satisfying $-\pi/2 < u < \pi/2$. In fact, with $u = \text{Tan}^{-1} x$, we have

$$\sin u \ge 0 \quad \text{if } 0 \le u < \pi/2,$$

so $\qquad\qquad\qquad\sin \mathrm{Tan}^{-1} x \geq 0 \quad$ if $x \geq 0,$

while $\qquad\qquad\qquad\sin u < 0 \quad$ if $-\pi/2 < u < 0,$

so $\qquad\qquad\qquad\sin \mathrm{Tan}^{-1} x < 0 \quad$ if $x < 0.$

Hence, $\qquad\qquad G(x) = \sqrt{\dfrac{x^2}{x^2+1}}, \quad$ if $x \geq 0,$

and $\qquad\qquad G(x) = -\sqrt{\dfrac{x^2}{x^2+1}}, \quad$ if $x < 0.$

A final simplification results from the fact that $\sqrt{x^2} = |x|$, which gives $G(x) = \dfrac{x}{\sqrt{x^2+1}}$, valid for all real numbers x.

Examples 8 and 9 illustrate once more how one must be prepared to see on his own that a certain identity between circular functions will be useful in a given situation. They also emphasize how important it is to know what the domain of a given function is, and how that function behaves on different parts of its domain.

The premise for introducing examples like these, however, was that they occur in certain situations in calculus, and as a practical matter, one usually does not have the time when these situations arise to stop and perform the sort of algebraic manipulations that appear in Examples 8 and 9. Fortunately, there is an approach through the use of angle trigonometry that simplifies matters a great deal.

Example 10 Let C be any one of the six basic circular functions. Find a simple description of $C \circ \mathrm{Sin}^{-1}$.

First, suppose x is a number such that $0 < x < 1$, and let $\theta(x) = \mathrm{Sin}^{-1} x$. This means that $0 < \theta(x) < \pi/2$ and $\sin \theta(x) = x$, and these conditions can be depicted in the following right triangle.

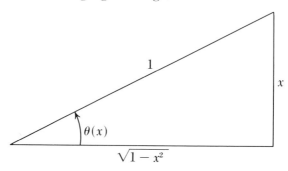

That is, since $0 < \theta(x) < \pi/2$, we have

$$\sin \theta(x) = \frac{\text{length of a side opposite } \theta(x)}{\text{length of hypotenuse}} = \frac{x}{1} = x.$$

Hence, we can see immediately that

$$\cos (\operatorname{Sin}^{-1} x) = \cos \theta(x) = \sqrt{1 - x^2}/1 = \sqrt{1 - x^2},$$

$$\tan (\operatorname{Sin}^{-1} x) = \tan \theta(x) = x/\sqrt{1 - x^2}, \quad \text{and so on,}$$

so that for any circular function C, the value of $C \circ \operatorname{Sin}^{-1}$ at the number x can be read off the above triangle, provided $0 < x < 1$.

Now, what happens if $-1 < x \leq 0$, or $x = -1$, or $x = 1$? The remarkable thing is this: If C is any basic circular function, and a formula for $C(\operatorname{Sin}^{-1} x)$ is found for $0 < x < 1$ from the above triangle, then that formula is valid for *all* x in the domain of $C \circ \operatorname{Sin}^{-1}$.

The reader should not accept this as a solemn decree; indeed, you should carefully verify this assertion in the process of working Exercise 4 below. Also, one still has the problem of determining the domain of $C \circ \operatorname{Sin}^{-1}$; there is no formal gadgetry for circumventing this problem.

Example 11   Let C be one of the basic circular functions. Find a simple description of $C \circ \operatorname{Cos}^{-1}$.

Suppose $0 < x < 1$ and $\theta(x) = \operatorname{Cos}^{-1} x$. This means that $0 < \theta(x) < \pi/2$ and $\cos \theta(x) = x$, and this relation between $\theta(x)$ and x can be seen in this right triangle:

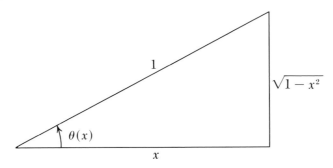

Here, we can see that, for example,

$$\sin(\operatorname{Cos}^{-1} x) = \sin \theta(x) = \sqrt{1 - x^2}, \quad \text{if } 0 < x < 1,$$

$$\cot (\operatorname{Cos}^{-1} x) = \cot \theta(x) = x/\sqrt{1 - x^2}, \quad \text{if } 0 < x < 1.$$

Again, you should be able to show in working Exercise 4 that if C is any basic circular function, and a formula for $C(\operatorname{Cos}^{-1} x)$ is found for $0 < x < 1$ from this triangle, then that formula is valid for *all* x in the domain of $C \circ \operatorname{Cos}^{-1}$.

Example 12 Let C be one of the basic circular functions. Find a simple description of $C \circ \mathrm{Tan}^{-1}$.

Suppose $x \in (0, \infty)$ and $\theta(x) = \mathrm{Tan}^{-1} x$, so that $0 < \theta(x) < \pi/2$ and $\tan \theta(x) = x$. The corresponding trigonometric picture is as follows:

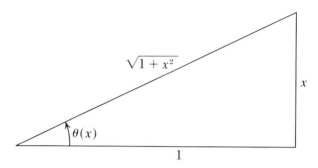

Here, whatever formula is discovered for $C(\mathrm{Tan}^{-1} x)$ from the right triangle above is also valid for *all* x in the domain of $C \circ \mathrm{Tan}^{-1}$.

Since we have yet to discuss the definition of the principal secant and principal cosecant functions, one might get the impression that they are not as important as the others. This is not the case — the principal secant function is especially useful in working certain calculus problems.

The trouble is, there is no universal agreement on what the domain of either Sec or Csc should be. Some authors choose the option of defining Sec to be 1/Cos, which appears to be a natural definition, but it leads to some clumsy formulas later on. Another popular choice is

$$\mathrm{Sec}: \mathrm{Sec}\, x = \sec x \quad \text{for} \quad -\pi \le x < -\pi/2 \quad \text{or} \quad 0 \le x < \pi/2.$$

This seems strange, since the domain in this case consists of two intervals, $[-\pi, -\pi/2)$ and $[0, \pi/2)$, which are separated by a whole interval of numbers. But, there are advantages to this choice of Sec. For example, if $u = \mathrm{Sec}^{-1} x$, then either $-\pi \le u < -\pi/2$ or $0 \le u < \pi/2$, so $\tan u \ge 0$. This implies that the formula

$$\tan \mathrm{Sec}^{-1} x = \sqrt{x^2 - 1}$$

is valid whenever $|x| \ge 1$, and this would not be the case with the first choice of Sec = 1/Cos. Other authors attempt a compromise by defining

$$\mathrm{Sec}: \mathrm{Sec}\, x = \sec x, \quad 0 \le x < \pi/2,$$

since both of the first two schools of thought agree that this piece of sec should be included. But, this also results in formulas which have easily forgotten subtleties.

The situation regarding Csc is much the same, and it is our position that it is pointless to try to make a choice for either Sec or Csc at this stage when it is likely that you will have to learn a different choice later on.

EXERCISES

1. Compute:
   (a) $\text{Tan}^{-1}(-1)$
   (b) $\text{Sin}^{-1} 0$
   (c) $\text{Sin}^{-1} \sqrt{3}/2$
   (d) $\text{Cos}^{-1} 1/\sqrt{2}$
   (e) $\text{Tan}^{-1} 0$
   (f) $\text{Cos}^{-1} 1/2$
   (g) $\text{Cot}^{-1}(-1/\sqrt{3})$
   (h) $\text{Sin}^{-1} 1$
   (i) $\text{Cos}^{-1}(-1)$

2. Verify:
   (a) $\cos \text{Cos}^{-1} a = a$ for $-1 \le a \le 1$
   (b) $\text{Cos}^{-1} \cos b = b$ for $0 \le b \le \pi$

3. For what values of a and b do these relations hold:
   $\cot \text{Cot}^{-1} a = a$ and $\text{Cot}^{-1} \cot b = b$?

4. Let C be in turn one of the six basic circular functions sin, cos, tan, cot, sec, csc. Find a simple description of:
   (a) $C \circ \text{Sin}^{-1}$
   (b) $C \circ \text{Cos}^{-1}$
   (c) $C \circ \text{Tan}^{-1}$

5. Find a simple description of the following.
   (a) $\text{Cos} \circ \text{Sin}^{-1}$ (d) $\text{Sin} \circ \text{Tan}^{-1}$
   (b) $\text{Sin} \circ \text{Cos}^{-1}$ (e) $\text{Tan} \circ \text{Sin}^{-1}$
   (c) $\text{Cos} \circ \text{Tan}^{-1}$ (f) $\text{Tan} \circ \text{Cos}^{-1}$

6. In Example 12 of Section 5.6, the following problem arose: Given real numbers B_1 and B_2 with $B_1^2 + B_2^2 = 1$, find a number θ such that $\cos \theta = B_1$ and $\sin \theta = B_2$.
   Show that $\theta = \text{Cos}^{-1} B_1$ is a solution if $B_2 \ge 0$, and $\theta = 2\pi - \text{Cos}^{-1} B_1$ works if $B_2 \le 0$. (Exercise 4(b) is useful here.)

7. Find all the solutions to the following equations. Your solutions may not be "exact," but they will be expressible in terms of $\text{Sin}^{-1} a_0$ for some number a_0.
   (a) $4 \sin(6x - 1) = 3$
   (b) $3 \sin 2x + \cos 2x = 1/2$
   (c) $\sin 3x - \cos 3x = 1.25$
   (d) $\cos 4x - 2 \sin 4x = -3$.

8. Graph each equation in the XY plane.
   (a) $y = \text{Sin} \, 2x$
   (b) $y = 2 \, \text{Tan}^{-1} 3x$
   (c) $y = \text{Cos}^{-1}(x - 2)$
   (d) $y = \text{Tan}(-x)$
   (e) $y = 4 \, \text{Sin}^{-1}(2x + 1)$
   (f) $y = \cos \text{Cos}^{-1} x$

9. Show that $\text{Tan}^{-1} \tan x = x - \left[\dfrac{2x + \pi}{2\pi} \right] \pi$ is an identity on $\mathscr{D}_{\tan}$. The point of the formula is to emphasize that $\text{Tan}^{-1} \tan x = x$ is *not* an identity. It is certainly not a formula to be memorized; given $x \in \mathscr{D}_{\tan}$, what is needed is a corresponding integer n such that $-\pi/2 < x - n\pi < \pi/2$. If you see why n should be chosen this way, it is then easy to conclude that $n = \left[\dfrac{2x + \pi}{2\pi} \right]$.

10. Find formulas similar to the one in Exercise 9 for $\text{Sin}^{-1} \sin x$ and $\text{Cos}^{-1} \cos x$.

11. Show that $\text{Cos}^{-1} u = \pi/2 - \text{Sin}^{-1} u$ for every u in $[-1, 1]$. *Hint:* If $-1 \le u \le 1$, then for some x in $[-\pi/2, \pi/2]$, $\text{Cos}^{-1} u = \pi/2 - x$.

12. Express Cot^{-1} in terms of Tan^{-1}.

CHAPTER 7

EXPONENTIAL AND LOGARITHM FUNCTIONS

■ 7.1 Rational Exponents

It is easy to give a recipe for computing a number like 3^r, where r is a positive rational number; we write $r = n/m$, where n and m are positive integers, compute 3^n, and then find the positive mth root of 3^n. (We didn't say that it is easy to carry out these computations, only that it is easy to give a recipe.) Now, what sort of recipe could be given for computing something like $3^{\sqrt{2}}$, or $2^{-\pi}$, where the exponent is an irrational number? Is it even worth while to try to construct such a recipe?

That the answer to the second question is "yes" will become clear in calculus. Some examples are given in Section 7.3 that indicate why we want to be able to talk about expressions like b^x, where b is a positive number and x is an arbitrary real number. The answer to the first question is not easy to come by, because it requires some of the deeper properties of the real number system that we have not used here. We can give an idea of how the question is answered, and what some of the difficulties are.

Suppose, for example, that we try to define what $3^{\sqrt{2}}$ is. We know that 3^r means when r is a positive rational number, and we have an algorithm for "computing" $\sqrt{2}$ that really amounts to finding approximations of $\sqrt{2}$ by rational numbers, so that if

$$r_1 = 1,$$
$$r_2 = 1.4 = 14/10,$$
$$r_3 = 1.41 = 141/100,$$
$$r_4 = 1.414 = 1,414/1,000,$$
$$r_5 = 1.4142 = 14,142/10,000, \ldots,$$

the rational numbers $r_1, r_2, r_3, \ldots$ give better and better approximations of the actual value of $\sqrt{2}$. Given this, we should expect that the numbers 3^{r_1}, $3^{r_2}, 3^{r_3}, \ldots$ should be giving better and better approximations to *some* number, and it should be reasonable to denote that number by $3^{\sqrt{2}}$.

Since these ideas and the question of whether or not they work are all tied to a knowledge of how rational powers of numbers behave, it is clear that such knowledge must be firmly in mind before proceeding any further.

DEFINITION   Suppose $b > 0$ and r is a rational number. Then

(i)   If $r > 0$, write $r = n/m$ where m and n are natural numbers, and define
$$b^r = (b^n)^{1/m} = \sqrt[m]{b^n}.$$

(ii)   If $r = 0$, define $b^r = 1$.

(iii)   If $r < 0$, define $b^r = 1/b^{-r}$.

Theorem 7.1.1 summarizes the fundamental facts about rational powers of positive numbers.

THEOREM 7.1.1   Let a and b be positive real numbers, and let r and s be rational numbers. Then

(i) $b^{r+s} = b^r b^s$.

(ii) $(ab)^r = a^r b^r$.

(iii) $(b^r)^s = b^{rs}$.

Suggestions for a proof of the theorem are given in Appendix II, Mathematical Induction. And, if you are uncertain of yourself in doing elementary manipulations that involve rational exponents, there is an opportunity to practice in Appendix I, Basic Algebra.

Example 1   If $b > 0$ and r and s are rational, then $b^{s-r} = b^s/b^r$.

For, $b^s = b^{(s-r)+r} = b^{s-r}b^r$,   so $b^{s-r} = b^s/b^r$.

Example 2   If $b > 0$ and r is any rational number, then $b^{-r} = 1/b^r$.

Notice that if $r < 0$, then the result follows from the definition of b^r. In general, the result of Example 1 can be applied with $s = 0$ to give
$$b^{-r} = b^0/b^r = 1/b^r.$$

Example 3   (Rational powers of negative numbers)

   This subject is a rather awkward one. Nevertheless, you should be aware of which results about exponents hold in this case.

   First, if $b < 0$ and r is a rational number of the form n/m where n and m are integers with m *odd*, then we define $b^r = (b^n)^{1/m} = \sqrt[m]{b^n}$ just as before. Otherwise, b^r is left undefined.

   Then, the results of Theorem 7.1.1 hold *provided* that in each part, we are considering only rational numbers r and s, which are both of the form n/m with m odd. The most common abuse of this last statement is found in applying part (iii) of Theorem 7.1.1 incorrectly. We can legitimately declare that the following simplification is valid, even if $b < 0$:

$$(b^{2/3})^{3/5} = b^{2/3 \cdot 3/5} = b^{2/5}.$$

The reason is that both the rational numbers 2/3 and 3/5 have odd denominators. But it is not correct to conclude that

$$(b^2)^{1/2} = b^{2 \cdot 1/2} = b^1 = b,$$

when $b < 0$, for a negative number just cannot be the positive square root of a number. What has happened here is that, while $2 = \frac{2}{1}$ is a rational number with an odd denominator, $\frac{1}{2}$ most certainly is not.

   Let us return for a moment to the problem of defining b^x when x is an irrational number. Example 3 indicates that we shouldn't even consider this problem for $b < 0$ in the setting of the real number system, since there are already difficulties with b^x when x is rational. Since the case where $b = 0$ is trivial, we will only look at what happens when $b > 0$. Our discussion of the particular example $3^{\sqrt{2}}$ suggests that a definition of b^x for x irrational may be arrived at by considering numbers of the form b^r, where r is rational and is in some sense "close" to x. The first step in making this idea more precise is the following result.

THEOREM 7.1.2   Suppose $b > 0$ with $b \neq 1$, and f_b is the function

$$f_b : f_b(r) = b^r, \ r \text{ rational.} \quad \text{Then}$$

(i) f_b is a positive, increasing function if $b > 1$;
(ii) f_b is a positive, decreasing function if $0 < b < 1$.

   PROOF   **(i)**   Assume that $b > 1$. First, we show that if p is a positive rational number, then $f_b(p) > 1$.

Let $p = n/m$, where n and m are positive integers. Then $f_b(p) = b^p = (b^n)^{1/m}$. But $b > 1$ is given, so $b^n > 1$ follows by Theorem 1.3.2. By the same theorem, we cannot have $(b^n)^{1/m} \leq 1$, else

$$b^n = [(b^n)^{1/m}]^m \leq 1^m = 1,$$

which is a contradiction. Hence, $f_b(p) = (b^n)^{1/m} > 1$.

Thus, we have for any rational number r,

$$\begin{aligned} f_b(r) &> 1 > 0 \quad \text{if} \quad r > 0 \\ f_b(r) &= 1 > 0 \quad \text{if} \quad r = 0 \\ f_b(r) &= 1/f_b(-r) > 0 \quad \text{if} \quad r < 0. \end{aligned}$$

To show that f_b is an increasing function, let r and s be rational numbers such that $r < s$. Then $p = s - r$ is a positive rational number, and

$$f_b(s) = f_b(r + p) = f_b(r)f_b(p),$$

by Theorem 7.1.1, part (i). But $f_b(p) > 1$, since p is a positive rational number, and $f_b(r) > 0$. Hence,

$$f_b(s) = f_b(r)f_b(p) > f_b(r).$$

Thus, $f_b(r) < f_b(s)$ whenever $r < s$, so f_b is an increasing function.

(ii)   If $0 < b < 1$, then an argument similar to that for (i) gives the conclusion that f_b is a positive, decreasing function. Or, you might notice that

$$f_b = \frac{1}{f_{1/b}},$$

and apply the result of (i) to the function $f_{1/b}$.

A typical example of f_b for $b > 1$ is graphed in Figure 1, and for $0 < b < 1$ in Figure 2. The graphs are drawn as dotted curves because they are full of "holes"; there is no point on either graph whose first coordinate is an irrational number.

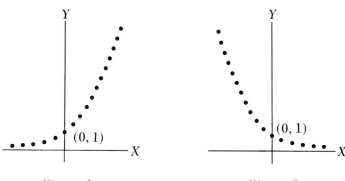

Figure 1   Figure 2

The discussion of the problem of irrational exponents continues in Section 7.2.

EXERCISES

1. Calculate.
   (a) $4^{-1/2}$
   (b) $8^{2/3}$
   (c) $16^{-3/4}$
   (d) $27^{4/3}$
   (e) $(9/16)^{-3/2}$
   (f) $(1/64)^{1/6}$
   (g) $32^{-4/5}$
   (h) $((2/7)^{3/7})^{-7/3}$
   (i) $25^{-5/2}$

2. Simplify each expression as much as possible. Remember that in factoring expressions such as $2x^5 + 3x^2$, which involve only integral powers of x, the power of x whose exponent is the *smallest* (in this case, x^2) is the power that is factored out. The same idea applies when rational powers are involved. Remember also that negative exponents are smaller than positive exponents.
   (a) $\dfrac{x^2 y^{-5}}{x^{-3} y^4}$
   (b) $\dfrac{a^{1/2} b^{-2/3}}{a^{4/3} b^{-3}}$
   (c) $(x^{1/3} - y^{1/3})(x^{2/3} + x^{1/3}y^{1/3} + y^{2/3})$
   (d) $(b^r - b^s)(b^r + b^s)$
   (e) $\dfrac{x^{-1/2} + x^2}{1 - x^5}$
   (f) $(a^2)^{-3}(b^{1/2})^4 + (a^{1/4})^{-12}(b^{-1/3})^3$
   (g) $x(2x + 1)^{1/2} - x^2(2x + 1)^{-1/2}$
   (h) $(a^{1/2} + a^{-1/2})^2 - (a^{1/2} - a^{-1/2})^2$

Note: If you have had a lot of difficulty with Exercises 1 and 2, you should consult Appendix I, Basic Algebra.

3. Here are some examples of simplification problems that arise in calculus. In each case, alter the left member of the equation so as to obtain the right member.
   (a)
   $$\dfrac{(3x^2)(1 + x^2)^3 - (x^3)(3)(1 + x^2)^2(2x)}{((1 + x^2)^3)^2}$$
   $$= (3x^2)(1 - x^2)(1 + x^2)^{-4}$$
   (b) $(2)(2x)(x^2 + 1)(x^2 - 1)^{-2}$
   $$- 2(x^2 + 1)^2(x^2 - 1)^{-3}(2x)$$
   $$= (-8x)(x^2 + 1)(x^2 - 1)^{-3}$$

   (c) $(16 - x^2)^{-1/2}$
   $$+ (x)(-1/2)(16 - x^2)^{-3/2}(-2x)$$
   $$= \dfrac{16}{(16 - x^2)^{3/2}}$$
   (d) $(2x)(x^2 - 4)^{1/2}$
   $$+ (x^2 - 1)(1/2)(x^2 - 4)^{-1/2}(2x)$$
   $$= \dfrac{(3x)(x - 3)(x + 3)}{\sqrt{x^2 - 4}}$$
   (e) $(3x^2)(2x - 1)^{-1/3}$
   $$+ (x^3)(-1/3)(2x - 1)^{-4/3}(2)$$
   $$= \dfrac{(16x - 9)(x^2)}{3(2x - 1)^{4/3}}$$
   (f) $(x - 5)^{2/3}(x + 4)^{1/3}$
   $$+ (x)(2/3)(x - 5)^{-1/3}(x + 4)^{1/3}$$
   $$+ (x)(x - 5)^{2/3}(1/3)(x + 4)^{-2/3}$$
   $$= 2(x-5)^{-1/3}(x+4)^{-2/3}(x^2 - 10)$$

4. Show that for any real number x, $(x^2)^{1/2} = |x|$.

5. In each case, find all real numbers for which the given statement is true. (Remember that *some* powers of negative numbers can be defined in the real number system, others cannot be.)
   (a) $(x^{1/3})^3 = x$
   (b) $(a^3)^{1/3} = a$
   (c) $(b^{1/2})^2 = b$
   (d) $(x^4)^{1/2} = x^2$
   (e) $(y^4)^{1/8} = y^{1/2}$
   (f) $(a^{-1/5})^5 = 1/a$
   (g) $(x^2 y^2)^{1/2} = xy$
   (h) $(ab)^{1/2} = a^{1/2}b^{1/2}$

6. For $b > 0$ and $b \ne 1$, let $f_b: f_b(r) = b^r$, r rational.
   (a) Show that $f_{1/b} = \dfrac{1}{f_b}$.
   (b) Show that for every rational number r,
   $$f_{1/b}(r) = f_b(-r).$$
   What does this say about the relation between the graph of $f_{1/b}$ and the graph of f_b?

■ 7.2 Exponential Functions

Suppose b is a positive number that is different from 1, and let

$$f_b\colon f_b(r) = b^r,\ r \text{ rational.}$$

One way to look at the problem of defining irrational powers of b is this: what we want to do is construct a new function F_b whose domain is all of R, has the same key properties which f_b does, and has the same value that f_b does at each rational number. If we refer to Figures 1 and 2 of Section 7.1, we imagine that the graph of this new function F_b should fill in the "holes" in the graph of f_b.

The one problem we have is that the ability to do all this depends upon a basic axiom for the real number system that was not assumed in Section 1.2. It is the same axiom that leads to Theorem 4.3.2, which says that polynomial functions have the intermediate value property on every interval. Roughly speaking, it asserts that the real number system doesn't have any "holes" in it, and this is exactly why we can fill in the "holes" in the graph of the function f_b. To give a precise formulation of these ideas, we introduce the following terminology.

DEFINITION Let S be a set of real numbers. Then

(i) S is **bounded above** if, and only if, there exists a number U such that for every x in S, $x \le U$. In this case, U is called an **upper bound** of S.

(ii) S is **bounded below** if, and only if, there exists a number L such that for every x in S, $x \ge L$. In this case, L is called a **lower bound** of S.

Example 1 Let $S = [0, 1]$.

Then S is bounded above, because if $U = 1$, for example, then $x \le U$ whenever $x \in S$. Notice also that any number $U > 1$ is an upper bound of S. This illustrates the fact that there is no such thing as *the* upper bound of a set.

Similarly, S is bounded below, because if L is any number with $L \le 0$, then whenever $x \in S$, we have $x \ge 0 \ge L$. Thus, there is also no such thing as *the* lower bound of a set.

Example 2 Let $S = (-\infty, 2) = \{x\colon x < 2\}$.

Then, if U is any number with $U \ge 2$, U is an upper bound of S, so S is bounded above. But S is not bounded below, because for any number L we try, there is at least one number in S that is smaller than L, so no number L can serve as a lower bound of S.

Example 3 Let b be a real number with $b > 1$. Let x be an irrational number, and let

$$S = \{b^r : r \text{ is a rational number and } r < x\}.$$

(See Figure 1.)

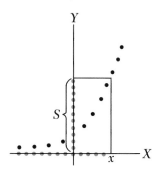

Figure 1

By Theorem 7.1.2, we know that the function

$$f_b : f_b(r) = b^r, \ r \text{ rational}$$

is an increasing function. Therefore, if we let s be any rational number that is larger than x, and we let $U = b^s$, then U will be an upper bound of S. For, if $b^r \in S$, then r is rational and $r < x < s$, so $b^r < b^s$, *i.e.*, every number in S is smaller than U.

The sets in Examples 1, 2, and 3 have this much in common: in each case, it is quite easy to find a number U that serves as an upper bound of the set. Indeed, in each case we were able to find many numbers U that have this property.

But there is a vital difference between Example 3 and Examples 1 and 2. In Example 1 with $S = [0, 1]$, we have not only that $U = 1$ is an upper bound of S, but also that $U = 1$ is the *smallest* of the upper bounds of S. In Example 2 where $S = (-\infty, 2)$, $U = 2$ is not only an upper bound of S but also is the *smallest* of the upper bounds of S. But in Example 3, it isn't clear that there even *exists* a smallest number U that will serve as an upper bound of S. In fact, Figure 1 suggests that if there is a smallest upper bound U of S at all, then U should occupy the same position on the number line as the elusive number b^x.

The only satisfactory solution to this problem may seem to be a bit cowardly: we have to *assume* that sets like the set in Example 3 do have a smallest upper bound. This assumption is made in the following axiom that bears the name of the German mathematician Richard Dedekind (1831–1916).

DEDEKIND AXIOM   Let S be a nonempty set of real numbers. Then

(i)   If S is bounded above, then among all the upper bounds of S there is a smallest one. It is called the **least upper bound** of S, and is denoted **LUB(S)**.

(ii) If S is bounded below, then among all the lower bounds of S there is a largest one. It is called the **greatest lower bound** of S, and is denoted **GLB(S)**.

This axiom doesn't have anything exciting to say about the sets in Examples 1 and 2. Without it, we could still say that if $S = [0, 1]$, then $GLB(S) = 0$ and $LUB(S) = 1$, or that if $S = (-\infty, 2)$, then $LUB(S) = 2$. In Example 3 comes the pay-off, for the Dedekind Axiom guarantees that $LUB(S)$ exists. Then, unless something is very wrong with our intuition in studying Figure 1, the following definition is a most reasonable one.

DEFINITION   Let b be a real number with $b > 1$, and let x be an irrational number. Then

$$b^x = LUB \ \{b^r : r \text{ is rational and } r < x\}.$$

Return for a moment to our original idea in Section 7.1 of how to go about defining $3^{\sqrt{2}}$. There we considered using the usual algorithm for approximating square roots of numbers to define the numbers

$$r_1 = 1,$$
$$r_2 = 1.4,$$
$$r_3 = 1.41,$$
$$r_4 = 1.414,$$
$$r_5 = 1.4142, \ \ldots,$$

which give closer and closer approximations to $\sqrt{2}$. Notice that

$$r_1 < r_2 < r_3 < r_4 < r_5 < \cdots < \sqrt{2},$$

so that the numbers 3^{r_1}, 3^{r_2}, 3^{r_3}, and so on, are in the set $S = \{3^r : r \text{ is rational} \text{ and } r < \sqrt{2}\}$. Now, we have defined $3^{\sqrt{2}}$ to be $LUB(S)$, but with some hard work we could show that our original notion of "approximating" $3^{\sqrt{2}}$ by rational powers of 3 and our definition of $3^{\sqrt{2}}$ based on the Dedekind Axiom are in agreement.

The situation for the case that $0 < b < 1$ can be handled in a fashion similar to the case $b > 1$, as Figure 2 suggests.

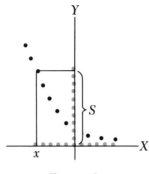

Figure 2

In this case, Theorem 7.1.2 implies that the function $f_b: f_b(r) = b^r$, r rational, is a decreasing function. Hence, if x is an irrational number, and

$$S = \{b^r : r \text{ is rational and } r > x\},$$

then S is bounded above. For example, let s be any rational number with $s < x$. Then if $b^r \in S$, we have $r > x > s$, so $b^r < b^s$, *i.e.*, b^s is an upper bound of S.

DEFINITION   Let b be a real number with $0 < b < 1$, and let x be an irrational number. Then

$$b^x = LUB \ \{b^r : r \text{ is rational and } r > x\}.$$

We can now define the function whose graphs fills in the "holes" in the graph of f_b.

DEFINITION   Given $b > 0$ and $b \neq 1$, the **exponential function with base b** is the function

$$F_b: F_b(x) = b^x, \ x \in R.$$

A typical example of the graph of F_b for $b > 1$ is sketched in Figure 3, and an example for $0 < b < 1$ is sketched in Figure 4.

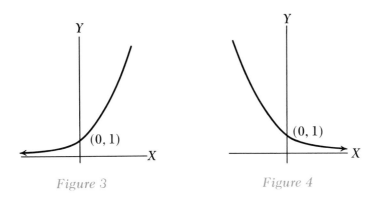

Figure 3   Figure 4

The case where $b = 1$ is not included in the previous discussion because this case can be handled so easily. Since $1^r = 1$ whenever r is a rational number, the only natural thing to do is to define $1^x = 1$ when x is irrational. For the sake of completeness, we will use the notation

$$F_1: F_1(x) = 1^x.$$

The next two theorems constitute the final test that shows that the definition of irrational powers of numbers that has been given is a reasonable one.

THEOREM 7.2.1 Suppose a and b are positive numbers, and x and y are real numbers. Then

(i) $\qquad\qquad\qquad b^{x+y} = b^x b^y$

(ii) $\qquad\qquad\qquad (ab)^x = a^x b^x$

(iii) $\qquad\qquad\qquad (b^x)^y = b^{xy}$

THEOREM 7.2.2 Suppose $b > 0$ and $b \neq 1$. Then

(i) The function $F_b: F_b(x) = b^x$, $x \in R$, is increasing in case $b > 1$, and is decreasing in case $0 < b < 1$.

(ii) The range of F_b is the set of all positive numbers.

The proofs of these two very sophisticated theorems will not be attempted here, since they involve concepts that are discussed in calculus. The Dedekind Axiom, however, is the foundation of those concepts. So, we are not dodging proofs because we don't have enough artillery, but because the proofs would not be appearing in the proper context.[*]

Theorem 7.2.1 states the essential tools needed to find other properties of the exponential functions and to perform algebraic manipulations.

Example 4   If $b > 0$ and x, y are real numbers, then $b^{x-y} = b^x/b^y$.

For, $b^x = b^{(x-y)-y} = b^{x-y} \cdot b^y$, by Theorem 7.2.1(i) and $b^y \neq 0$, so $b^{x-y} = b^x/b^y$.

Example 5   Let a be a positive number different from 1. Define functions s and c by:

$$s: s(x) = \frac{a^x - a^{-x}}{2}, \quad c: c(x) = \frac{a^x + a^{-x}}{2}.$$

Then

$$(c(x))^2 - (s(x))^2 = 1 \quad \text{for every } x \text{ in } R.$$

For

$$(c(x))^2 - (s(x))^2 = \frac{a^{2x} + 2 + a^{-2x}}{4} - \frac{a^{2x} - 2 + a^{-2x}}{4}$$

$$= \frac{2}{4} + \frac{2}{4} = 1.$$

There is a wealth of interesting relationships between the functions s and c, some of which are given in the exercises.

Example 6   If $b > 0$, then $F_{1/b} = 1/F_b$.

For any real number x,

$$F_{1/b}(x) = \left(\frac{1}{b}\right)^x \quad (\text{even if } b = 1)$$

$$= (b^{-1})^x, \quad \text{by Example 4}$$

$$= b^{-x}, \quad \text{by (iii) of Theorem 7.2.1,}$$

$$= \frac{1}{b^x}, \quad \text{by Example 4,}$$

$$= \frac{1}{F_b(x)}.$$

Hence, the functions $F_{1/b}$ and F_b have the same domain, namely R, and for each x in R, $F_{1/b}(x) = \left(\frac{1}{F_b}\right)(x)$. Therefore, $F_{1/b} = 1/F_b$.

---

[*] A proof of the fact that the Dedekind Axiom implies Theorem 4.3.1 on the intermediate value property for polynomial functions would also be out of place here, although you might begin to think about how to start such an argument. Incidentally, you might notice that Theorem 4.3.1 was used to establish the result in Exercise 10 of Section 4.3 that positive numbers have unique positive mth roots. Apparently, then, we cannot even discuss b^r for r rational completely without the Dedekind Axiom!

EXERCISES

In Exercises 1 through 6, let a be a real number greater than 1, and let s and c be the functions

$$s: s(x) = \frac{a^x - a^{-x}}{2},$$

$$c: c(x) = \frac{a^x + a^{-x}}{2}$$

defined in Example 5.

1. Verify that for all real numbers x,

   $$s(-x) = -s(x) \quad \text{and} \quad c(-x) = c(x).$$

   What does this say about the graphs of s and c?

2. Show that s is an increasing function on R. (*Hint:* If $x_1 < x_2$, let $p = x_2 - x_1$, and show that

   $$s(x_2) - s(x_1)$$
   $$= \left(\frac{1}{2}\right)(a^p - 1)(a^{x_1} + a^{-x_2}).$$

   Remember that $a > 1$ is given.)

3. Show that c is an increasing function on the ray $[0, \infty)$.

4. Use the results of Exercises 1, 2, 3 to sketch the graphs of s and c.

5. You should have discovered in working Exercise 4 that $c(x) \geq 1$ for all $x \in R$, so the domain of the function $t = s/c$ is R. Verify that
   (a) $t(-x) = -t(x)$ for all $x \in R$.
   (b) t is an increasing function.
   (c) $-1 < t(x) < 1$ for all $x \in R$.
   Now sketch the graph of t.

6. Verify that the following hold for all x, y in R.
   (a) $s(x + y) = s(x)c(y) + c(x)s(y)$
   (b) $c(x + y) = c(x)c(y) + s(x)s(y)$
   (c) $t(x + y) = \dfrac{t(x) + t(y)}{1 + t(x)t(y)}$

7. Let a and b be positive numbers with $a \neq 1$. Let $H: H(x) = a^{b^x}$, that is, $H(x)$ is a raised to the b^x power for each $x \in R$.

   Show that there is no positive number d such that $H(x) = d^x$ for every x in R. In particular, the "formula"

$$a^{b^x} = (a^b)^x, x \in R$$

does *not* hold.

8. Let a and b be positive numbers.
   (a) Show that $F_{ab} = F_a \cdot F_b$. Which law of exponents is stated implicitly in this relationship?
   (b) Let H be the function defined in Exercise 7. What is the relationship between H and the functions F_a and F_b?

†9. There has not been much made of the fact that if $b > 0$, $b \neq 1$, then the range of F_b is the set of *all* positive numbers. (This is the final statement of Theorem 7.2.2.)

   Use this fact together with the knowledge that F_b is monotone to show that F_b has the intermediate value property on every interval.

10. For each of the following sets, if the set is bounded above find its least upper bound; if it is bounded below find its greatest lower bound.
   (a) $[-2, 3]$
   (b) $(4, 5]$
   (c) $(0, \pi)$
   (d) $[3, \infty)$
   (e) $(3, \infty)$
   (f) $\{x: x > 0\}$
   (g) $\{n: n \text{ is an integer}\}$
   (h) $\{1/n: n \text{ is a natural number}\}$

†11. It is easy to show that there is no largest integer. However, that is not the same as saying that $\{n: n \text{ is an integer}\}$ fails to be bounded above. Use the Dedekind Axiom to show that this set indeed does not have an upper bound. (*Hint:* If it did have an upper bound, it would have a least upper bound.)

†12. Prove that part (i) of the Dedekind Axiom implies part (ii). *Hint:* Suppose S is a nonempty set of numbers that is bounded below. Let $T = \{L: L \text{ is a lower bound of } S\}$. Apply (i) to the set T.

■ 7.3 Logarithm Functions

Logarithms were invented in the seventeenth century for the purpose of dealing with certain kinds of computational problems, and this use of logarithms is still in evidence today. For example, the operation of the slide rule is based on logarithms. But the real power in the study of logarithms is found in tying this idea up with the function concept. The groundwork for doing this has been laid in Chapter 6 and in Section 7.2.

Let b be a positive number different from 1, and let

$$F_b\colon F_b(x) = b^x.$$

According to Theorem 7.2.2, the function F_b is a monotone function, being an increasing function if $b > 1$ and a decreasing function if $0 < b < 1$. Therefore, F_b is invertible, and it is the inverse of F_b in which we are presently interested.

DEFINITION If $b > 0$ and $b \neq 1$, then F_b^{-1} is denoted $\log_b$, and is called the **logarithm function of base b**.

Theorem 7.2.2 provides that the domain of F_b is R, and the range of F_b is the set R^+ of all positive numbers. Hence, the domain of the function $\log_b$ is R^+ and its range is R.

Moreover, Theorem 6.1.2 (ii) gives the result that if $y > 0$, then $\log_b y = x$, where x is the unique solution of the equation $b^x = y$. Hence, the statements

$$\text{``}\log_b y = x\text{''} \quad \text{and} \quad \text{``}b^x = y\text{''}$$

mean the same thing. If you are familiar with computations involving logarithms, you are aware that the fact that these two statements are equivalent is what allows many logarithms to be calculated easily. What you may not have been aware of previously is that the symbol $\log_b$ stands for a function, namely, the inverse of the exponential function with base b, and that computing $\log_b y$ by finding the unique number x such that $b^x = y$ is really a special example of the more general process described in Theorem 6.1.2 (ii).

Before launching a general discussion of the algebraic properties of the logarithm functions, we want to emphasize how remembering what the graph of a function looks like helps one to remember certain properties of the function. In Figure 1 is sketched the graph of $\log_b$ where $b > 1$, and in Figure 2 is the case where $0 < b < 1$. If these are remembered, it is easy to recall the monotonicity properties of $\log_b$, where the values of $\log_b$ are positive and where they are negative, and where the one and only zero of $\log_b$ is. Included in each figure is a sketch of the corresponding function F_b.

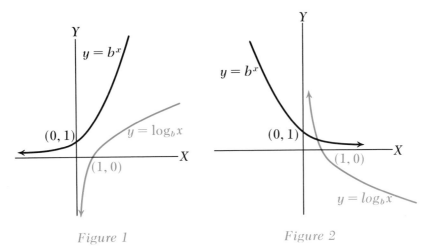

Figure 1   Figure 2

Here is a summary of the properties of the logarithm functions that correspond to those stated in parts (i) and (iii) of Theorem 7.2.1 for exponential functions.

THEOREM 7.3.1 Suppose $b > 0$ and $b \neq 1$. Then:

(i) For any positive real numbers u and v,

$$\log_b(uv) = \log_b u + \log_b v.$$

(ii) If $a > 0$ and $x \in R$, then

$$\log_b(a^x) = x \cdot \log_b a.$$

PROOF **(i)** Given $u > 0$ and $v > 0$, choose x and y such that $u = b^x$ and $v = b^y$ (*i.e.*, let $x = \log_b u$, $y = \log_b v$.) Then

$$
\begin{aligned}
\log_b(uv) &= \log_b(b^x b^y) \\
&= \log_b(b^{x+y}), \quad \text{by (i) of Theorem 7.2.1,} \\
&= x + y, \quad \text{by definition of } \log_b, \\
&= \log_b u + \log_b v.
\end{aligned}
$$

(ii) Given $a > 0$ and $x \in R$, we know that $a^x > 0$ by the last statement of Theorem 7.2.2, so $\log_b(a^x)$ is defined. To verify the formula, we need only ask, "To what power must b be raised in order to obtain a^x?" Realizing that

$$a = b^{\log_b a}, \quad \text{by definition of } \log_b a,$$

we have
$$b^{x \cdot \log_b a} = b^{(\log_b a) \cdot x}$$
$$= (b^{\log_b a})^x, \quad \text{by (iii) of Theorem 7.2.1,}$$
$$= a^x,$$

so
$$\log_b (a^x) = x \cdot \log_b a.$$

A formula in terms of logarithms that corresponds to the formula

$$a^x b^x = (ab)^x$$

can be written, but it is fairly obscure, so it will be omitted.

Example 1 Find (a) $\log_5 \left(\dfrac{1}{125} \right)$ and (b) $\log_{1/8} 2$.

(a): $x = \log_5 \left(\dfrac{1}{125} \right)$ if, and only if,

$$5^x = \frac{1}{125},$$

so
$$x = -3.$$

Note: It may help in problems like this to use (ii) of Theorem 7.3.1. For,

$$\log_5 \left(\frac{1}{125} \right) = \log_5 (125)^{-1}$$
$$= -\log_5 (125).$$

(b): $x = \log_{1/8} 2$ if, and only if

$$(1/8)^x = 2,$$
$$(2^{-3})^x = 2,$$
$$2^{-3x} = 2,$$
$$-3x = 1,$$
$$x = -1/3.$$

Example 2 Find all real solutions of

$$\log_2 (t + 4) + \log_2 (t + 1) = \log_2 4.$$

First, if t is a solution, then both $t + 4 > 0$ and $t + 1 > 0$, since only positive numbers are in the domain of $\log_2$. Now, $t + 4 > 0$ and $t + 1 > 0$ is equivalent to $t > -4$ and $t > -1$, which boils down to $t > -1$.

So, *if t is a solution, then*

$$\log_2 4 = \log_2(t+4)(t+1), \quad \text{by Theorem 7.3.1 (i)},$$

so $4 = (t+4)(t+1), \quad \text{since } \log_2 \text{ is one-to-one.}$

This can be written

$$t^2 + 5t = 0,$$

so the only possible solutions are $t = 0$ and $t = -5$. But $t = -5$ is eliminated, because $-5 \not> -1$, and the fact that $t = 0$ is indeed a solution can be checked by direct substitution.

Example 3   Let $f \colon f(x) = \log_{1/2}\left(\dfrac{x^2}{2x+1}\right)$. Find $\mathscr{D}_f$, and solve the inequality $f(x) > 0$.

$$x \in \mathscr{D}_f \quad \text{if, and only if,}$$

$$x^2/(2x+1) > 0,$$

which is equivalent to

$$x > -1/2 \quad \text{and} \quad x \neq 0.$$

Thus, $\mathscr{D}_f = \{x \colon x > -1/2 \text{ and } x \neq 0\}$.
  We have $f(x) > 0$ if, and only if,

$$0 < \frac{x^2}{2x+1} < 1. \quad \text{(Remember Figure 2)}$$

The condition $0 < \dfrac{x^2}{2x+1}$ says that $x \in \mathscr{D}_f$, and

$$\frac{x^2}{2x+1} < 1$$

is equivalent to

$$\frac{x^2}{2x+1} - 1 < 0,$$

$$\frac{x^2 - 2x - 1}{2x+1} < 0.$$

But already $2x + 1 > 0$, since $x \in \mathscr{D}_f$,

so $x^2 - 2x - 1 < 0,$

which says $1 - \sqrt{2} < x < 1 + \sqrt{2}$.

Thus, we have

$$\{x: f(x) > 0\} = \{x: x \neq 0, \ x > -1/2, \ \text{ and } \ 1 - \sqrt{2} < x < 1 + \sqrt{2}\}$$
$$= \{x: 1 - \sqrt{2} < x < 1 + \sqrt{2} \ \text{ and } \ x \neq 0\}$$

The results of Theorem 7.3.1 are used for more than computational problems like these examples. Our next theorem is a very easy consequence of Theorem 7.3.1 (ii), but it is a result that is fairly important in calculus.

THEOREM 7.3.2 Let b be a positive number different from 1. Suppose g is a real function, and f is any real function with $\mathcal{R}_f \subset R^+$. Then for all t in both $\mathcal{D}_f$ and $\mathcal{D}_g$,

$$f(t)^{g(t)} = b^{g(t)\log_b f(t)}$$

PROOF   Given t in both $\mathcal{D}_f$ and $\mathcal{D}_g$, replace a by $f(t)$ and x by $g(t)$ in Theorem 7.3.1 (ii), obtaining

$$\log_b(f(t)^{g(t)}) = g(t) \cdot \log_b(f(t)).$$

The conclusion follows by definition of $\log_b$.

The reason that the result of this theorem is attractive is that the function

$$h: h(t) = f(t)^{g(t)},$$

which is expressed in terms of a "variable" base, can also be written in terms of any "constant" base $b > 0$, $b \neq 1$.

Example 4   Let $h: h(t) = t^t$, $t \geq 1$. Then h is an increasing function.
     For we have $h(t) = 2^{t \log_2 t}$, by Theorem 7.3.2. (There is no particular reason for using the base 2 here; any other constant base $b > 0$, $b \neq 1$ would serve as well.) Notice that h is pieced together using the following functions.

$$u: u(t) = t, \quad t \geq 1$$
$$v: v(t) = \log_2 t, \quad t \geq 1$$
$$w: w(x) = 2^x$$

That is, for all $t \geq 1$, we have $h(t) = w(u(t) \cdot v(t))$, so that $h = w \circ (u \cdot v)$. But both u and v are positive, increasing functions, so their product $u \cdot v$ is an increasing function. (Exercise 13(a), Section 3.3.) The function w is also an increasing function, so the composite $h = w \circ (u \cdot v)$ is an increasing function. (Exercise 11, Section 3.4.)

EXERCISES

1. Prove that

$$\log_b(x/y) = \log_b x - \log_b y \quad \text{for}$$
$$x > 0 \quad \text{and} \quad y > 0.$$

2. Verify the formula

$$\log_b y = \frac{\log_a y}{\log_a b}.$$

(This formula shouldn't be memorized. It can be discovered by using Theorem 7.3.1 (ii) if you take the point of view that you are trying to express $\log_b y$ in terms of $\log_a y$.)

3. Compute.
   (a) $\log_3(27)$
   (b) $\log_{1/4}(1/16)$
   (c) $\log_6\left(\dfrac{1}{216}\right)$
   (d) $\log_\pi(\pi^2)$
   (e) $\log_x(x^z)$
   (f) $\log_{ab}(a^{-2}b^{-2})$
   (g) $\log_{x^2}(x^3)$
   (h) $\log_{4t}(2\sqrt{t})$

4. Find the solutions of each condition.
   (a) $\log_4(x + 2) = -1$
   (b) $\log_3(3x^2 - 5x + 7) = 2$
   (c) $\log_6(t + 7) + \log_6(t + 2) = 2$
   (d) $\log_3\left(\dfrac{2t + 1}{t + 1}\right) = 2$
   (e) $\log_3(2t + 1) - \log_3(t + 1) = 2$
   (f) $\log_x(36) = 2$
   (g) $\log_{|x|}(36) = 2$
   (h) $\log_4(3t - 2) < 1$
   (i) $\log_{1/2}(2t - 5) < 2$
   (j) $\log_{10}|6x - 1| < 3$

5. Sketch the graph of each function.
   (a) $f: f(x) = \log_2(-x)$
   (b) $g: g(x) = \log_2|x|$
   (c) $h: h(x) = -\log_2(x)$
   (d) $k: k(x) = \log_{1/2}(x^2)$
   (e) $u: u(x) = \log_{10}(2x)$
   (f) $v: v(x) = \log_{1/3}(1/x)$
   (g) $w: w(x) = \log_4\left(\dfrac{x}{x + 1}\right)$

6. Given a and b positive numbers different from 1, let $H: H(x) = a^{b^x}$.

Show that H is invertible, and compute H^{-1}.

7. Given $b > 0$, $b \neq 1$, find the set D on which the identity

$$\log_b\left(\frac{x - \sqrt{x^2 - 1}}{x + \sqrt{x^2 - 1}}\right)$$
$$= 2 \log_b(x - \sqrt{x^2 - 1})$$

holds.

8. Write each of the following in terms of the exponential function of base 10. In each case, determine the set of numbers for which the expression is defined.
   (a) $x^{\sin x}$
   (b) $(\sin x)^x$
   (c) $(\sin x)^{\cos x}$
   (d) $(\log_2 x)^x$
   (e) $x^{\log 3 x}$
   (f) x^{x^x}
   (g) $x^{1/x}$
   (h) 2^x

9. It is known that a radioactive substance decays at a rate that is proportional to the amount of the substance present at any given time t. If we let $f(t)$ denote the amount of the substance that is present at time $t \geq 0$, it can be shown by using methods of calculus that

$$f: f(t) = C \, 10^{-kt}, \, t \geq 0,$$

where $C = f(0)$ is the amount present at time $t = 0$, and k is a positive constant that depends only on the substance.
   (a) Show that f is a decreasing function.
   (b) Write the unique number t_0 that satisfies $f(t_0)/f(0) = 1/2$ in terms of $\log_{10}$. (The number t_0 is called the half-life of the substance.)
   (c) Show that $f(t + t_0)/f(t) = 1/2$ for all $t \geq 0$. What is the physical interpretation of this result?

APPENDIX I

BASIC ALGEBRA

This Appendix is intended as a brief review of the basic rules and manipulative techniques of algebra that are used in this text.

Since the first six sections involve the central rules of the arithmetic of real numbers, the basic assumptions (axioms) about addition and multiplication of numbers are listed here for ready reference.

It is assumed that given any two real numbers a and b, there corresponds a unique real number $a + b$, called the **sum** of a and b, and also that there is a unique real number ab (also written $a \cdot b$), called the **product** of a and b. The operations of taking the sum and product of two numbers are called **addition** and **multiplication**, respectively, and they satisfy the following conditions:

A1 Associative Law for Addition. If a, b, and c are any real numbers, then

$$(a + b) + c = a + (b + c).$$

A2 Commutative Law for Addition. If a and b are any real numbers, then

$$a + b = b + a.$$

A3 Existence of an Additive Identity. There is a unique real number denoted by 0, such that

$$a + 0 = 0 + a = a$$

for every real number a.

A4 Existence of Additive Inverses. For each real number a, there is a unique real number $-a$, such that

$$a + (-a) = (-a) + a = 0.$$

M1 Associative Law for Multiplication.   If a, b, and c are any real numbers, then

$$(ab)c = a(bc).$$

M2 Commutative Law for Multiplication.   If a and b are any real numbers, then

$$ab = ba.$$

M3 Existence of a Multiplicative Identity.   There is a unique nonzero real number denoted by 1, such that

$$1 \cdot a = a \cdot 1 = a$$

for every real number a.

M4 Existence of Multiplicative Inverses.   For each real number a different from 0, there is a unique real number a^{-1}, such that

$$a \cdot a^{-1} = a^{-1} \cdot a = 1.$$

D   Distributive Law.   If a, b, and c are any real numbers, then

$$a(b + c) = ab + ac$$

and
$$(b + c)a = ba + ca.$$

We adopt the usual conventions that if a, b, and c are real numbers, then the common value of $(a + b) + c$ and $a + (b + c)$ will be denoted $a + b + c$, *i.e.*,

$$(a + b) + c = a + (b + c) = a + b + c,$$

and similarly the common value of $(ab)c$ and $a(bc)$ will be denoted abc, *i.e.*,

$$(ab)c = abc = a(bc).$$

I.1 ADDITION AND SUBTRACTION OF NUMBERS

Given real numbers a and b, it is reasonable to expect that the number $a - b$ should be one whose sum with b is a. That is, we want it to be true that $(a - b) + b = a$. (This is just a statement of the usual "check" of computation in a subtraction problem.) But the axioms governing the real numbers imply that the number $a + (-b)$ has this property:

$$(a + (-b)) + b = a + (-b + b) = a + 0 = a.$$

Hence, we define the **difference** $a - b$ of a and b as:

(1) $$a - b = a + (-b).$$

There are several other basic formulas that are useful both in performing computations with specific numbers and in simplifying algebraic expressions.

(2)   For any number a,

$$-(-a) = a.$$

(3)   For any two numbers a and b,

$$-(a + b) = -a - b.$$

(4)   For any two numbers a and b,

$$-(a - b) = -a + b.$$

(5)   For any two numbers a and b,

$$a + b = a - (-b).$$

Some suggestions for the derivation of these formulas are given in the exercises that follow this section.

Before proceeding with some examples of how these five rules can be used, a comment is in order concerning the symbol $-$. This symbol is used both to denote the operation of subtraction and as part of the name of certain numbers, as in -2, $-a$, $-(-b)$, and so on. There is a tendency to think of symbols like $-b$ as standing for "minus numbers," from which it is easy to take the fatal step: $-b$ always stands for a negative number. This conclusion is obviously false, because if $b = -3$, for example, then $-b = -(-3) = 3$, according to Rule (2), so $-b$ is evidently not a negative number in this case. You will have to make a choice as to whether you prefer to read the symbol $-b$ as "minus b," or "the negative of b," or "the opposite of b," but whichever you choose, keep this in mind:

The symbol $-b$ does not always stand for a negative number.

Turning to our five rules, we first notice how Rules (1) and (4) can be used to compute the sum of numbers of unlike signs.

EXAMPLE 1

(i)
$$\begin{aligned} -2 + 4 &= 4 + (-2), &&\text{by Axiom A2,} \\ &= 4 - 2, &&\text{by (1),} \\ &= 2. \end{aligned}$$

(ii)
$$\begin{aligned} -1 + 5 &= 5 + (-1), &&\text{by Axiom A2,} \\ &= 5 - 1, &&\text{by (1),} \\ &= 4. \end{aligned}$$

(iii)
$$\begin{aligned} -6 + 2 &= -(6 - 2), &&\text{by (4),} \\ &= -4. \end{aligned}$$

(iv)
$$\begin{aligned} -2 + 1 &= -(2 - 1), &&\text{by (4),} \\ &= -1. \end{aligned}$$

Next, Rule (3) is useful in computing the sum of two negative numbers.

EXAMPLE 2

(i)
$$\begin{aligned} -3 - 10 &= -(3 + 10), &&\text{by (3),} \\ &= -13. \end{aligned}$$

(ii)
$$-1 - \sqrt{2} = -(1 + \sqrt{2}), \qquad \text{by (3),}$$

and that is about as far as we can go.

Finally, Rule (5) is useful in subtracting a negative number from any number.

EXAMPLE 3

(i)
$$\begin{aligned} 4 - (-3) &= 4 + 3, &&\text{by (5),} \\ &= 7. \end{aligned}$$

(ii)
$$-2 - (-6) = -2 + 6, \qquad \text{by (5)},$$
$$= 6 + (-2), \qquad \text{by Axiom A2},$$
$$= 6 - 2, \qquad \text{by (1)},$$
$$= 4.$$

Using all these rules in various combinations is demanded in simplifying certain algebraic expressions.

EXAMPLE 4

(i)
$$x - (y - z) = x + (-(y - z)), \qquad \text{by (1)},$$
$$= x + (-y + z), \qquad \text{by (4)},$$
$$= x + (-y) + z, \qquad \text{by Axiom A1},$$
$$= x - y + z, \qquad \text{by (1)}.$$

(ii)
$$-(-c - d) = -(-(c + d)), \qquad \text{by (3)},$$
$$= c + d, \qquad \text{by (2)}.$$

(iii)
$$u - (-(-v)) = u - v, \qquad \text{by (2)}.$$

(iv)
$$a - (-(-(b - c))) = a - (b - c), \qquad \text{by (2)},$$
$$= a - b + c, \qquad \text{as in part (i)}.$$

For quick reference in working the exercises, we list the five basic rules discussed in this section.

Addition and Subtraction of Signed Numbers

(1) $a - b = a + (-b)$
(2) $-(-a) = a$
(3) $-(a + b) = -a - b$
(4) $-(a - b) = -a + b$
(5) $a + b = a - (-b)$

Exercises

1. Find the sum and difference of each pair of numbers.
   (a) $-1, 2$
   (b) $-3, -4$
   (c) $6, -2$
   (d) $0, -5$
   (e) $4, 7$
   (f) $-2, 5$
2. Find the sum of each list of numbers.
   (a) $7, -6, 5, -2$
   (b) $16, 2, -8, -3, 4$
   (c) $-47, -1, 0, 3, -5$
3. Compute:
   (a) $3 - 2 + [4 - (5 - 7)]$
   (b) $-6 - [-(2 - 3) + 4]$
   (c) $8 + [3 - \{2 - (1 - 5)\}]$
4. Simplify:
   (a) $x - y + [z - (u - w)]$

   (b) $-a - [-(b - c) + d]$
   (c) $x + [y - \{z - (w - v)\}]$
   Do your results check with your answers to Exercise 3?
5. Simplify:
   (a) $ax + by - [by - (by - ax)]$
   (b) $[-(uv - zw) + uv] + zw - uv$
   (c) $[-(xyz - rs)] - (xyz + rs)$
6. Use Axiom A4 to derive Rule (2).
7. Use Axiom A4 to derive Rule (3).
   Hint: Given real numbers a and b, what is the result of adding $a + b$ to $-a - b$?
8. Use Rules (1), (2), and (3) to derive Rule (4).
9. Use Rules (1) and (2) to derive Rule (5).

I.2 MULTIPLICATION OF NUMBERS

Here are several basic rules covering computations of products of real numbers.

Multiplication of Signed Numbers

(**1**) $a \cdot 0 = 0$

(**2**) $a \cdot (-b) = -(ab)$

(**3**) $(-a) \cdot b = -(ab)$

(**4**) $(-a) \cdot (-b) = ab$

The essential tool in establishing the properties is Axiom D, the Distributive Law. For example, Rule (1) follows from the observation that

$$a \cdot 0 = a \cdot (0 + 0), \qquad \text{by Axiom A3,}$$
$$= a \cdot 0 + a \cdot 0, \qquad \text{by Axiom D,}$$

and adding $-(a \cdot 0)$ to the first and last members of this sequence of equalities gives $0 = a \cdot 0$. Or, to obtain Rule (2), notice that

$$a \cdot (-b) + ab = a \cdot (-b + b), \qquad \text{by Axiom D,}$$
$$= a \cdot 0, \qquad \text{by Axiom A4,}$$
$$= 0, \qquad \text{by (1).}$$

Rules (3) and (4) can then be derived from (2).

EXAMPLE 1

(**i**) $2 \cdot (-3) = -6, \qquad \text{by (2),}$

(**ii**) $(-2) \cdot 3 = -6, \qquad \text{by (3),}$

(**iii**) $(-2)(-3) = 6, \qquad \text{by (4).}$

EXAMPLE 2

(**i**) $a(-b)(-c) = a[(-b)(-c)], \qquad \text{by Axiom M1,}$
$$= a(bc), \qquad \text{by (4),}$$
$$= abc.$$

(**ii**) $(-a)(-b)(-c) = (-a)(bc), \qquad \text{as in part (i),}$
$$= -(a(bc)), \qquad \text{by (3),}$$
$$= -abc.$$

EXAMPLE 3

For any numbers a, b, c,

$$a \cdot (b - c) = ab - ac.$$

For
$$a \cdot (b - c) = a \cdot (b + (-c))$$
$$= ab + a \cdot (-c)$$
$$= ab + (-(ac))$$
$$= ab - ac.$$

The reader should give reasons for each of the steps taken here. Indeed, he should always approach claims of truth suspiciously, especially if they are made in a textbook. As much as possible, do not let statements go by until *you* are satisfied that they are true, and can defend them yourself.

Exercises

1. Compute each product.
   (a) $(-2)(-4)(3)(-1)$
   (b) $(16)(-5)(4)(-8)$
   (c) $(-7)(3)(-4)(2)(-15)$
   (d) $(-1)(-1)(-1)(-1)(-1)(-1)$
2. Simplify.
   (a) $(-x)(y)(-z)$
   (b) $(-x)(-y - z)$
   (c) $(-3a)(2b)$
   (d) $(4a)(-5b)(c)$
   (e) $(-6a)(3a^2)$
   (f) $(cx)(-dx)$
   (g) $(-ax)(bx - cx)$
3. Use Axiom M2 and Rule (2) to derive Rule (3).
4. Derive Rule (4) from Rule (3).

I.3 DIVISION OF NUMBERS

If a and b are numbers with $b \neq 0$, then we define the **quotient** of a and b, denoted a/b or $a \div b$, as

(1) $$a/b = a \cdot b^{-1}.$$

Thus, a/b is the number whose product with b is a:

$$\begin{aligned}
a/b \cdot b &= (a \cdot b^{-1}) \cdot b \\
&= a \cdot (b^{-1} \cdot b), \quad \text{by Axiom M1,} \\
&= a \cdot 1, \quad \text{by Axiom M4,} \\
&= a, \quad \text{by Axiom M3.}
\end{aligned}$$

There is an important point about the definition of division that is easy to memorize but is also easy to forget:

Division by the number 0 is not defined. Don't forget it.

Quotients of numbers can be multiplied, divided, added, and subtracted according to the following rules:

(2) $\qquad (a/b) \cdot (c/d) = ac/bd, \qquad$ if $b \neq 0$ and $d \neq 0$
(3) $\qquad a/b \div c/d = ad/bc, \qquad$ if $b \neq 0, d \neq 0$ and $c \neq 0$
(4) $\qquad a/b + c/d = (ad + bc)/bd, \qquad$ if $b \neq 0$ and $d \neq 0$
(5) $\qquad a/b - c/d = (ad - bc)/bd, \qquad$ if $b \neq 0$ and $d \neq 0$

These rules can be derived using the idea illustrated by this argument for Rule (2).

Assuming $b \neq 0$ and $d \neq 0$, let $x = a/b$, $y = c/d$. We must show that $x \cdot y$ is the number whose product with bd is ac. But

$$\begin{aligned}
(bd) \cdot (xy) &= (bx) \cdot (dy), \qquad \text{using Axioms M1 and M2,} \\
&= a \cdot c, \qquad \text{by definition of } x \text{ and } y.
\end{aligned}$$

Hence, since
$$bd \neq 0,$$
$$a/b \cdot c/d = xy = ac/bd.$$

EXAMPLE 1

(i)
$$1/2 \cdot 3/4 = \frac{1 \cdot 3}{2 \cdot 4}, \quad \text{by (2)},$$
$$= 3/8.$$

(ii)
$$1/8 \div 3/16 = \frac{1 \cdot 16}{8 \cdot 3}, \quad \text{by (3)},$$
$$= 16/24 = 2/3.$$

(iii)
$$2/3 + 3/5 = \frac{2 \cdot 5 + 3 \cdot 3}{3 \cdot 5}, \quad \text{by (4)},$$
$$= 19/15.$$

(iv)
$$1/4 - 1/3 = \frac{1 \cdot 3 - 1 \cdot 4}{4 \cdot 3}, \quad \text{by (5)},$$
$$= -1/12.$$

EXAMPLE 2   (Cancellation)

If $b \neq 0$ and $x \neq 0$, then $ax/bx = a/b$.

Because,
$$\frac{ax}{bx} = \frac{a}{b} \cdot \frac{x}{x}, \quad \text{by (2)},$$
$$= \frac{a}{b} \cdot 1 = \frac{a}{b}.$$

EXAMPLE 3

If $c \neq 0$, then $a/c + b/c = (a + b)/c$.

For, by Rule (4),
$$\frac{a}{c} + \frac{b}{c} = \frac{ac + bc}{c \cdot c}$$
$$= \frac{(a + b) \cdot c}{c \cdot c}, \quad \text{by Axiom D},$$
$$= \frac{a + b}{c}, \quad \text{by Example 2}.$$

Rules governing manipulation of signed numbers in quotients are similar to those for products.

(6) $(-a)/b = -(a/b), \quad$ if $b \neq 0$.

(7) $a/(-b) = -(a/b), \quad$ if $b \neq 0$.

(8) $(-a)/(-b) = a/b, \quad$ if $b \neq 0$.

In fact, these rules can be derived from the rules given in Section I.2 for multiplying signed numbers, with the help of these two basic observations.

(i)   If $y \neq 0$, then $x/y = x \cdot y^{-1}$.

(ii)   If $y \neq 0$, then $-(y^{-1}) = (-y)^{-1}$,

that is,
$$-(1/y) = 1/(-y).$$

Statement (i) is just the definition of the quotient of two numbers, whereas (ii) follows from the fact that the product of $-(y^{-1})$ and $-y$ is 1:

$$(-(y^{-1})) \cdot (-y) = y^{-1} \cdot y, \quad \text{by the rules of sign for products,}$$
$$= 1, \quad \text{by Axiom M4.}$$

Hence, (ii) follows by Axiom M4.

EXAMPLE 4

(i)
$$\frac{-a}{b} \cdot \frac{c}{-d} = \left(-\frac{a}{b}\right)\left(-\frac{c}{d}\right), \quad \text{by (6) and (7)}$$
$$= \frac{a}{b} \cdot \frac{c}{d} = \frac{ac}{bd};$$

or, we could notice that

(ii)
$$\frac{-a}{b} \cdot \frac{c}{-d} = \frac{(-a)c}{b(-d)}, \quad \text{by (2),}$$
$$= \frac{-ac}{-bd}$$
$$= \frac{ac}{bd}, \quad \text{by (8).}$$

EXAMPLE 5   Division by zero is meaningless in the real number system.

The reason is that if the arithmetic of quotients is going to make sense, then a/b must represent the *unique* number whose product with b is a.
So, if $b = 0$, then the statement

$$a/b = x$$

would have to imply that

$$a = b \cdot x = 0 \cdot x = 0.$$

This says that the only chance for making $a/0$ meaningful is to have $a = 0$. But this chance vanishes also, for the statement

$$0/0 = x$$

would have to mean that x is the *unique* number satisfying

$$0 = 0 \cdot x.$$

But *every* number x satisfies this equation.
Hence, no matter what the real number a is, we conclude that no meaning can be assigned to the symbol $a/0$ that will be consistent with the arithmetic of quotients. The rules for quotients are summarized as follows:

Arithmetic of Quotients

(1) $\frac{a}{b} = a \cdot b^{-1}$

(2) $\left(\frac{a}{b}\right)\left(\frac{c}{d}\right) = \frac{ac}{bd}$

(3) $\frac{a}{b} \div \frac{c}{d} = \frac{ad}{bc}$

(4) $\dfrac{a}{b} + \dfrac{c}{d} = \dfrac{ad + bc}{bd}$

(5) $\dfrac{a}{b} - \dfrac{c}{d} = \dfrac{ad - bc}{bd}$

Division of Signed Numbers

(6) $\dfrac{-a}{b} = -\left(\dfrac{a}{b}\right)$

(7) $\dfrac{a}{-b} = -\left(\dfrac{a}{b}\right)$

(8) $\dfrac{-a}{-b} = \dfrac{a}{b}$

Exercises

1. Find the sum and difference of each pair of numbers:
   (a) 1/2, 1/3
   (b) −3/4, 1/12
   (c) −5/3, 1/3
   (d) −1/5, −2/15
   (e) 3, −1/6
   (f) −2, −1/4

2. Find the quotient of each pair of numbers given in Exercise 1.

3. Compute each product:
   (a) $\left(\dfrac{-2}{3}\right)\left(\dfrac{1}{6}\right)$

   (b) $\left(\dfrac{-1}{4}\right)\left(\dfrac{-3}{8}\right)$

   (c) $(-2)\left(\dfrac{-3}{5}\right)$

   (d) $\left(\dfrac{-3}{16}\right)\left(\dfrac{4}{3}\right)\left(\dfrac{-8}{5}\right)$

   (e) $\left(\dfrac{3}{7}\right)\left(\dfrac{54}{-9}\right)\left(\dfrac{-14}{6}\right)$

4. Simplify:
   (a) $\left[(3)(-2)\left(\dfrac{-1}{5}\right)\right] \div \left[\left(\dfrac{4}{7}\right)\left(\dfrac{-2}{3}\right)\right]$

   (b) $\left[\left(\dfrac{-1}{3}\right)\left(\dfrac{-2}{5}\right)\left(\dfrac{-3}{4}\right)\right]$
   $\div \left[(-2)\left(\dfrac{5}{3}\right)\left(\dfrac{-1}{6}\right)\right]$

   (c) $1 \div \left[\left(\dfrac{-1}{2}\right) \div \left\{\left(\dfrac{3}{4}\right) \div \left(\dfrac{-4}{3}\right)\right\}\right]$

5. Simplify:
   (a) $\dfrac{a}{(-b)} + \dfrac{c}{(-d)}$

   (b) $\dfrac{(-a)}{b} \div \dfrac{(-c)}{(-d)}$

(c) $\dfrac{x}{y} - \dfrac{z}{y}$

(d) $\dfrac{u}{(v/w)}$

(e) $\dfrac{(u/v)}{w}$

6. Each of the following statements about numbers is fallacious. For each statement, give specific examples of numbers for which the statement is not true. Also, try to explain the fallacy in your own words.
   (a) $\dfrac{1}{x} + \dfrac{1}{y} = \dfrac{1}{(x + y)}$

   (b) $\dfrac{1}{x} + \dfrac{1}{y} = \dfrac{2}{(x + y)}$

   (c) $\dfrac{a}{b} + \dfrac{c}{d} = \dfrac{(a + c)}{(b + d)}$

   (d) $\dfrac{u}{(u + v)} = \dfrac{\cancel{u}}{(\cancel{u} + v)} = \dfrac{1}{(1 + v)}$

   (e) $\left(\dfrac{1}{a}\right)(a + b) = \left(\dfrac{1}{\cancel{a}}\right)(\cancel{a} + b)$
   $= 1 + b$

   (f) $\dfrac{a}{(b + c)} = \dfrac{a}{b} + \dfrac{a}{c}$

   (g) $\dfrac{x}{(y/z)} = \dfrac{(x/y)}{z}$

7. Here is a derivation of Rule (3) for quotients. Supply the reasons for each step.
   Let a, b, c, d be numbers with $b \neq 0$, $c \neq 0$, $d \neq 0$.

   Let $x = \dfrac{a}{b}$ and let $y = \dfrac{c}{d}$.

   To show: $(bc)x = (ad)y$. (Why do we want to show *this*?)

Now, $(bc)x = (cb)x$ (Why?)

$\qquad = c(bx)$ (Why?)

$\qquad = ca$ (Why?)

$\qquad = (dy)a$ (Why?)

$\qquad = a(dy)$ (Why?)

$\qquad = (ad)y$ (Why?)

Hence, $x/y = ad/bc$ (Why?)

8. Give a derivation of Rule (4) for quotients. *Hint:* Let a, b, c, d be numbers with $b \neq 0$, $d \neq 0$. Let $x = a/b$ and let $y = c/d$. Show that $(bd)(x+y) = ac + bd$.

9. Give a derivation of Rule (5) for quotients.

10. Show how the rules of signs for multiplication yield the rules of signs for quotients.

I.4   SUMS AND DIFFERENCES OF ALGEBRAIC EXPRESSIONS

Simplification of expressions involving sums and differences of algebraic quantities can be obtained by careful use of the rules given in Section I.1 for addition and subtraction of signed numbers, together with the Associative and Commutative Laws for addition and the Distributive Law.

EXAMPLE

(i)

$$2x - 3y - (x - 2y) = 2x - 3y - x + 2y$$
$$= (2x - x) + (-3y + 2y)$$
$$= (2 - 1)x + (-3 + 2)y$$
$$= x - y.$$

(ii)

$$7a - 4b + c + 5b - 3a = (7a - 3a) + (5b - 4b) + c$$
$$= 4a + b + c.$$

(iii)

$$xy - 3y^2 - (x^2 + y^2) + 2(xy - x^2) = xy - 3y^2 - x^2 - y^2 + 2xy - 2x^2$$
$$= (xy + 2xy) + (-3y^2 - y^2) + (-x^2 - 2x^2)$$
$$= 3xy - 4y^2 - 3x^2.$$

(iv)

$$a - \{b + c - [c - (-b - a)]\} = a - \{b + c - [c + b + a]\}$$
$$= a - \{b + c - c - b - a\}$$
$$= a - (-a) = 2a.$$

Exercises

1. Find the sum of the numbers in each list.

  (a) $3x - 2y + 4z$, $-5x + y - z$

  (b) $8xy - 2z$, $4x + 3xy$, $z - x - 4xy$

  (c) $(4/3)a - (1/2)b + c$, $(-1/6)a - 3b + (1/4)c$

  (d) $-4x^2 + ax - by^3 + 2$, $2x + 3y^3$, $-3 + 6x^2$

2. Subtract:

  (a) $6x - 2y + 3z$ from $x + y - 4z$

  (b) $-2(a + b) + 7(a - b)$ from $3(a + b) + 5(a - b)$

  (c) $-3x^2 + 4y - 7$ from $2x^2 + 6y - 3$

  (d) $4a^2 - 3ab + b^2$ from the sum of $2a^2 - ab + 6b^2$ and $-a^2 + b^2$

3. Simplify:

  (a) $2y - 4[z - (x + y)]$

  (b) $3(uv - w) + 2uv - 3w$

  (c) $8a^2 - 3ab - (2b^2 - 3a^2) + 2(ab - b^2)$

  (d) $3x - \{2y - [4y + 7(x - z)] + 2x + 1\}$

  (e) $-2\{x + 3[y - (2y - z)]\} + 4[z - 2(y - x)]$

  (f) $3\{abc - 2[xy + abc] + x\} - 2(x + y - abc)$

  (g) $-4[x^2y - 3(y^3 + 2xy)] + 5\{3[x^2y + 2(-y^3 + x)]\}$

I.5 PRODUCTS OF ALGEBRAIC EXPRESSIONS

Some products of algebraic expressions can be simplified just by using the rules for multiplication of signed numbers given in Section I.2, with an assist from the Associative and Commutative Laws of Multiplication.

EXAMPLE 1

(i) $\qquad (-2a)(3b) = -((2a)(3b)) = -6ab$
(ii) $\qquad (-4x)(-2x^2) = (4x)(2x^2) = 8x^3$
(iii) $\qquad (xy)(-ax)(by^2) = -abx^2y^3$

It is sometimes desirable to write certain products as sums of algebraic expressions. Here is a list of some of the most common examples.

Expansion Formulas

(1) $\qquad (a + b)(a - b) = a^2 - b^2$
(2) $\qquad (a + b)^2 = a^2 + 2ab + b^2$
(3) $\qquad (a - b)^2 = a^2 - 2ab + b^2$
(4) $\qquad (a + b)^3 = a^3 + 3a^2b + 3ab^2 + b^3$
(5) $\qquad (a - b)^3 = a^3 - 3a^2b + 3ab^2 - b^3$
(6) $\qquad (ax + b)(cx + d) = acx^2 + (bc + ad)x + bd$

EXAMPLE 2

(i) $\qquad (2x + 3y)(2x - 3y) = (2x)^2 - (3y)^2, \qquad \text{by (1)},$
$$= 4x^2 - 9y^2.$$

(ii) $\qquad (4t - 3)^2 = (4t)^2 - 2 \cdot 4t \cdot 3 + 3^2, \qquad \text{by (3)},$
$$= 16t^2 - 24t + 9.$$

(iii) $\qquad (5x - 2)^3 = 125x^3 - 150x^2 + 60x - 8, \qquad \text{by (5)}.$

(iv) $\qquad (4x - y)(5x + 2y) = 20x^2 + (-5 + 8)xy + (-2y^2), \qquad \text{by (6)},$
$$= 20x^2 + 3xy - 2y^2.$$

Exercises

1. Multiply:
   (a) $-xy$ by $2x^2$
   (b) $3abc$ by $-4ac^2$
   (c) $-9uvw$ by $-3xy$
   (d) $4ac$ by the product of $-2a$ and $5bc$.

2. Multiply:
   (a) $3x - 4y$ by $2x$
   (b) $5ab - 2c$ by abc
   (c) $2u - 4v + 3w$ by $-6uv$
   (d) $13x^2$ by $2x - 3xy + 4y^2$

3. Expand each product.
   (a) $(x + y)^2$
   (b) $(3v + 1)^2$
   (c) $(8y - 3)^2$
   (d) $(2 - 3t)^2$
   (e) $(6z + 4u)^2$
   (f) $(ab - cd)^2$

4. Expand each product.
   (a) $(3u + 1)^3$
   (b) $(2 - 5x)^3$
   (c) $(a^2 - b)^3$
   (d) $(x - 1)^3$
   (e) $(2y + 3z)^3$
   (f) $(ax + by)^3$

5. Expand each product.
   (a) $(5a + 4b)(5a - 4b)$
   (b) $(3x - 2)(x + 1)$

(c) $\left(4a - \dfrac{3}{2}\right)\left(a - \dfrac{1}{3}\right)$

(d) $(6ax^2 - y^2)(6ax^2 + y^2)$

(e) $(5 - 4z)(z + 2);$

(f) $\left(\dfrac{3}{2}x + \dfrac{1}{4}\right)\left(2x - \dfrac{8}{9}\right)$

6. Expand each product.

(a) $(x - 2y)(x + 2y)(2x - y)$

(b) $(a - 2b)^2(a + 2b)$

(c) $(5x + 2y)^3(x - y)$

(d) $(x - y + z)(x - y - z)$

(e) $(4a - b + c)^2$

(f) $(2a^2 + 1 - b)^3$

7. Use the axioms to verify each of the expansion formulas (1)–(6).

I.6 FACTORING

The most elementary form of factoring appears when the Distributive Law (Axiom D) is read backward:

$$ab + ac = a(b + c)$$
$$ba + ca = (b + c)a$$

EXAMPLE 1

(i)
$$6x - 2xy = 2x \cdot 3 - 2x \cdot y$$
$$= 2x(3 - y)$$

(ii)
$$4x^2 + 8x^3 = 4x^2 \cdot 1 + 4x^2 \cdot 2x$$
$$= 4x^2(1 + 2x)$$

(iii)
$$a^2b^2 - 2ab + 3ab^2 = ab \cdot ab - 2 \cdot ab + 3b \cdot ab$$
$$= (ab - 2 + 3b) \cdot ab$$

(iv)
$$2ax + 2ay - abx - aby = 2a(x + y) - ab(x + y)$$
$$= (2a - ab)(x + y)$$
$$= a(2 - b)(x + y)$$

Beyond examples of this type are certain standard forms that should be recognized.

Factorization Formulas

(1) $\quad x^2 - y^2 = (x + y)(x - y)$

(2) $\quad x^2 + 2xy + y^2 = (x + y)^2$

(3) $\quad x^2 - 2xy + y^2 = (x - y)^2$

(4) $\quad x^3 + y^3 = (x + y)(x^2 - xy + y^2)$

(5) $\quad x^3 - y^3 = (x - y)(x^2 + xy + y^2)$

(6) $\quad px^2 + qx + r = (ax + b)(cx + d)$ by inspection

Notice that Rules (1), (2), and (3) here are just the corresponding expansion formulas from Section I.5 read backwards. Notice also that the expansion formula (6) from Section I.5 gives some clues as to how to go about the "inspection" involved in Rule (6): one tries different combinations of numbers a and c such that $ac = p$, together with different combinations of b and d satisfying $bd = r$, until one discovers a combination yielding $bc + ad = q$.

EXAMPLE 2

(i)
$$16a^2 - 49b^2 = (4a)^2 - (7b)^2$$
$$= (4a - 7b)(4a + 7b), \quad \text{by (1).}$$

(ii)
$$9a^2 + 6ab + b^2 = (3a)^2 + 2 \cdot 3ab + b^2$$
$$= (3a + b)^2, \qquad \text{by (2).}$$

(iii)
$$4z^2 - 4z + 1 = (2z - 1)^2, \qquad \text{by (3).}$$

(iv)
$$8a^3 + 27b^3 = (2a)^3 + (3b)^3$$
$$= (2a + 3b)(4a^2 - 6ab + 9b^2), \qquad \text{by (4).}$$

(v)
$$u^6 - 64v^9 = (u^2)^3 - (4v^3)^3$$
$$= (u^2 - 4v^3)(u^4 + 4u^2v^3 + 16v^6), \qquad \text{by (5).}$$

(vi)
$$6x^2 + 5x - 4 = (2x - 1)(3x + 4), \qquad \text{by inspection.}$$

Exercises

1. Use the Distributive Law to factor each expression.
  (a) $5ax - 2bx$
  (b) $3x^2 + 4xy$
  (c) $a(x - 2) - 3(x - 2)$
  (d) $x(y + z) - x(y - z)$
  (e) $6x^2 - ax + bx^3$
  (f) $(c - d)^2 + 4(c - d)$
  (g) $3b^2(b - 1) - (1 - b)$
  (h) $4x^2(y - z) + 3x^2y$
  (i) $2(x + y) - 4(x - y)$
  (j) $a^2b^2 - 3ab^3 + 2ab^4$

2. Use the Factorization Formulas to factor.
  (a) $y^2 + 8y + 16$
  (b) $a^2 - 10a + 25$
  (c) $9 - 6x + x^2$
  (d) $36 - 4b^2$
  (e) $16x^2 - 9y^2$
  (f) $25a^2 - 36$
  (g) $8x^3 - y^3$
  (h) $a^3 - 1$
  (i) $z^3 + 1$
  (j) $27b^3 + 1$
  (k) $125 - 64x^3$
  (l) $1000a^3 + 8b^3$
  (m) $x^2 - 5x + 4$
  (n) $y^2 - 16y + 55$
  (o) $28 + 3z - z^2$

  (p) $x^2 + 12x + 20$
  (q) $4b^2 - 28b + 45$
  (r) $2a^2 + 9a + 9$
  (s) $15y^2 + y - 6$
  (t) $6x^2 - x - 2$

3. Factor each of the following.
  (a) $2ax^3y^2 - 8axy^4$
  (b) $xy - 3x + 2y - 6$
  (c) $ab - a - 5b + 5$
  (d) $(x - y)^2 + 4(x - y) + 4$
  (e) $(2c - d)^2 + 2(2c - d) - 3$
  (f) $y^2(3y + 1)^2 - (x + 4)^2$
  (g) $(4x + y)^2 - (2x - 3)^2$
  (h) $a^4b^4 - 9b^4$
  (i) $45x^3 + 18x^2 - 20x - 8$
  (j) $21b^3 + 14b^2 - 24b - 16$
  (k) $a^2b^3 + a^2y^3 - b^3x^2 - x^2y^3$
  (l) $(x + 2y)^3 - x(x^2 - 4y^2)$
  (m) $(a^3 - 8b^3) - a(a - 2b)^2$
  (n) $y^4 - 81$
  (o) $9x^2(3x + 2) + 6x(3x + 2) + 1$
  (p) $(x^2 + y^2)^3 - 4x^2y^2(x^2 + y^2)$
  (q) $(8y^3 - 27)$
$$+ (2y - 3)(4y^2 + 4y - 6)$$
  (r) $(4b^2 + 9)^2 - 24b(4b^2 + 9)$
$$+ 144b^2$$
  (s) $x^3 + 2x^2 + 2x + 1$
  (t) $(a^2 - 9a)^2 + 4(a^2 - 9a) - 140$

I.7 QUOTIENTS OF ALGEBRAIC EXPRESSIONS

Simplification of expressions involving quotients is usually a multistep process that uses many of the techniques that have been discussed in the first six sections of this Appendix. There are a few basic principles of technique that can be used in an orderly fashion in problems of this type.

(1) First, examine each quotient involved in the expression for the possibility of factoring both numerator and denominator, and cancel any common factors that appear.

(2) If the expression is the sum, difference, product, or quotient of two or more algebraic fractions, examine each part as in (1), and then use the rules of arithmetic for quotients stated in Section I. 3 to write the expression as a single quotient.

(3) Examine the final quotient obtained in (2) for the possibility of canceling factors common to the numerator and denominator.

EXAMPLE 1

$$\frac{3}{x^2 + x - 2} + \frac{x}{x^3 + 5x^2 + 6x}$$

Step (1)
$$= \frac{3}{(x - 1)(x + 2)} + \frac{x \cdot 1}{x(x + 2)(x + 3)}$$

Step (2)
$$= \frac{3(x + 3) + (x - 1)}{(x - 1)(x + 2)(x + 3)}$$

Step (3)
$$= \frac{4x + 8}{(x - 1)(x + 2)(x + 3)} = \frac{4(x + 2)}{(x - 1)(x + 2)(x + 3)}$$
$$= \frac{4}{(x - 1)(x + 3)}.$$

EXAMPLE 2

$$[x^2 - 1/x] \div [(x^2 - x)/x^2]$$

Step (1) $= [x^2 - 1/x] \div [x(x - 1)/x \cdot x]$

Step (2) $= [(x^3 - 1)/x] \div [(x - 1)/x]$

Step (2) again
$$= \frac{(x^3 - 1)(x)}{(x)(x - 1)}$$

Step (3)
$$= \frac{(x - 1)(x^2 + x + 1)(x)}{(x)(x - 1)} = x^2 + x + 1$$

EXAMPLE 3

$$\frac{x}{1 - \dfrac{1 - x}{1 + x}}$$

Step (2)
$$= x \div \frac{1 + x - (1 - x)}{1 + x}$$

$$= x \div \frac{2x}{1 + x}$$

Step (2) again
$$= \frac{(x)(1 + x)}{2x}$$

Step (3)
$$= \frac{1 + x}{2}.$$

Exercises

1. Verify each of the following by simplifying the left member of the equation in order to obtain the right member.

(a) $\left(\dfrac{x^2+2x}{x^2+x-6}\right)\cdot\left(\dfrac{x^2-9}{x^2-4}\right)=\dfrac{x(x-3)}{(x-2)^2}$

(b) $\left(\dfrac{x^2+9xy+18y^2}{x^2-9xy+20y^2}\right)$

$\qquad\cdot\left(\dfrac{xy^2-4y^3}{x^2+6xy+9y^2}\right)$

$\qquad\qquad=\dfrac{y^2(x+6y)}{(x-5y)(x+3y)}$

(c) $\dfrac{9x^2-4y^2}{x^2-y^2}\div\dfrac{3x+2y}{x-y}=\dfrac{3x-2y}{x+y}$

(d) $\dfrac{a^2-ab-2b^2}{a^3-9ab^2}\div\dfrac{a-2b}{a+3b}$

$\qquad\qquad=\dfrac{(a+b)}{a(a-3b)}$

(e) $\dfrac{a}{3+a}+\dfrac{a}{3-a}-\dfrac{2a^2}{a^2-9}=\dfrac{-2a}{a-3}$

(f) $\dfrac{3y+2}{3y-2}-\dfrac{9y^2+4}{9y^2-4}$

$\qquad\qquad=\dfrac{12y}{(3y-2)(3y+2)}$

(g) $\dfrac{1}{x^2-3x+2}-\dfrac{2}{x^2-4x+3}$

$\qquad\qquad+\dfrac{1}{x^2-5x+6}=0$

(h) $\left(3b+\dfrac{10b^2-9b-25}{2b+3}\right)$

$\qquad\cdot\left(2b-\dfrac{4b^2-22b-9}{4b-5}\right)$

$\qquad\qquad=(2b+3)(4b+5)$

(i) $\dfrac{t-7+(10/t)}{2t-9-(5/t)}=\dfrac{t-2}{2t+1}$

(j) $\dfrac{\dfrac{3x}{(x+2)^2}+\dfrac{x-2}{x+2}}{\dfrac{2x^2+2x-1}{x^2-4}-\dfrac{x}{x-2}}$

$\qquad\qquad=\dfrac{(x+4)(x-2)}{(x+1)(x+2)}$

2. Simplify each expression. That is, write each expression as a single quotient in which the numerator and denominator are factored as much as possible.

(a) $\dfrac{4}{3x-3}-\dfrac{1}{2-2x}$

(b) $\dfrac{3x}{x^2-16}+\dfrac{2}{4-x}$

(c) $\left(\dfrac{4y^2+8y+3}{2y^2-5y+3}\right)\left(\dfrac{6y^2-9y}{4y^2-1}\right)$

(d) $\left(\dfrac{b^2-3b}{b^2-25}\right)\left(\dfrac{b^2-11b+30}{b^3-6b^2+9b}\right)$

$\qquad\qquad\cdot\left(\dfrac{b^2-9}{b^2+3b-54}\right)$

(e) $\left(\dfrac{x^2-3xy}{x^3-y^3}\right)\div\left(\dfrac{x^2-10xy+21y^2}{x^2+xy+y^2}\right)$

(f) $\left(\dfrac{a^3+2a^2+a+2}{a^3-a^2-a+1}\right)$

$\qquad\qquad\div\left(\dfrac{a^4+3a^2+2}{a^4-2a^2+1}\right)$

(g) $2y^2-5y+\dfrac{2y^2+35y}{4y+9}$

(h) $\dfrac{1}{(x-y)(x-z)}-\dfrac{1}{(y-x)(y-z)}$

$\qquad\qquad-\dfrac{1}{(z-x)(z-y)}$

(i) $\dfrac{5c+4}{c-4}-\dfrac{3c-2}{c+1}-\dfrac{2c^2+19c-8}{c^2-3c-4}$

(j) $\dfrac{(1+1/x)(1+1/x^2)}{x+2+1/x}$

(k) $\left(\dfrac{3a^2+b^2}{(a-b)^2}-\dfrac{a+b}{a-b}\right)$

$\qquad\qquad\div\left(\dfrac{a}{a+b}+\dfrac{b}{a-b}\right)$

(l) $\dfrac{\dfrac{x^2-y^2-z^2}{2yz}-1}{\dfrac{x^2+y^2-z^2}{2xy}-1}$

(m) $\dfrac{\dfrac{x+1}{x-1}-\dfrac{x^2+1}{x^2-1}}{\dfrac{x-1}{x+1}+\dfrac{x^2-1}{x^2+1}}$

(n) $\left[\left(\dfrac{1}{y-z}-\dfrac{1}{x}\right)\div\left(\dfrac{1}{y+z}-\dfrac{1}{x}\right)\right]$

$\qquad\qquad\cdot\left[\dfrac{x^2-y^2-z^2-2yz}{x^2-y^2-z^2+2yz}\right]$

I.8 LINEAR AND QUADRATIC EQUATIONS

Recall that in solving a given equation, any of the following operations can be performed:

(1) Addition or subtraction of the same number to each side of the equation.
(2) Multiplication or division of each side of the equation by the same *nonzero* number.

The result in each case will be an equation that is equivalent to the original one.

LINEAR EQUATIONS   A linear equation in an unknown x is one that can be transformed by operations (1) and (2) to the form

$$ax = b.$$

This equation has the solution $x = b/a$ provided $a \neq 0$, by operation (2).

EXAMPLE 1

(i)
Solve

$$5x - 3 = 2 + x - 3x.$$
$$5x - 3 = 2 - 2x,$$
$$7x = 5,$$
$$x = 5/7.$$

(ii)
Solve

$$4y - 3x = 2 \quad \text{for} \quad x.$$
$$-3x = 2 - 4y,$$
$$x = \frac{2 - 4y}{-3} = \frac{4y - 2}{3}.$$

(iii)
Solve

$$a^2 y + xy - zx = 2b^2 \quad \text{for} \quad x.$$
$$(y - z)x = 2b^2 - a^2 y,$$
$$x = \frac{2b^2 - a^2 y}{y - z}, \quad \text{if} \quad y - z \neq 0.$$

QUADRATIC EQUATIONS   A quadratic equation in an unknown x is one that can be transformed by operations (1) and (2) to the form

$$ax^2 + bx + c = 0, \quad \text{where} \quad a \neq 0.$$

A quadratic equation may be solved by any of these methods.

EXAMPLE 1   *Factoring*

Solve

$$3x^2 + 4x - 2 = x^2 - x + 1.$$
$$2x^2 + 5x - 3 = 0,$$
$$(2x - 1)(x + 3) = 0,$$
$$2x - 1 = 0 \quad \text{or} \quad x + 3 = 0,$$
$$x = 1/2 \quad \text{or} \quad x = -3.$$

EXAMPLE 2   *Completing the square*

In this method, one observes that

$$ax^2 + bx + c = a\left(x^2 + \frac{b}{a}x\right) + c$$
$$= a\left(x^2 + \frac{b}{a}x + \left(\frac{b}{2a}\right)^2\right) + c - a \cdot \left(\frac{b}{2a}\right)^2$$
$$= a\left(x + \frac{b}{2a}\right)^2 + c - \frac{b^2}{4a}.$$

Thus, to solve

$$4x^2 + 12x - 7 = 0,$$

we proceed as follows:

$$4(x^2 + 3x) - 7 = 0,$$
$$4(x^2 + 3x + (3/2)^2) - 7 - 4(3/2)^2 = 0,$$
$$4(x + 3/2)^2 = 7 + 9 = 16,$$
$$(x + 3/2)^2 = 4,$$
$$x + 3/2 = \pm\sqrt{4} = \pm 2,$$
$$x = -3/2 \pm 2,$$
$$x = 1/2 \quad \text{or} \quad x = -7/2.$$

EXAMPLE 3   *Quadratic Formula*

If the method of completing the square is carried through for the general quadratic equation $ax^2 + bx + c = 0$, the result is the solution

$$x = \frac{-b \pm \sqrt{b^2 - 4ac}}{2a}.$$

Notice that the **discriminant** $b^2 - 4ac$ of the quadratic expression $ax^2 + bx + c$ plays an important role:

If $b^2 - 4ac$ is positive, there are two distinct solutions.

If $b^2 - 4ac = 0$, there is only one solution.

If $b^2 - 4ac$ is negative, there are no real-number solutions, since $\sqrt{b^2 - 4ac}$ will be an imaginary number.

Thus

(i) $$6x^2 - 4x - 3 = 0 \quad \text{has}$$
$$x = \frac{4 \pm \sqrt{(-4)^2 - 4(6)(-3)}}{12} \quad \text{for its solutions.}$$

To simplify this expression, don't be in a great rush to carry out all the indicated arithmetic under the radical sign right away.

Observe: $$x = \frac{4 \pm \sqrt{4^2 + 4 \cdot 6 \cdot 3}}{12}$$
$$= \frac{4 \pm \sqrt{4(4 + 18)}}{12}, \qquad \text{by Axiom D,}$$
$$= \frac{4 \pm 2\sqrt{22}}{12}$$
$$= \frac{2 \pm \sqrt{22}}{6}.$$

The point is, rules like the Distributive Law are sometimes useful when simplifying expressions involving specific numbers as well as when there is a profusion of a's, b's, x's, and y's in attendance!

(ii) Solve $\qquad\qquad\qquad yx^2 - xy^3 + 3y^2 = 1$ for x.

This is a quadratic equation in x, provided $y \neq 0$:

$$yx^2 - y^3x + (3y^2 - 1) = 0,$$

and has the solution

$$x = \frac{y^3 \pm \sqrt{y^6 - 4y(3y^2 - 1)}}{2y}, \quad \text{if}\quad y \neq 0.$$

Exercises

1. Solve each equation.
   (a) $6x - 28 = 15x - 13$
   (b) $13 + 12x = 37x + 43$
   (c) $98 - 16y = 23 - 41y$
   (d) $-29a + 31 = 19 - 13a$
   (e) $5/2 - 14b = (3/4)b + 6/5$
   (f) $\frac{7}{3}b - \frac{2}{5}b = b + 1$

2. Solve each equation.
   (a) $8x(3x + 2) - 27$
   $\qquad = 4x(6x - 1) - 147$
   (b) $(3a - 2)^2 - 9(a - 1)(3a - 8)$
   $\qquad = -18a^2 + 51a - 38$
   (c) $(y + 4)^3 - (y - 4)^3$
   $\qquad = 2(3y - 2)(4y + 1)$
   (d) $\dfrac{6x + 1}{15} - \dfrac{2x - 4}{7x - 16} = \dfrac{2x - 1}{5}$
   (e) $\dfrac{21x^2 + 7x + 11}{7x^2 - 4x - 9} - 3 = 0$
   (f) $\dfrac{2}{y - 2} - \dfrac{5}{y + 2} - \dfrac{2}{y^2 - 4} = 0$

3. Solve each equation.
   (a) $2x^2 - 15x + 25 = 0$
   (b) $15x^2 + 26x + 7 = 0$
   (c) $27x - 9 - 8x^2 = 0$

   (d) $7a^2 + 20a = -12$
   (e) $4b^2 - 8b = 45$
   (f) $13y = 10y^2 - 3$
   (g) $3 = 6t^2 + 17t$
   (h) $30r^2 + 1 = -17r$
   (i) $9s^2 = 18s - 8$
   (j) $-48x^2 + 22x + 15 = 0$

4. Find the real number solutions of each equation.
   (a) $x^4 - 2x^2 + 1 = 0$
   (b) $2u^4 - 3u^2 - 5 = 0$
   (c) $2y^6 - 18y^3 + 16 = 0$
   (d) $a^4 + 9a^2 - 36 = 0$
   (e) $x^8 - 5x^4 + 6 = 0$
   (f) $b^4 - 29b^2 + 98 = -2$

5. Solve:
   (a) $x^2 - 4ax - 10x = -40a$ for x
   (b) $y^2 + by + y = -y$ for y
   (c) $(a - 1)c^2 - 2a^2c = -4a^2$ for c
   (d) $6x^2 + 4ax - 15bx = 10ab$ for x
   (e) $y^2 + ay - by - ab = 0$ for y
   (f) $x^2 - 2xy + y^2 - y - 2 = 0$ for x
   (g) $\dfrac{x^2}{a + b} + a + b = \dfrac{2x(a^2 + b^2)}{a^2 - b^2}$
   $\qquad\qquad\qquad\qquad\qquad$ for x

I.9 EXTRANEOUS SOLUTIONS OF EQUATIONS

In solving certain equations, it is often convenient to use operations other than those stated at the beginning of Section I.8 in order to simplify the equation. But, there may result a new equation that has either more solutions or fewer solutions than the original equation. This happens most often in equations that contain radicals or fractions.

EXAMPLE 1

Solve

$$\sqrt{x-1} = 2x - 3.$$

$$\sqrt{x-1} = 2x - 3,$$
$$(\sqrt{x-1})^2 = (2x-3)^2,$$
$$x - 1 = 4x^2 - 12x + 9,$$
$$4x^2 - 13x + 10 = 0,$$
$$x = \frac{13 \pm \sqrt{169 - 160}}{8} = \frac{13 \pm 3}{8},$$

so

$$x = 2 \quad \text{or} \quad x = \frac{5}{4}.$$

What we know so far is that *if* x is a solution of our original equation, *then* $x = 2$ or $x = 5/4$, that is, 2 and 5/4 are the only *possible* solutions.

Now, if $x = 2$, then

$$\sqrt{x-1} = 1 = 2x - 3$$

so 2 is a solution.

But if $x = \frac{5}{4}$, then

$$\sqrt{x-1} = \sqrt{1/4} = 1/2, \quad \text{whereas}$$
$$2x - 3 = -1/2 \neq \sqrt{x-1},$$

so $\frac{5}{4}$ is not a solution.

Hence, the only solution is 2.

The reason for the appearance of the extraneous solution 5/4 is that the equations

$$\sqrt{x-1} = 2x - 3$$

and

$$x - 1 = (2x - 3)^2$$

are *not* equivalent. The first equation says that $2x - 3$ is the *positive* square root of $x - 1$, the second that $2x - 3$ is *one* of the square roots of $x - 1$. (Remember that for a positive number a, $\sqrt{a}$ denotes the positive square root of a, $-\sqrt{a}$ the negative square root of a.)

EXAMPLE 2

Solve

$$\sqrt{x^2 + 1} - 4x = 1.$$
$$\sqrt{x^2 + 1} = 4x + 1,$$
$$x^2 + 1 = 16x^2 + 8x + 1,$$
$$15x^2 + 8x = 0,$$
$$x(15x + 8) = 0,$$

so $x = 0$ and $x = -\frac{8}{15}$ are the only *possible* solutions.

If $x = 0$,

then

$$\sqrt{x^2 + 1} - 4x = \sqrt{1 - 0} = 1;$$

If $x = -\frac{8}{15}$,

then

$$\sqrt{x^2 + 1} - 4x = \sqrt{(8/15)^2 + 1} + 32/15 \neq 1.$$

Hence, 0 is the only solution.

EXAMPLE 3   If more than one radical appears in the equation, isolate the most complicated one on one side of the equation, square both sides, collect terms, and repeat the process. Then check for extraneous solutions.

Solve

$$\sqrt{2x-7} - \sqrt{x} = 1.$$
$$\sqrt{2x-7} = \sqrt{x} + 1,$$
$$2x - 7 = x + 2\sqrt{x} + 1,$$
$$x - 8 = 2\sqrt{x},$$
$$x^2 - 16x + 64 = 4x,$$
$$x^2 - 20x + 64 = 0,$$
$$(x - 16)(x - 4) = 0,$$
$$x = 16 \quad \text{or} \quad x = 4.$$

If $x = 16$,

then
$$\sqrt{2x-7} - \sqrt{x} = \sqrt{25} - \sqrt{16} = 5 - 4 = 1.$$

If $x = 4$,

then
$$\sqrt{2x-7} - \sqrt{x} = \sqrt{1} - \sqrt{4} = 1 - 2 \neq 1.$$

Hence,   16 is the only solution.

In solving equations that contain algebraic expressions, extraneous solutions may be introduced by multiplying each member of the equation by an expression that contains the unknown. Conversely, dividing each member of an equation by an expression that contains an unknown may yield an equation that has fewer solutions than the original equation.

EXAMPLE 4

Solve
$$\frac{2}{x^2} - \frac{1}{x} = \frac{2 - x^2}{x^2}.$$

If x is a solution, then multiplying each member of the equation by x^2 yields

$$2 - x = 2 - x^2,$$
$$x^2 - x = 0,$$
$$x(x - 1) = 0.$$

So $x = 0$ and $x = 1$ are the only *possible* solutions. However, the original equation is meaningless if $x = 0$, whereas if $x = 1$, then $2/x^2 - 1/x^2 = 2 - 1 = (2 - x^2)/x^2$. Hence, $x = 1$ is the only solution.

EXAMPLE 5

Solve
$$\frac{7x + 58}{(x + 10)(x + 6)} = \frac{7x + 58}{(x + 8)(x + 9)}.$$

If both terms of the equation are multiplied by

$$(x + 10)(x + 6)(x + 8)(x + 9), \quad \text{we have}$$
$$(7x + 58)(x + 8)(x + 9) = (7x + 58)(x + 10)(x + 6),$$
$$(7x + 58)(x^2 + 17x + 72) = (7x + 58)(x^2 + 16x + 60),$$
$$(7x + 58)(x^2 + 17x + 72 - x^2 - 16x - 60) = 0,$$
$$(7x + 58)(x + 12) = 0,$$

so $x = -\frac{58}{7}$ or $x = -12$.

Notice that if we had simply divided both members of the original equation by $7x + 58$, we would have "lost" the solution $x = -\frac{58}{7}$.

In problems such as those appearing in Examples 4 and 5, it is probably best to first add or subtract numbers to both sides of the equation so that the right member becomes zero. Then, simplify the left member according to the rules in Section 1.7.

Thus, in Example 4,

$$\frac{2}{x^2} - \frac{1}{x} - \frac{2 - x^2}{x^2} = 0,$$

$$\frac{2 - x - (2 - x^2)}{x^2} = 0,$$

$$\frac{x(x - 1)}{x^2} = 0,$$

are all equivalent to the original equation, and it becomes clear that $x = 1$ is a solution but $x = 0$ is not.

Similarly, in Example 5,

$$\frac{(7x + 58)}{(x + 10)(x + 6)} - \frac{(7x + 58)}{(x + 8)(x + 9)} = 0,$$

$$\frac{(7x + 58)(x^2 + 17x + 72 - x^2 - 16x - 60)}{(x + 10)(x + 6)(x + 8)(x + 9)} = 0,$$

$$\frac{(7x + 58)(x + 12)}{(x + 10)(x + 6)(x + 8)(x + 9)} = 0,$$

are all equivalent to the original equation, and we can see that $x = -\frac{58}{7}$ and $x = -12$ are the solutions, without any question of either having lost possible solutions or having introduced extraneous solutions.

The only price paid for treating equations involving fractions in this way is a physical one, that of having to write down a common denominator for a sum of quotients. Besides the advantage this method has in solving equations, you will find its use mandatory when solving inequalities, so it will be best if you practice its use now.

Exercises

1. Solve.
  (a) $\sqrt{4x + 1} + 5 = 0$
  (b) $\sqrt{x^2 - 5} - x = -1$
  (c) $\sqrt{2x - 5} + x = 0$
  (d) $\sqrt{3y + 1} - y = 0$
  (e) $\sqrt{2z - 1} - \sqrt{2z + 6} = 7$
  (f) $\sqrt{3t - 2} - \sqrt{3t + 1} = 0$
  (g) $\sqrt{x^2 - 2x + 3} = x$
  (h) $\sqrt{a^2 + 4a + 5} = 0$
  (i) $\sqrt{c^2 + 7c - 4} + \sqrt{c^2 - 3c + 1} = 5$
  (j) $\sqrt{x - 1} - \sqrt{x + 2} = -\sqrt{4x - 5}$
  (k) $\sqrt{u - 2} - \sqrt{u - 6} = 2\sqrt{u - 5}$
  (l) $\sqrt{3 - x} + \sqrt{1 - x} - \sqrt{4 - 2x} = 0$

2. Solve.
  (a) $\dfrac{2t + 7}{2t + 1} + \dfrac{2t - 3}{t - 2} = 3$
  (b) $\dfrac{1}{y - 3} + \dfrac{1}{y - 2} = \dfrac{3y - 7}{y^2 - 5y + 6}$
  (c) $\dfrac{2x + 3}{2x - 3} - \dfrac{2x - 3}{2x + 3} = \dfrac{36}{4x^2 - 9}$
  (d) $\dfrac{4z + 11}{z^2 + z - 20} = \dfrac{1}{z + 5} - \dfrac{1}{z - 4}$
  (e) $\dfrac{2u + 5}{u + 7} - \dfrac{3u^2 + 24u + 19}{u^2 + 8u + 7} = -1$
  (f) $\dfrac{3}{x + 9} - \dfrac{1}{x + 3} = \dfrac{4}{x + 18} - \dfrac{2}{x + 4}$

(g) $\dfrac{a}{x-a}-\dfrac{b}{x-b}=\dfrac{a-b}{x-c}$

(h) $\dfrac{a}{x+b}-\dfrac{b}{x+a}=\dfrac{a-b}{x+a+b}$

3. Solve, by first altering the equation so as to obtain a single fraction set equal to zero; then find the numbers that make the numerator zero, remembering to check for extraneous solutions.

(a) $3\sqrt{3-x}+\sqrt{x}=3/\sqrt{x}$

(b) $\sqrt{x-2}+\sqrt{x}=1/\sqrt{x-2}$

(c) $\dfrac{3\sqrt{x}+4}{5\sqrt{x}-2}=\dfrac{3\sqrt{x}+5}{5\sqrt{x}-3}$

(d) $\dfrac{-3\sqrt{1+2t}+4}{-6\sqrt{1+2t}-1}=\dfrac{-\sqrt{1+2t}+6}{-2\sqrt{1+2t}-5}$

(e) $\dfrac{\sqrt{34-x}+\sqrt{34+x}}{\sqrt{34-x}-\sqrt{34+x}}=-4$

(f) $\dfrac{\sqrt{3u+2}+\sqrt{3u}}{\sqrt{3u+2}-\sqrt{3u}}=\dfrac{1}{4}$

I.10 SIMULTANEOUS LINEAR EQUATIONS

The problem of solving a system

$$ax+by=c,$$
$$a'x+b'y=c',$$

of two linear equations in two unknowns simultaneously is that of determining all values, if any exist, of the numbers x and y that satisfy both equations. Any such pair of numbers is called a **solution of the system**.

It may happen that every choice of x and y that satisfies one equation satisfies the other also, in which case the equations are called **equivalent**. Thus,

(**1**) $2x-y=3$ and

(**2**) $4x-2y=6$

are equivalent.

If the two equations are not equivalent, they are called **independent**, in which case exactly one of two things can happen:

(**i**)   There is no solution common to the two equations, *i.e.*, they are **inconsistent**. For example,

$$x+y=2$$
$$2x+2y=-1$$

are inconsistent.

(**ii**)   There is exactly one solution common to the equations:

$$3x-y=2$$
$$x+2y=3$$

has only $x=1$, $y=1$ as a common solution.

We will discuss two methods of solving systems of linear equations, both of which are essentially applications of the two principles stated in Section I.8 for transforming a given equation into an equivalent equation.

EXAMPLE 1   *Elimination by Addition or Subtraction*

(**i**)

(**1**) $4x-3y=-2$

(**2**) $3x+5y=13$

If equation (1) is multiplied by 3 and equation (2) is multiplied by 4, and then corresponding members of the new equations are subtracted, we obtain

$$
\begin{aligned}
12x - 9y &= -6 \\
12x + 20y &= 52 \\
\hline
-29y &= -58 \\
y &= 2.
\end{aligned}
$$

Setting $y = 2$ in equation (1) gives

$$
\begin{aligned}
4x &= 3y - 2 = 4 \\
x &= 1,
\end{aligned}
$$

so the simultaneous solution is $x = 1$, $y = 2$. This result can be checked by substituting these values in equation (2).

This system could also be solved by multiplying (1) by 5, multiplying (2) by 3, and adding:

$$
\begin{aligned}
20x - 15y &= -10 \\
9x + 15y &= 39 \\
\hline
29x &= 29 \\
x &= 1.
\end{aligned}
$$

Setting $x = 1$ in equation (1) gives

$$
\begin{aligned}
-3y &= -2 - 4x = -6, \\
y &= 2.
\end{aligned}
$$

(ii)

(1) $\qquad\qquad 3x - 2y = 1$

(2) $\qquad\qquad 9x - 6y = 0.$

Here, if (1) is multiplied by 3 and (2) is left unchanged, we obtain

$$
\begin{aligned}
9x - 6y &= 3, \\
9x - 6y &= 0,
\end{aligned}
$$

which is inconsistent, so the system has no solution.

EXAMPLE 2   *Elimination by Substitution*

In this method, one of the equations is solved for one of the unknowns in terms of the other, and the result is substituted in the remaining equation.

(1) $\qquad\qquad 2x - 3y = 4$

(2) $\qquad\qquad 3x + 4y = 6$

If (1) is solved for x in terms of y, we obtain

(3) $\qquad\qquad x = \dfrac{1}{2}(4 + 3y)$

Substituting this expression in (2) yields

$$
\begin{aligned}
3\left[\frac{1}{2}(4 + 3y)\right] + 4y &= 6, \\
6 + \frac{9}{2}y + 4y &= 6, \\
\frac{17y}{2} &= 0, \\
y &= 0.
\end{aligned}
$$

From (3), then, $x = \frac{1}{2}(4 + 3 \cdot 0) = 2$, so $x = 2$, $y = 0$ is the solution.

Or, we could just as well have solved either equation for y in terms of x first. For example,

$$y = \frac{1}{4}(6 - 3x), \quad \text{from (2).}$$

Substitution in (1) yields

$$2x - \frac{3}{4}(6 - 3x) = 4,$$

$$2x - \frac{9}{4}x - \frac{9}{2} = 4,$$

$$\frac{17}{4}x = \frac{17}{2},$$

$$x = 2,$$

$$y = \frac{1}{4}(6 - 3x) = \frac{1}{4}(0) = 0.$$

Exercises

1. Solve simultaneously.
   (a) $x + 2y = 11$
        $3x + 5y = 29$
   (b) $25x - 12y = -19$
        $10x + 4y = -1$
   (c) $4s - 11t = -71$
        $9s + 8t = 4$
   (d) $8u - 15v = 18$
        $12u + 7v = 48$
   (e) $7x - 9y = -22$
        $4y + 11x = -89$
   (f) $10h + 6k = -15$
        $14k - 15h = -48$
   (g) $\frac{x}{2} + \frac{2y}{3} = 0$
        $-x + 2y = 4$
   (h) $5w + 3z - 2 = 0$
        $2w - z + 1 = 0$
   (i) $\frac{2t}{5} - \frac{3s}{7} = 1$
        $28t - 30s = -4$
   (j) $7a - 9b = 15$
        $8a - 5b = -17$

   (k) $\frac{1}{x} - \frac{1}{y} = 3$
        $\frac{2}{x} + \frac{5}{y} = 1$
   (l) $\frac{3}{x^2} - \frac{2}{y} = 4$
        $\frac{1}{x^2} - \frac{1}{y} = 0$

2. A man can row 10 miles in 50 minutes downstream, and 12 miles in $1\frac{1}{2}$ hours against the stream. What is his speed in miles per hour, and what is the speed of the current?

3. Find the number such that the sum of its two digits is 14, and such that if 36 is added to the number, the digits will be reversed.

4. Of two mixtures of alcohol and water, the one is $\frac{5}{6}$ alcohol, the other is $\frac{8}{9}$ alcohol. How many gallons of each mixture is needed to obtain 24 gallons of a mixture that is $\frac{7}{8}$ alcohol?

I.11 EXPONENTS

Integral powers of nonzero numbers are defined as follows.

Definition   Let a be a nonzero number.

(i)   If n is a positive integer, then $a^n = a \cdot a \cdots \cdots a$, with n factors.
(ii) $a^0 = 1$.
(iii) If n is a negative integer, then $a^n = 1/a^{-n}$.

Rational exponents, that is, exponents that are quotients of integers, require careful handling. In considering rational powers of a number, much depends on whether the number is positive or negative. The former case is more coherent, and we look at it first.

Definition   Let a be a positive number. If m and n are integers with n positive, then

$$a^{m/n} = \sqrt[n]{a^m},$$

the positive n^{th} root of a^m.

EXAMPLE 1

(i) $2^2 = 4; \ 2^{-2} = 1/4; \ 2^{2/3} = \sqrt[3]{4}; \ 2^{-2/3} = 1/\sqrt[3]{4}$

(ii) $4^{3/2} = \sqrt{4^3} = \sqrt{64} = 8$

(iii) $8^{2/3} = \sqrt[3]{8^2} = \sqrt[3]{64} = 4$

As is discussed in Chapter 7, it is possible to use the definition of rational powers of positive numbers to define what is meant by a^x, where a is a positive number and x is any real number, rational or irrational. This can be done in such a way that the following rules hold.

**Laws of Exponents
For Positive Bases**

Let a and b be positive real numbers, and let x and y be any two real numbers. Then

(1) $a^{x+y} = a^x \cdot a^y$

(2) $(a^x)^y = a^{xy}$

(3) $(ab)^x = a^x b^x$

(4) $a^{-x} = 1/a^x$

These rules are useful both in performing algebraic computations and in computing rational powers of positive numbers.

EXAMPLE 2

(i) $8^{-5/3} = (8^{-1/3})^5, \qquad$ by (2),

$$= \left(\frac{1}{8^{1/3}}\right)^5, \qquad \text{by (4)},$$

$$= \left(\frac{1}{2}\right)^5$$

$$= \frac{1}{32}.$$

Notice that this is easier than using the definition:

$$8^{-5/3} = \sqrt[3]{8^{-5}},$$

because $8^{1/3}$ is easily computed.

(ii)
$$16^{7/2} = (16)^{3+1/2} = 16^3 \cdot 16^{1/2}$$
$$= 4096 \cdot 4$$
$$= 16384.$$

(iii)
$$(5^{-2} + 12^{-2}) = \left(\frac{1}{5^2} + \frac{1}{12^2}\right)^{1/2}$$
$$= \left(\frac{169}{5^2 \cdot 12^2}\right)^{1/2}$$
$$= \frac{13}{60}.$$

Notice that we do *not* have the result that
$$(5^{-2} + 12^{-2})^{1/2} = (5^{-2})^{1/2} + (12^{-2})^{1/2}.$$

EXAMPLE 3

(i)   One use of the laws of exponents is that of eliminating negative exponents:
$$(a^{-1} + b^{-1})/(a^{-2} - b^{-2}) = (1/a + 1/b)/(1/a^2 - 1/b^2)$$
$$= (b + a)/ab \div (b^2 - a^2)/a^2 b^2$$
$$= (b + a)(ab)/(b^2 - a^2)$$
$$= ab/(b - a).$$

(ii)   Rule (1) is often useful in factoring expressions.
$$x^{-2} y^{1/2} + 2x^4 y^{-3/2} = x^{-2} y^{-3/2} (y^2 + 2x^6).$$

Notice that we have followed the principle of factoring out the *lowest* power of each expression that appears in both terms.

(iii)   A more complicated example of the technique used in part (ii):
$$x^{-1/2} (4 - x^2)^{3/4} - 3x^{3/2} (4 - x^2)^{-1/4}$$
$$= x^{-1/2} (4 - x^2)^{-1/4} [(4 - x^2)^1 - 3x^2]$$
$$= x^{-1/2} (4 - x^2)^{-1/4} (4 - 4x^2)$$
$$= 4x^{-1/2} (4 - x^2)^{-1/4} (1 - x)(1 + x).$$

We now turn briefly to the problem of rational powers of negative numbers.

Definition   Let a be a negative number, and let r be a rational number. If r can be written in the form m/n where n is a positive odd integer, then
$$a^r = \sqrt[n]{a^m}.$$
Otherwise, a^r is not defined.

EXAMPLE 4

(i) $(-8)^{2/3} = \sqrt[3]{-64} = -4$
(ii) $(-2)^{4/2} = (-2)^{2/1} = (-2)^2 = 4$
(iii) $(-2)^{2/4}$ is not defined, since no integers m and n with n odd can be found that satisfy $2/4 = m/n$.

Part (iii) indicates that the laws of exponents cannot be expected to hold when rational powers of negative numbers are involved. We might argue that $(-2)^{2/4}$ *should* be defined as $[(-2)^2]^{1/4} = 4^{1/4}$. But we would certainly want $(-2)^{2/4} = (-2)^{1/2}$, and there is no way to make sense out of $(-2)^{1/2}$ in the system of real numbers. However, the following modifications of the laws of exponents hold.

Laws of Exponents For Negative Bases

Let a and b be negative real numbers, and let m, n, p, q be integers with n and q odd. Then

(1) $\qquad\qquad\qquad\qquad a^{m/n + p/q} = a^{m/n} a^{p/q}$

(2) $\qquad\qquad\qquad\qquad (a^{m/n})^{p/q} = a^{mp/nq}$

(3) $\qquad\qquad\qquad\qquad (ab)^{m/n} = a^{m/n} \cdot b^{m/n}$

(4) $\qquad\qquad\qquad\qquad a^{-m/n} = 1/a^{m/n}$

Exercises

1. Compute:
   (a) $16^{3/2}$
   (b) $27^{2/3}$
   (c) $(-8)^{4/3}$
   (d) $8^{-4/3}$
   (e) $(-8)^{-4/3}$
   (f) $[(-2)^2]^{1/2}$
   (g) $(-27^5)^{1/3}$

2. Express with positive exponents.
   (a) $a^{-5/3} b^2$
   (b) $a^{-2} b^{-1/4} c^{1/6}$
   (c) $6x^2 y^{-2/5} z^{-3/7}$
   (d) $2x^{-4} y^{-5/4} \div 8z^{-3} w^{-2/3}$
   (e) $4a^{-3/2} b^{-1/4} \div 6c^{4/5} d^{-5}$

3. Write each of the following expressions in nonfractional form, and simplify as much as possible.
   (a) $a^{4/9} \div a^{1/3}$
   (b) $x^{-1/5} \div x^{-3/10}$
   (c) $6b^{-3/4} \cdot b^{-5/8}$
   (d) $(x^{-2/3} y^{6/5})^{-1/4}$
   (e) $(\sqrt[4]{a^3} \sqrt[5]{b^{-8}})^{5/6}$
   (f) $(\sqrt[4]{x} \sqrt{y^3})^{2/3}$.

4. Eliminate all negative exponents and simplify.
   (a) $\dfrac{x^{1/2} + y^{1/2}}{x^{1/2} - y^{1/2}} + \dfrac{x^{-1/2} + y^{-1/2}}{x^{-1/2} - y^{-1/2}}$
   (b) $\dfrac{a^{2/3} - b^{2/3}}{a - b}$
   (c) $\dfrac{x^{3/2} + y^{3/2}}{x^{1/2} + y^{1/2}}$
   (d) $(x^{(n+1)/(n-1)} \div x^{(n-1)/(n+1)})^{(n-1)/2n}$
   (e) $(a^{1/m^2} \div a^{1/n^2})^{mn/(m+n)} \div a^{-1/n}$

5. Factor:
   (a) $a^{-2} b^3 + a^4 b^{-1}$
   (b) $x^2 y^{-1/2} + 2y^{5/2}$
   (c) $u^{-3} v^{5/3} - u^{-1} v^{-1/3}$
   (d) $a^{-1} b^{1/4} - a^2 b^{-11/4}$
   (e) $x^{2/3} - 2x^{1/3} y^{1/3} + y^{2/3}$
   (f) $4b^{2/5} - 7b^{1/5} - 2$
   (g) $(8 - x^2)^{1/2} - x^2(8 - x^2)^{-1/2}$
   (h) $3x(1 - x)^{2/3} - x^2(1 - x)^{-1/3}$
   (i) $3x^2(4x - x^2)^{-1/2}$
   $\qquad\qquad + x^3(4x - x^2)^{-3/2}(x - 2)$
   (j) $2x^{-2}(28 - x^3)^{3/2} + 9x(28 - x^3)^{1/2}$

I.12 LOGARITHMS

Given a positive number $b \neq 1$, it is known that for any positive number M, the equation $b^x = M$ has one and only one solution x.

Definition

If b is positive and different from 1, then $\log_b M = x$ means that x is the unique number such that $b^x = M$.

EXAMPLE 1

(i) $$\log_2 32 = 5, \text{ because } 2^5 = 32.$$

(ii) $$\log_{10} 0.01 = -2, \text{ because } 10^{-2} = 0.01$$

(iii) $$\log_9\left(\frac{1}{27}\right) = -\frac{3}{2}, \text{ because } 9^{-3/2} = \frac{1}{27}.$$

EXAMPLE 2

If $\log_{10} M = -1/3$, what is M?
  From the definition, $M = 10^{-1/3} = 1/\sqrt[3]{10}$.

EXAMPLE 3

If $\log_b 16 = 4$, what is b?
  We have $16 = b^4$, so $b = 2$. Notice that the possible solution $b = -2$ is not admissible since $\log_b 16$ wouldn't be meaningful if $b = -2$.

  Computations with logarithms are often made easier with the use of the following rules.

Laws of Logarithms

Let b be a positive number different from 1. If M and N are positive, then

(1) $\log_b (MN) = \log_b M + \log_b N.$
(2) $\log_b (M/N) = \log_b M - \log_b N.$
(3) $\log_b (M^p) = p \log_b M, \; p$ any number.
(4)   If a is also positive and different from 1,

$$\log_b M = \frac{\log_a M}{\log_a b}.$$

EXAMPLE 4

Assuming $\log_{10} 2 = 0.3010$, $\log_{10} 3 = 0.4771$, and $\log_{10} 5 = 0.6990$, find

(i) $\log_{10} 18$ (ii) $\log_{10} 30$ (iii) $\log_{10} (.015)$

  Solutions:

(i) $$\log_{10} 18 = \log_{10} (2 \cdot 3^2) = \log_{10} 2 + \log_{10} 3^2$$
$$= .3010 + 2(.4771) = 1.2552.$$

(ii) $$\log_{10} 30 = \log_{10} (3 \cdot 10) = \log_{10} 3 + \log_{10} 10$$
$$= .4771 + 1 = 1.4771.$$

(iii) $$\log_{10} (.015) = \log_{10} (15/1000) = \log_{10} (5 \cdot 3) - \log_{10} 1000$$
$$= .6990 + .4771 - 3 = -1.8239.$$

EXAMPLE 5

Rule (3) can be used to yield the following formula for converting powers of one number into powers of another number:

$$a^x = b^{x \log_b a}$$

For $$b^{x \log_b a} = b^{\log_b (a^x)}, \qquad \text{by (3)},$$
$$= a^x, \qquad \text{by definition of logarithms.}$$

Exercises

1. Compute:
   (a) $\log_3 27$
   (b) $\log_2 (1/4)$
   (c) $\log_4 64$
   (d) $\log_{1/2} 4$
   (e) $\log_{2/3}(9/4)$
   (f) $\log_{10} 1$
   (g) $\log_{6/7}(6/7)$

2. Find M for each statement.
   (a) $\log_5 M = -2$
   (b) $\log_{10} M = 1$
   (c) $\log_4 M = -1/2$
   (d) $\log_{1/8} M = 1/3$
   (e) $\log_{2/5} M = -2$

3. Assuming $\log_{10} 2 = .3010$, $\log_{10} 3 = .4771$, and $\log_{10} 5 = .6990$, find the following.
   (a) $\log_{10} 12$

   (b) $\log_{10} 6000$
   (c) $\log_{10} .0075$
   (d) $\log_2 3$
   (e) $\log_5 (1/2)$
   (f) $\log_6 16$

4. Express each as a power of 10.
   (a) 3^x
   (b) a^2
   (c) x^x
   (d) $(4x)^{2x+1}$
   (e) $(1 + x)^{1/x}$.

5. Simplify.
   (a) $\log_2 2^x$
   (b) $\log_{10} (x^2 - 4) - \log_{10} (x - 2)$
   (c) $\log_3 (a + b) + \log_3 (a - b)$
   (d) $\log_x x^2$
   (e) $\log_2 (4^{x \log_4 8})$

APPENDIX II

MATHEMATICAL INDUCTION

The set of natural numbers can be thought of as being constructed one step at a time by the following process.

Beginning with the natural number 1, we have

$$2 = 1 + 1$$
$$3 = 2 + 1$$
$$4 = 3 + 1$$

and so forth, at each stage adding the natural number 1 to the previous number in the list. What is being described here is an infinite process, because no matter at what stage of the process we are, the number 1 can be added once more to produce a new number. Thus, what is needed is some way of being sure that this construction actually yields all the natural numbers. This is accomplished by the assumption of the following axiom.

Axiom of Induction

Let S be a set of natural numbers having the following two properties:

(i) $1 \in S$,

(ii)   If k is any natural number such that $k \in S$, then $k + 1 \in S$.

Then every natural number is a member of S.

The biggest hurdle to cross in understanding how to use this axiom is that of knowing what it means for a set S to satisfy condition (ii). This condition does not say that we already know that every natural number k is a member of S. Rather, to show that a given set S satisfies (ii) is to do the following: assuming that k is any natural number that happens to belong to S, prove (somehow) that $k + 1 \in S$.

To use this axiom in proving statements about natural numbers, it is convenient to notice that the following principle holds.

Principle of Mathematical Induction

For each natural number n, let $P(n)$ denote some statement about n. Then $P(n)$ is true for every natural number n if the following conditions hold:

   (**i'**) $P(1)$ is true, and
   (**ii'**) If k is a natural number for which $P(k)$ is true, then it follows that $P(k+1)$ is also true.

To see that this principle follows from the axiom of induction, let
   $S = \{n\colon n$ is a natural number such that $P(n)$ is true$\}$, and assume that conditions (i') and (ii') hold.
   Then $1 \in S$, because (i') is assumed to hold.
   Now, suppose k is a natural number that belongs to S. This means that $P(k)$ is true, by definition of S. Hence, $P(k+1)$ must be true, by condition (ii'), that is, $k+1 \in S$. Thus, we have verified that

$$\text{if } k \in S, \text{ then } k+1 \in S.$$

   Therefore, S satisfies conditions (i) and (ii) of the induction axiom, so every natural number is in S, *i.e.*, $P(n)$ is true for every natural number n.

EXAMPLE 1

Let a be a number between 0 and 1. Prove that $0 < a^n < 1$ for every natural number n.
   First, for each natural number n, let $P(n)$ denote the statement $0 < a^n < 1$.
   (**i'**)   Since $a^1 = a$, and it is given that $0 < a < 1$, it follows immediately that $P(1)$ is true.
   (**ii'**) Assume k is a natural number for which $P(k)$ is true, that is, assume that k is a natural number such that $0 < a^k < 1$. Multiplying each member in this chain of inequalities by the positive number a, we obtain

$$0 < a^k \cdot a < a.$$

But $a^k \cdot a = a^{k+1}$, and we also know $a < 1$, so it follows that

$$0 < a^{k+1} < 1.$$

   Hence, we have shown that *if $P(k)$ is true, then $P(k+1)$ is also true.*
   Therefore, $P(n)$ is true for every natural number n.

EXAMPLE 2

Prove that for every natural number n, the sum of the first n odd integers is n^2.
   For each natural number n, let $P(n)$ be the statement that

$$1 + 3 + 5 + \cdots + (2n - 1) = n^2.$$

   (**i'**) $P(1)$ is just the statement $1 = 1^2$, so $P(1)$ is true.
   (**ii'**) Assume that k is a natural number for which $P(k)$ is true, *i.e.*,

$$1 + 3 + 5 + \cdots + (2k - 1) = k^2.$$

Then the sum of the first $k + 1$ odd integers is

$$
\begin{aligned}
1 + 3 + 5 + \cdots &+ (2k - 1) + [2(k + 1) - 1] \\
&= k^2 + [2(k + 1) - 1], \qquad \text{by assumption on } k, \\
&= k^2 + 2k + 1 \\
&= (k + 1)^2.
\end{aligned}
$$

Thus, on the basis of the assumption that $P(k)$ is true, we can conclude that $P(k+1)$ is also true.

Therefore, $P(n)$ is true for every natural number n.

EXAMPLE 3

Prove that for every natural number n, $6n^2 + 2n$ is divisible by 4.

For each natural number n, let $P(n)$ be the statement that $6n^2 + 2n$ is divisible by 4.

(i′) $P(1)$ is true, because $6 \cdot (1)^2 + 2 \cdot 1 = 8 = 4 \cdot 2$.

(ii′)   Assume that k is a natural number for which $P(k)$ is true, *i.e.*, k is such that $6k^2 + 2k$ is divisible by 4.

Then,

$$6(k+1)^2 + 2(k+1) = 6(k^2 + 2k + 1) + 2k + 2$$
$$= 6k^2 + 12k + 6 + 2k + 2$$
$$= (6k^2 + 2k) + (12k + 8).$$

But $6k^2 + 2k$ is assumed to be divisible by 4, and $12k + 8$ is clearly divisible by 4, so the sum of these numbers is also divisible by 4.

Hence, the assumption that $P(k)$ is true leads to the conclusion that $P(k+1)$ is also true.

Therefore, $P(n)$ is true for every natural number n.

EXAMPLE 4   (Recursive Definition)

Consider the problem of defining what is meant by a^n, where n is a natural number. Proceeding naïvely, we might state that

$$a^n = a \cdot a \cdots \cdot a, \quad \text{with } n \text{ factors,}$$

or $a^1 = a$, $a^2 = a \cdot a$, $a^3 = a \cdot a \cdot a$, and so on.

For purposes of doing elementary computations, these "definitions" will probably suffice, but for doing more sophisticated work the following scheme is more helpful.

First, define $a^1 = a$.

Then, for each natural number k for which a^k has been defined, define

$$a^{k+1} = a^k \cdot a.$$

Now, if $S = \{n: n$ is a natural number and a^n is defined$\}$, the axiom of induction implies that every natural number is a member of S.

EXAMPLE 5

Let a be a real number, and let m and n be natural numbers. Then

$$a^{m+n} = a^m \cdot a^n.$$

The point of view we take is this: given a real number a and a natural number m, then for every natural number n, let $P(n)$ be the statement $a^{m+n} = a^m \cdot a^n$.

(i′)   By our recursive definition in Example 4, we have

$$a^{m+1} = a^m \cdot a = a^m \cdot a^1.$$

Therefore, $P(1)$ is true.

(**ii'**)   Assume that k is a natural number for which $P(k)$ is true, *i.e.*, $a^{m+k} = a^m \cdot a^k$.

Then
$$a^{m+(k+1)} = a^{(m+k)+1}$$
$$= a^{m+k} \cdot a, \quad \text{by definition,}$$
$$= (a^m \cdot a^k) \cdot a, \quad \text{by assumption on } k,$$
$$= a^m \cdot (a^k \cdot a)$$
$$= a^m \cdot a^{k+1} \quad \text{by definition.}$$

Therefore, $P(k+1)$ is true whenever $P(k)$ is true.

By the principle of mathematical induction, it follows that $P(n)$ is true for every natural number n.

You are urged to continue this mode of attack on the properties of exponents in Exercises 20–22. You are also urged not to work any of the exercises carelessly. In fact, you should go to possibly painful lengths in writing down arguments by induction, at least until the axiom of induction seems as natural to you as do the rules of arithmetic.

Exercises

Use mathematical induction to prove that each of the statements in Exercises 1–19 is true for every natural number n.

1. n is a positive number. (Use the Order Axiom O2, Section 1.2 of Chapter 1.)
2. $1^n = 1$
3. $(-1)^{2n} = 1$
4. $(-1)^{2n-1} = -1$
5. The product of $n+1$ positive numbers is positive.
6. The sum of the first n positive integers is $\frac{1}{2}n(n+1)$.
7. $2 + 4 + 6 + \cdots + 2n = n(n+1)$
8. $1^2 + 2^2 + 3^2 + \cdots + n^2 = \frac{1}{6}n(n+1) \cdot (2n+1)$
9. The sum of the cubes of the first n positive integers is $\frac{1}{4}n^2(n+1)^2$.
10. $n^2 - n + 2$ is an even integer.
11. $n(n+1)$ is an even integer.
12. $n(n+1)(n+2)$ is divisible by 6.
13. $x - y$ is a factor of $x^n - y^n$.
14. If $a > 1$, then $a^n > 1$.
15. $3^n \geq 2n + 1$
16. $2^n \geq n + 1$
17. $2^n < 3^n$
18. For any real number x, $|\sin nx| \leq n|\sin x|$.
19. $\sin x + \sin 3x + \cdots + \sin (2n-1)x = \sin^2 nx / \sin x$, if $\sin x \neq 0$.
20. (**i**) Let a be a real number. Prove that if m and n are natural numbers,

then $(a^m)^n = a^{mn}$. *Hint:* Given a and m, let $P(n)$ be the statement $(a^m)^n = a^{mn}$. You will need to use the result of Example 5.

(**ii**) Let a and b be real numbers. Prove that if n is any natural number, then $(ab)^n = a^n b^n$.

21. Let a and b be positive real numbers, and let r and s be positive rational numbers. Prove that

(**i**) $a^{r+s} = a^r \cdot a^s$
(**ii**) $(a^r)^s = a^{rs}$
(**iii**) $(ab)^r = a^r b^r$.

Suggestion: To prove (i), let $r = m/n$, $s = p/q$ with m, n, p, q natural numbers. Then $a^r = (a^m)^{1/n}$, $a^s = (a^p)^{1/q}$ by definition. Use the results of Example 5 and Exercise 20 to show that $(a^r \cdot a^s)^{nq} = a^{mq+np}$. (No use of induction is necessary.) Proceed in a similar fashion for (ii) and (iii).

22. Show that if a and b are positive real numbers and r and s are any two rational numbers, then the laws of exponents (parts (i), (ii), (iii) of Exercise 21) hold. Recall that for $a \neq 0$, we have $a^0 = 1$, by definition, and that $a^{-r} = 1/a^r$, by definition.

23. Prove that if M is a nonempty set of natural numbers, then M contains a

smallest element. (*Hint:* Assume there is a nonempty set M that does not contain a smallest element and let $P(n)$ be the statement that $n \notin M$. Use mathematical induction to show that $P(n)$ is true for every natural number n. This contradicts the fact that M is not empty.)

24. Let f be a real function whose domain is the set of all real numbers and such that $f(x + y) = f(x) \cdot f(y)$ for all x, y in R. Then show that $f(nx) = [f(x)]^n$ for each $x \in R$ and each natural number n.

25. Let g be a real function for which $\mathscr{D}_g = \{x : x > 0\}$ and $g(xy) = g(x) + g(y)$ for all x, y in $\mathscr{D}_g$. Show that $g(x^n) = ng(x)$ for all $x \in \mathscr{D}_g$ and each natural number n.

†26. Let T_1 be a real function with $\mathscr{D}_{T_1} = R$. If k is a natural number for which T_k is defined, let $T_{k+1} = T_1 \circ T_k$. If $|T_1(x) - T_1(y)| \leq \frac{1}{2}|x - y|$ for all x and y, prove that

(a) $|T_n(1) - T_n(0)| \leq 1/2^n$ for every natural number n.

(b) $|T_n(-3) - T_n(0)| \leq 3/2^n$ for every natural number n.

(c) $|T_n(x) - T_n(0)| \leq |x|/2^n$ for every natural number n and every real number x.

(d) $|T_{n+1}(x) - T_n(x)| \leq \dfrac{|T_1(x) - x|}{2^n}$

for every natural number n and real number x.

APPENDIX III

ANGLE TRIGONOMETRY

In this Appendix we review briefly some topics from angle trigonometry. It will be assumed that the reader is acquainted with the notation and properties of coordinate planes and functions as discussed in Chapters 2 and 3.

The subject of trigonometry evolved from the use of similar triangles to calculate distances that could not be measured directly. In similar right triangles, for example, the ratios of any corresponding pairs of sides are the same and are determined uniquely by the nonright angles. That is, in right triangles the ratio of any pair of sides can be thought of as a function of one of the nonright angles of the triangle. Before defining these functions there must be some agreement on what is meant by an angle and the methods for assigning a measure to an angle.

III.1 ANGLES AND ANGLE MEASUREMENT

The term *angle* is given various meanings or definitions depending on the context in which it is used. In trigonometry one usually thinks of an angle as being an ordered pair of half-lines or rays emanating from a common point, together with a rotation of the first ray to the second. That is, one starts with a ray r_1 with endpoint O as in Figure 1(a) and rotates r_1 about the point O to obtain a second ray r_2 as in Figure 1(b). (The rays r_1 and r_2 may coincide.) The ordered pair (r_1, r_2) with the rotation is called an **angle**. If we let A denote the angle, r_1 is called the **initial side** of A and r_2 is called the **terminal side** of A and O is called the **vertex** of A.

It is important to note that the angle is not determined by the initial and terminal sides alone. There are many different angles having the same initial and terminal sides, but with different rotations, a few of which are indicated in Figure 1(c). If the rotation of the angle A is in the counterclockwise sense A is said to be a **positive angle**, and if it is in the clockwise sense A is called a **negative angle**.

One appealing aspect of this definition is that an angle has a "built-in" measure — the number of revolutions about O and the sense of the rotation. If an angle has a rotation of x revolutions, we say the angle has measure x **revolutions**, or x rev, where the algebraic sign of x indicates the sense of the rotation — counterclockwise

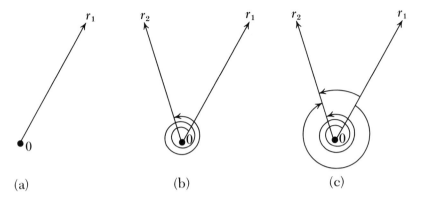

(a)   (b)   (c)

Figure 1

if x is positive and clockwise if x is negative. Although this notion of the measure of an angle is intuitively appealing and in a sense is automatic from the definition, it is not as convenient in practice as some others.

The most common way to assign a measure to an angle is a refinement of the revolution measure. A rotation of one revolution in the positive (counterclockwise) sense is divided into 360 equal parts, each of which is called a **degree**. Thus, one degree, written $1°$, is a positive rotation of 1/360 of a revolution.

The method of assigning a measure to an angle that is important for our purposes and that will be used most of the time in calculus is *radian* measure, which we will now describe.

An angle in a coordinate plane is said to be in **standard position** if its vertex is at the origin and its initial side coincides with the positive horizontal axis. Clearly, for any angle A, we can introduce a coordinate system in which A is in standard position.

Let A be an angle in the plane. Put a coordinate system in the plane, say the *ST* system, so that A is in standard position. Let P be the point of the initial side 1 unit from the vertex. As the initial side r_1 rotates about the origin, P will move on the unit circle $C = \{(s, t) : s^2 + t^2 = 1\}$, ending at the point P', which is the intersection of the terminal side r_2 and the circle C. (See Figure 2.) If ρ is the length

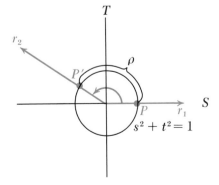

Figure 2

of the arc of the circle C traversed by P in the rotation then the **radian measure** of A is ρ if A is a positive angle and $-\rho$ if A is a negative angle.

For example, if A is a positive angle of one revolution, then the radian measure of A is 2π, the circumference of C. If B is a negative angle of one-half revolution, then the radian measure of B is $-\pi$.

The relation between the three types of angle measure is readily found. If A is an angle with revolution measure 1, then its degree measure is 360 and its radian measure is 2π. To describe this relation more conveniently, we write

$$1 \text{ revolution} = 360 \text{ degrees} = 2\pi \text{ radians,}$$

or more briefly,

$$1 \text{ rev} = 360° = 2\pi \text{ rad.}$$

From this it is clear that

$$1° = \frac{\pi}{180} \text{ rad} = \frac{1}{360} \text{ rev} \quad \text{and} \quad 1 \text{ rad} = \left(\frac{180}{\pi}\right)° = \frac{1}{2\pi} \text{ rev.}$$

These equations enable us to translate from any one method of assigning a measure to an angle to any other. Thus, an angle A with degree measure -45 has radian measure $(-45)\,\frac{\pi}{180} = -\frac{\pi}{4}$, and revolution measure $-\frac{1}{8}$. If we let $m(A)$ denote the measure of A, then

$$m(A) = -45° = -\pi/4 \text{ rad} = -1/8 \text{ rev.}$$

Similarly, if B is an angle having measure 2 rad, then

$$m(B) = 2 \text{ rad} = 2\left(\frac{180}{\pi}\right)° = (360/\pi)° = 1/\pi \text{ rev.}$$

If C is an angle with $m(C) = 27°$, then

$$m(C) = 27° = 27(\pi/180) \text{ rad} = 3\pi/20 \text{ rad} = 3/40 \text{ rev.}$$

If, in defining the radian measure of an angle A, we had considered the point Q on the initial side that was r units from the origin, then as the initial side r_1 rotated about the origin, Q would move on the circle $C_r = \{(s, t) : s^2 + t^2 = r^2\}$ of radius r, ending at the point Q' of intersection of the terminal side r_2 and the circle C_r. (See Figure 3.) Let σ denote the length of the arc traversed by Q in the rotation and ρ the length of the arc traversed by the point P one unit from the origin. Since the circular sectors POP' and QOQ' are similar the ratios of corresponding distances are equal. In particular,

$$\frac{\sigma}{\rho} = \frac{r}{1}$$

or

$$\sigma = \rho r.$$

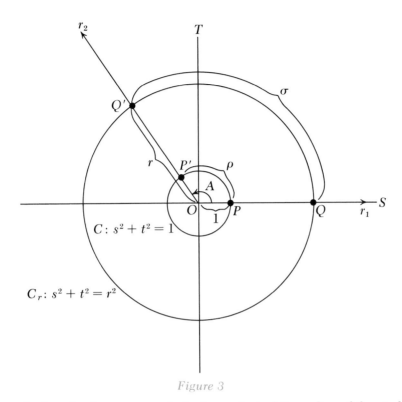

Figure 3

Thus, the length of arc on a circle is the product of the radius of the circle with the radian measure of the positive central angle subtended. Equivalently, one obtains the result that the radian measure of a positive central angle of any circle is the length of arc subtended divided by the radius of the circle. Indeed, this is often used as the definition of the radian measure of a positive angle.

EXAMPLE 1

Find the length of the arc of a circle having radius 7 inches that is subtended by a central angle with measure 75°.

If the degree measure of the angle is 75 then its radian measure is $75\pi/180 = 5\pi/12$. Hence, the length of the arc is $(5\pi/12)(7)$ inches $= 35\pi/12$ inches.

EXAMPLE 2

What must be the radius of a circle in which a central angle of 48° subtends an arc of 10 feet?

The radius will be the length of the arc subtended divided by the radian measure of the central angle. Now, since the central angle has degree measure 48, it has radian measure $48(\pi/180) = 4\pi/15$. Hence, the radius of the circle must be $10 \div (4\pi/15) = 75/2\pi$ feet.

Exercises

1. Find the measure of an angle A in each of the other systems if
  (a) $m(A) = 1/2$ rev
  (b) $m(A) = -15°$
  (c) $m(A) = 2$ rad
  (d) $m(A) = 1/10$ rev
  (e) $m(A) = 47°$
  (f) $m(A) = -3\pi$ rad
  (g) $m(A) = 315°$
  (h) $m(A) = \pi/2$ rad
  (i) $m(A) = 45°$
  (j) $m(A) = 30°$
  (k) $m(A) = \pi/3$ rad
  (l) $m(A) = 3\pi/2$ rad

2. If a flywheel is turning at the rate of 1500 rpm (revolutions per minute), what is its angular speed in
  (i)   degrees per minute?
  (ii)   radians per minute?
  (iii) revolutions per second?
  (iv)   radians per hour?

3. If the flywheel of Exercise 2 has radius 4.5 cm, through what distance does a point on its circumference travel in 1 second? 1 minute? one hour? What is the speed of the point in meters per hour?

III.2 TRIGONOMETRIC FUNCTIONS

Let A be any angle with initial side r_1 and terminal side r_2. Put a coordinate system in the plane so that A is in standard position and let $P = (s, t)$ be any point on r_2 except the origin. If d denotes the distance between $(0, 0)$ and P, define

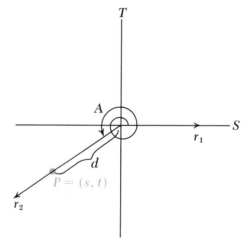

Figure 1

$$\sin A = \frac{t}{d}$$

$$\cos A = \frac{s}{d}$$

$$\tan A = \frac{t}{s} \qquad \text{for } s \neq 0$$

$$\cot A = \frac{s}{t} \qquad \text{for } t \neq 0$$

$$\sec A = \frac{d}{s} \qquad \text{for } s \neq 0$$

$$\csc A = \frac{d}{t} \qquad \text{for } t \neq 0.$$

It must be shown that these are well defined, in that the definition does not depend on which point P of r is chosen. This can be done with similar triangles or by using an algebraic description of the ray r_2. (See Exercise 6.) These equations define six functions, called the **sine, cosine, tangent, cotangent, secant,** and **cosecant** functions, respectively. Their domains are sets of angles and their ranges are subsets of the set of real numbers. They are called **trigonometric functions** .

If A and B are two angles for which $m(A) = m(B)$, then the values of each of the trigonometric functions at A and B are the same. For this reason it is common to write, for example, $\sin m(A)$, instead of $\sin A$. Thus, if $m(A) = 30°$, we write $\sin 30°$ instead of $\sin A$, or if we use radian measure $\sin \pi/6$ rad. Indeed, when we write $\sin \theta$, θ may be any one of three things: (i) an angle; (ii) the measure of an angle; (iii) a real number. In case (i) the meaning of $\sin \theta$ is obvious. In case (ii) $\sin \theta$ denotes the sine of any angle which has measure θ. In case (iii), $\sin \theta$ denotes the sine of any angle whose measure is θ radians.

EXAMPLE 1

Find $\sin 45°$ and $\tan 30°$.

The terminal side of a $45°$ angle in standard position will bisect the first quadrant. Hence, every point on the terminal side is of the form (x, x) with $x > 0$. In particular, $(2, 2)$ is on the terminal side and the distance from this point to the origin is $2\sqrt{2}$. Therefore,

$$\sin 45° = \frac{2}{2\sqrt{2}} = \frac{1}{\sqrt{2}}.$$

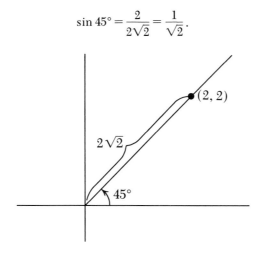

Figure 2

For an angle of $30°$ in standard position, if we drop a perpendicular from any point P on the terminal side to the horizontal axis as in Figure 3, then the triangle OQP is a 30–60 right triangle, so the length of the hypotenuse is twice the length of the side opposite the $30°$ angle. If for example we take P to be the point 2 units from the origin, then the vertical coordinate of P is 1 and by the Pythagorean Theorem the horizontal coordinate must be $\sqrt{3}$. Therefore,

$$\tan 30° = \frac{1}{\sqrt{3}}.$$

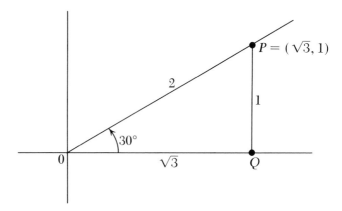

Figure 3

EXAMPLE 2

Compute the value of each trigonometric function at an angle whose radian measure is $-3\pi/2$.

Since $3\pi/2$ is $3/4$ of the circumference of the unit circle, the terminal side of the angle in standard position coincides with the positive vertical axis. Hence, $(0, 1)$ is a point of the terminal side 1 unit from the origin. Therefore,

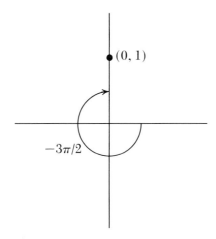

Figure 4

$$\sin\left(-\frac{3\pi}{2}\,\text{rad}\right) = 1/1 = 1$$
$$\cos\left(-\frac{3\pi}{2}\,\text{rad}\right) = 0/1 = 0$$

$$\csc\left(-\frac{3\pi}{2}\ \text{rad}\right) = 1/1 = 1$$
$$\cot\left(-\frac{3\pi}{2}\ \text{rad}\right) = 0/1 = 0.$$

The tangent and secant functions are not defined at $-3\pi/2$ radians because each point on the terminal side has first coordinate 0.

The values of the trigonometric functions are determined solely by the terminal sides of angles in standard position. Thus, the values of these functions at two angles in standard position that have the same terminal side (are **coterminal**) are the same. Now, two such angles are coterminal if and only if their rotations differ by an integral number of revolutions. Therefore, for every integer n,

$$\sin A° = \sin (A + 360n)°,$$
$$\cos A° = \cos (A + 360n)°,$$
$$\tan A° = \tan (A + 360n)°,$$

and also for the remaining trigonometric functions. Similarly, if θ is the radian measure of an angle and n is any integer, then

$$\sin (\theta + 2n\pi) = \sin \theta,$$
$$\cos (\theta + 2n\pi) = \cos \theta,$$
$$\tan (\theta + 2n\pi) = \tan \theta,$$

and so forth.

EXAMPLE 3

Find $\tan 765°$ and $\cos (-7\pi/4)$.

$$\tan 765° = \tan (45 + 360 \cdot 2)°$$
$$= \tan 45°$$
$$= 1$$

$$\cos (-7\pi/4\ \text{rad}) = \cos (\pi/4 + 2(-1)\pi)\ \text{rad}$$
$$= \cos (\pi/4\ \text{rad})$$
$$= 1/\sqrt{2}.$$

Given any angle A, if a coordinate system is introduced so that A is in standard position, A is said to be **in the quadrant** in which its terminal side lies. For example if the degree measure of A is greater than 90 but less than 180, then A is an angle in the second quadrant. If the radian measure of an angle B is between $-\pi/2$ and 0, then B is in the fourth quadrant.

The algebraic sign of each trigonometric function of an angle A is determined by the quadrant in which A lies. This is illustrated in Figure 5 in which $+$ denotes positive and $-$ denotes negative.

EXAMPLE 4

Find $\csc \theta$ if $\tan \theta = -7$ and $\cos \theta$ is negative.

For $\tan \theta$ and $\cos \theta$ to both be negative, θ must be in the second quadrant and its terminal side must contain the point $(-1, 7)$. The distance between $(-1, 7)$ and $(0, 0)$ is $\sqrt{50}$. Hence, $\csc \theta = \sqrt{50}/7$. (See Figure 6.)

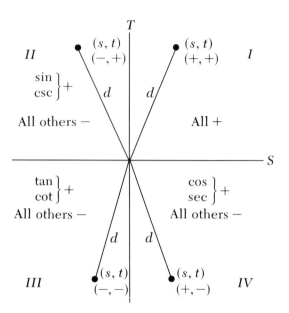

Figure 5

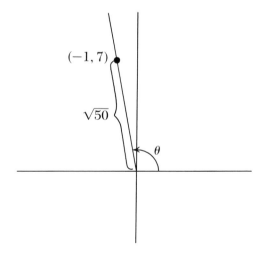

Figure 6

The definitions of the trigonometric functions yield several useful relationships between them. If (s, t) is a point on the terminal side of an angle A at a distance $d = \sqrt{s^2 + t^2}$ from the origin, then

(i) $\csc A = \dfrac{d}{t} = \dfrac{1}{t/d} = \dfrac{1}{\sin A}$ provided $t \neq 0$

(ii) $\sec A = \dfrac{d}{s} = \dfrac{1}{s/d} = \dfrac{1}{\cos A}$ provided $s \neq 0$

(iii) $\cot A = \dfrac{s}{t} = \dfrac{1}{t/s} = \dfrac{1}{\tan A}$ provided $s \neq 0$ and $t \neq 0$

(iv) $\tan A = \dfrac{t}{s} = \dfrac{t/d}{s/d} = \dfrac{\sin A}{\cos A}$ provided $s \neq 0$

(v) $\cot A = \dfrac{s}{t} = \dfrac{s/d}{t/d} = \dfrac{\cos A}{\sin A}$ provided $t \neq 0$

(vi) $\sin^2 A + \cos^2 A = \left(\dfrac{t}{d}\right)^2 + \left(\dfrac{s}{d}\right)^2 = \dfrac{t^2 + s^2}{d^2} = 1$ since $d^2 = s^2 + t^2$

(vii) $\tan^2 A + 1 = \left(\dfrac{t}{s}\right)^2 + 1 = \dfrac{t^2 + s^2}{s^2} = \dfrac{d^2}{s^2} = \left(\dfrac{d}{s}\right)^2 = \sec^2 A$ for $s \neq 0$

(viii) $1 + \cot^2 A = 1 + \left(\dfrac{s}{t}\right)^2 = \dfrac{t^2 + s^2}{t^2} = \left(\dfrac{d}{t}\right)^2 = \csc^2 A$ for $t \neq 0$.

These relationships are frequently used to simplify expressions involving trigonometric functions.

EXAMPLE 5

Show that $\dfrac{1}{\tan A + \cot A} = (\sin A)(\cos A)$ if $\tan A$ and $\cot A$ are defined.

Note first that $\tan A$ and $\cot A$ are both defined if the terminal side of A does *not* coincide with a coordinate axis. That is, if neither of the coordinates of points on the terminal side of A (other than the origin) is 0. For such angles A,

$$\frac{1}{\tan A + \cot A} = \frac{1}{\dfrac{\sin A}{\cos A} + \dfrac{\cos A}{\sin A}}, \qquad \text{by (iv) and (v),}$$

$$= \frac{1}{\dfrac{\sin^2 A + \cos^2 A}{(\sin A)(\cos A)}}$$

$$= \frac{(\sin A)(\cos A)}{\sin^2 A + \cos^2 A}$$

$$= (\sin A)(\cos A), \qquad \text{by (vi).}$$

EXAMPLE 6

Simplify $\dfrac{1 - \cos \theta}{\sin \theta} - \dfrac{\sin \theta}{1 + \cos \theta}$.

If θ is not an integral multiple of π, then

$$\frac{1 - \cos \theta}{\sin \theta} - \frac{\sin \theta}{1 + \cos \theta} = \frac{1 - \cos^2 \theta - \sin^2 \theta}{(\sin \theta)(1 + \cos \theta)}$$

$$= \frac{1 - (\sin^2 \theta + \cos^2 \theta)}{(\sin \theta)(1 + \cos \theta)}$$

$$= 0, \qquad \text{by (vi).}$$

Exercises

1. Find the values of each of the trigonometric functions for the following
angles (when they exist).
   (a) $0°$ (i) π rad
   (b) $30°$ (j) $-\pi/4$ rad
   (c) $45°$ (k) 1 rev
   (d) $60°$ (l) $3\pi/2$ rad
   (e) $90°$ (m) $-\pi/2$ rad
   (f) $120°$ (n) $-\pi$ rad
   (g) $135°$ (o) $1110°$
   (h) $150°$ (p) $-270°$

2. List all numbers α for which each of
the following does not exist.
   (a) $\tan \alpha°$ (c) $\sec \alpha°$
   (b) $\cot \alpha°$ (d) $\csc \alpha°$

3. Compute:
   (a) $\sin A$ if $\cos A = -1/2$ and
       $\tan A > 0$.
   (b) $\cos B$ if $\csc B = 4$ and $\sec B > 0$.
   (c) $\tan C$ if $\cot C = 1/10$.
   (d) $\cot \alpha$ if $\sin \alpha = 7/12$ and
       $90° < \alpha < 180°$.
   (e) $\sec \beta$ if $\tan \beta = 12$ and $\sin \beta < 0$.
   (f) $\csc \gamma$ if $\sec \gamma = -2$ and $\tan \gamma < 0$.

4. Verify each of the following statements.
   (a) If A is in the first quadrant, then
       $$\sin A = \sqrt{1 - \cos^2 A}.$$
   (b) If B is in the second quadrant,
       then $\cos B = -\sqrt{1 - \sin^2 B}$.
   (c) If the terminal side of A is not on
       one of the coordinate axes, then
       $\sec^2 A \csc^2 A = \sec^2 A + \csc^2 A$.
   (d) If $\csc A$ exists, then $\csc^4 A \cot^3 A$
       $= (\cot^3 A + \cot^5 A) \csc^2 A$.
   (e) $\sin^2 x \cos^3 x = (\sin^2 x - \sin^4 x)$
       $\cdot \cos x$ for every angle x.

5. Under what conditions on A is each
of the following true?
   (a) $\sin A = \sqrt{1 - \cos^2 A}$
   (b) $\sin A = -\sqrt{1 - \cos^2 A}$
   (c) $\tan A = \sqrt{\sec^2 A - 1}$
   (d) $\cot A = 1/\tan A$

6. Show that the value of each trigonometric function at any given angle
A does not depend on the point
chosen on the terminal side of A. (Let
$P = (s, t)$, $P' = (s', t')$ be any two
points on the terminal side of A.
Argue first that $s \cdot s' \geq 0$ and $t \cdot t' \geq$
0. If $Q = (s, 0)$ and $Q' = (s', 0)$,
argue that triangles OPQ and $OP'Q'$
are similar.)

III.3 RIGHT TRIANGLES

Let A, B, C be vertices of a right triangle, with the right angle located at C, and
let α, β denote the acute angles (or their measures) at A and B respectively, as in
Figure 1. Let a, b, and c denote the lengths of the sides of the triangle opposite
A, B, and C respectively.

We introduce a coordinate system in the plane, say the ST system, so that angle
α is a positive angle in standard position and B is in the first quadrant. Then the
point B is on the terminal side of α at a distance c (the length of the hypotenuse)
from the origin and has coordinates (b, a). The definition then gives

$$\sin \alpha = \frac{a}{c} = \frac{\text{opposite side}}{\text{hypotenuse}} \qquad \csc \alpha = \frac{c}{a} = \frac{\text{hypotenuse}}{\text{opposite side}}$$

$$\cos \alpha = \frac{b}{c} = \frac{\text{adjacent side}}{\text{hypotenuse}} \qquad \sec \alpha = \frac{c}{b} = \frac{\text{hypotenuse}}{\text{adjacent side}}$$

$$\tan \alpha = \frac{a}{b} = \frac{\text{opposite side}}{\text{adjacent side}} \qquad \cot \alpha = \frac{b}{a} = \frac{\text{adjacent side}}{\text{opposite side}}$$

It is clear that similar statements can be made about the values of the trigonometric
functions at the angle B. If the lengths of two sides of a right triangle or the length

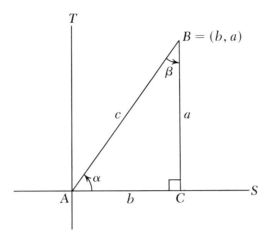

Figure 1

of one side and the measure of one of the nonright angles are known, these formulas can be used to determine the lengths of the remaining sides and measures of the other angles with the aid of a table listing approximate values of these functions. Indeed, by constructing triangles and measuring lengths of sides one can approximate the values of the trigonometric functions for acute angles. Such approximations, however, are too crude for most purposes, so different characterizations of these functions are used to construct tables.

There are several special angles for which the exact values of the trigonometric functions can easily be computed with the aid of right triangles. Thus, for a 45° angle we construct a right triangle with sides having length 1 so the hypotenuse has length $\sqrt{2}$ as in Figure 2. Then $\sin 45° = 1/\sqrt{2}$, $\cos 45° = 1/\sqrt{2}$, and $\tan 45° = 1/1 = 1$. Similarly,

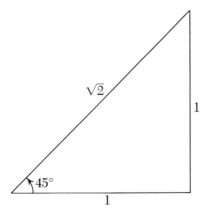

Figure 2

we construct a right triangle with acute angles of 30° and 60° by making the hypotenuse twice as long as the side opposite the 30° angle. Thus, as in Figure 3, we make the

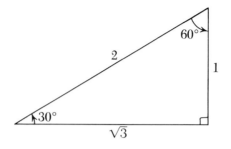

Figure 3

hypotenuse have length 2 and the side opposite the 30° angle have length 1, so the side opposite the 60° angle has length $\sqrt{3}$ by the Pythagorean Theorem. By inspection then,

$$\sin 30° = \cos 60° = 1/2. \qquad \sin 60° = \cos 30° = \sqrt{3}/2.$$
$$\tan 30° = \cot 60° = 1/\sqrt{3}. \qquad \tan 60° = \cot 30° = \sqrt{3}.$$
$$\sec 30° = \csc 60° = 2/\sqrt{3}. \qquad \sec 60° = \csc 30° = 2.$$

As one further illustration, we compute the tangent of an acute angle whose sine is $\tfrac{1}{8}$. Draw a right triangle ABC for which $\sin A = \tfrac{1}{8}$, by making the hypotenuse have length 8 and the side opposite A have length 1, as in Figure 4. Then the side adjacent

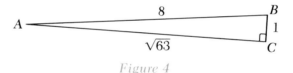

Figure 4

to A must have length $\sqrt{8^2 - 1} = \sqrt{63}$, and hence $\tan A = 1/\sqrt{63}$.

This characterization of the trigonometric functions for acute angles in a right triangle is especially convenient for "solving" right triangles. A triangle is said to be solved if the measure of each of its angles and the length of each of its sides is known.

EXAMPLE 1

Solve the triangle ABC in Figure 5 if $\beta = 52°$ and $b = 10$.

First, $\alpha = 90° - 52° = 38°$. Now, $\cot \beta = a/b$, so $a = 10 \cot 52°$. From the table on page 318,

$$\cot 52° \doteq .781.$$

Therefore, $a \doteq 7.81$. Similarly, $\csc \beta = c/b$, so $c = 10 \csc 52°$. Then, with the aid of the table again, $c \doteq 12.69$.

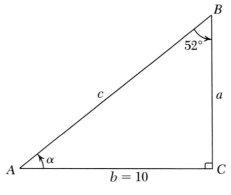

Figure 5

EXAMPLE 2

Determine the height of a vertical pole if the angle of elevation of its top is 73° when measured from a point 15 feet from its base.

   From Figure 6 we have

$$\tan 73° = h/15$$
$$h = 15 \cdot \tan 73° \doteq 15(3.271) = 49.065.$$

Hence, the height of the pole is approximately 49 feet.

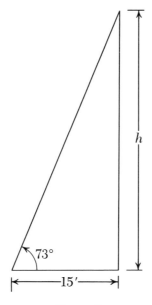

Figure 6

EXAMPLE 3

What is the smallest ball that can roll in a groove formed by straight sides at an angle of 80° if a clearance of at least 0.3 inches between the ball and the point of the groove is required?

Clearly the smallest ball will be that for which the clearance is exactly 0.3 in. Thus, let r be the radius of this ball and consider the cross section shown in Figure 7.

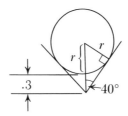

Figure 7

The geometry of the situation ensures us that r is the length of the side opposite a 40° angle in a right triangle with a hypotenuse of length $r + 0.3$.

Therefore, we obtain the equation

$$\sin 40° = \frac{r}{r + 0.3}.$$

With the help of a table of values for the trigonometric functions we find $\sin 40° \doteq 0.643$. We then solve the above equation to obtain

$$r \doteq 0.54 \text{ inches.}$$

Exercises

1. Solve the right triangle ABC as drawn in Figure 1 if
   (a) $\alpha = 30°$, $a = 12$.
   (b) $\alpha = 47°$, $c = 6$.
   (c) $\beta = 80°$, $a = 100$.
   (d) $\beta = 25°$, $c = 40$.
   (e) $\alpha = 20°$, $b = 9$.
   (f) $\beta = 75°$, $b = 4$.

2. In the right triangle ABC of Figure 1 show that each statement is true.
   (a) $a = c \sin \alpha = c \cos \beta = b \cot \beta$
       $= b \tan \alpha$
   (b) $b = c \sin \beta = c \cos \alpha = a \cot \alpha$
       $= a \tan \beta$.
   (c) $c = a \csc \alpha = b \sec \alpha = a \sec \beta$
       $= b \csc \beta$

III.4 REFERENCE ANGLES

It is possible to determine the values of the trigonometric functions of an arbitrary angle using right triangles if we recall the algebraic sign of these functions in each quadrant. Given an angle A in standard position, there corresponds a positive acute angle formed by the terminal side of A and the horizontal axis. This angle is called the **reference angle** for A and will be written $r(A)$. Figure 1 shows several angles and the associated reference angles.

If $P = (s, t)$ is any point on the terminal side of A, then OQP, where Q is the projection of P on the horizontal axis, is a right triangle containing the reference angle $r(A)$. It is clear that the value of any trigonometric function at A is in absolute value the same as that function evaluated at $r(A)$. (See Figure 2.)

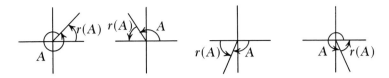

Figure 1

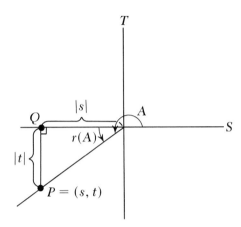

Figure 2

EXAMPLE 1

Find the value of each trigonometric function at an angle with measure 210°.
  In this case the reference angle has measure 30°. (See Figure 3.) Hence,

$$|\sin 210°| = \sin 30° = 1/2.$$

But 210° is in the third quadrant where the sine function is negative. Therefore,

$$\sin 210° = -\sin 30° = -1/2.$$

Similarly,

$$\cos 210° = -\cos 30° = -\sqrt{3}/2,$$
$$\tan 210° = \tan 30° = 1/\sqrt{3},$$
$$\cot 210° = \cot 30° = \sqrt{3},$$
$$\sec 210° = -\sec 30° = -2/\sqrt{3},$$

and

$$\csc 210° = -\csc 30° = -2.$$

EXAMPLE 2

Compute $\sin 315°$ and $\cos 315°$.

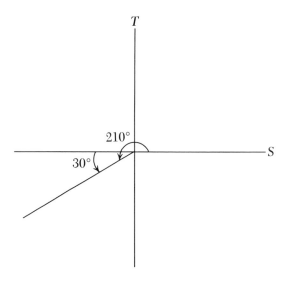

Figure 3

The given angle is in the fourth quadrant where the sine function is negative and the cosine function is positive. The reference angle here has measure 45°. Therefore,

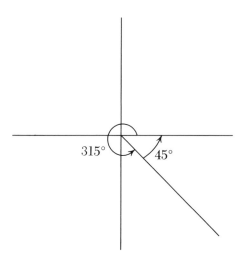

Figure 4

$$\sin 315° = -\sin 45° = -1/\sqrt{2},$$
$$\cos 315° = \cos 45° = 1/\sqrt{2}.$$

This use of reference angles enables us to evaluate the trigonometric functions at any angle (at least approximately) with a table of values of these functions for angles between 0° and 90°.

Exercises

1. For each angle whose measure is given below, state the measure of the associated reference angle.
   (a) 30°
   (b) −225°
   (c) −150°
   (d) 240°
   (e) 120°
   (f) 300°
   (g) 360°
   (h) −315°
   (i) $7\pi/4$ rad
   (j) $16\pi/3$ rad
   (k) $3\pi/2$ rad
   (l) $683\pi/6$ rad
   (m) 216°

   (n) −5 rad
   (o) 461°
   (p) 152°
   (q) −78°
   (r) $13\pi/18$ rad

2. Without referring to tables or previous work, evaluate each trigonometric function at each of the angles of parts (a) through (l) in Exercise 1.

3. Use the table at the end of this Appendix to find approximate values of the trigonometric functions at the angles in parts (m) through (r) of Exercise 1.

III.5 SOLUTION OF TRIANGLES

Recall that to solve a triangle means to find the measure of each angle and the length of each side of the triangle. Given any triangle, it is possible to consider it as being made up of one or more right triangles, and if sufficient information is at hand, to solve the triangle by repeated use of the methods discussed in Section 3 for right triangles.

It is more convenient, however, to have techniques that apply to all triangles. The results of the two theorems given below apply to arbitrary triangles and make it possible to solve any triangle for which enough information is known. When we refer to a triangle *ABC* it will always be assumed to be labeled as in Figure 1.

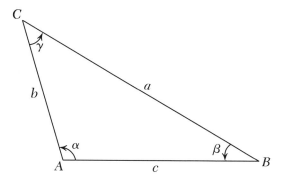

Figure 1

Law of Cosines

In any triangle ABC

(i) $a^2 = b^2 + c^2 - 2bc \cos \alpha$
(ii) $b^2 = a^2 + c^2 - 2ac \cos \beta$
(iii) $c^2 = a^2 + b^2 - 2ab \cos \gamma$

PROOF

Put a coordinate system in the plane as shown in Figure 2 so that $A = (0, 0)$, $B = (c, 0)$

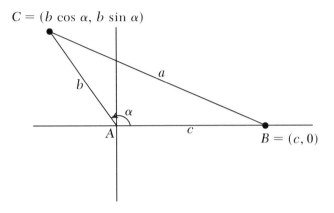

Figure 2

and $C = (b \cos \alpha, b \sin \alpha)$. We now use the distance formula and compute the distance between the points B and C, which is also the length a of the side opposite A to obtain

$$a = \sqrt{(b \cos \alpha - c)^2 + (b \sin \alpha)^2}.$$

Part (i) follows by squaring and simplifying this equation. Parts (ii) and (iii) are obtained by coordinatizing the plane so that angle β and angle γ, respectively, are in standard position and proceeding as above.

Law of Sines

In any triangle ABC, the lengths of the sides are proportional to the sines of the opposite angles. That is,

$$\frac{a}{\sin \alpha} = \frac{b}{\sin \beta} = \frac{c}{\sin \gamma}.$$

PROOF

First, introduce a coordinate system in the plane as in Figure 3 and drop a perpendicular from C to the horizontal axis at point D. If h is the vertical coordinate of

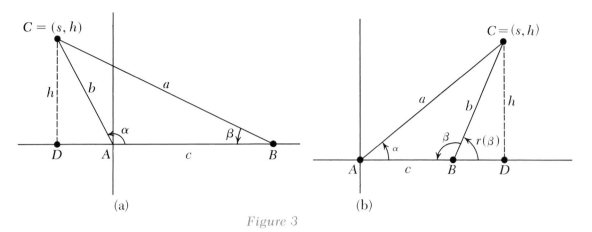

Figure 3

the point C, then h is the length of the side of the right triangle BCD (that is either opposite angle β, as in Figure 3(a), or opposite the reference angle $r(\beta)$, as in Figure 3(b). In the first case, $h = a \sin \beta$; in the second case, $h = a \sin r(\beta) = a \sin (\beta)$. Therefore, $h = a \sin \beta$. From the definition of the sine function, $\sin \alpha = h/b$ or equivalently, $h = b \sin \alpha$. Equating the two expressions for h and dividing by ab we obtain $a/\sin \alpha = b/\sin \beta$. The other equation can be obtained in the same manner by placing γ in standard position.

EXAMPLE 1

Solve the triangle ABC if $\alpha = 40°$, $\beta = 65°$, and $c = 12$.

Since the sum of the measures of the angles of a triangle is $180°$, $\gamma = 180° - (40 + 65)° = 75°$. From the Law of Sines,

$$a = \frac{c \sin \alpha}{\sin \gamma} = \frac{12 \sin 40°}{\sin 75°} \doteq \frac{12(.643)}{.966} \doteq 8.0.$$

Similarly,

$$b = \frac{c \sin \beta}{\sin \gamma} = \frac{12 \sin 65°}{\sin 75°} \doteq \frac{12(.906)}{.966} \doteq 11.3.$$

EXAMPLE 2

Solve triangle ABC if $a = 4$, $b = 7$, $c = 10$.

From the Law of Cosines,

$$\cos \alpha = \frac{b^2 + c^2 - a^2}{2bc} = \frac{49 + 100 - 16}{2 \cdot 7 \cdot 10} = \frac{133}{140} = .950$$

Hence, from the tables, $\alpha \doteq 18°$.

From the Law of Sines,

$$\sin \beta = \frac{b \sin \alpha}{a} = \frac{7 \sin 18°}{4} \doteq \frac{7(.309)}{4} \doteq .541,$$

so

$$\beta \doteq 33°.$$

Finally, $\gamma \doteq 180° - (18 + 33)° = 129°$.

EXAMPLE 3

Find the length of the chord of a circle having radius r if it is subtended by a central angle $\theta°$.

From Figure 4 we see that the Law of Cosines is applicable.

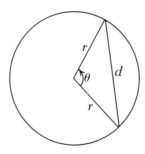

Figure 4

$$d^2 = r^2 + r^2 - 2 \cdot r \cdot r \cdot \cos \theta$$
$$= (2 - 2 \cos \theta)r^2.$$

Hence,
$$d = r\sqrt{2 - 2 \cos \theta}.$$

Exercises

1. Solve triangle ABC (if possible) for each of the following.
   (a) $\alpha = 27°$, $\beta = 74°$, $a = 16$
   (b) $\beta = 62°$, $\gamma = 42°$, $a = 24$
   (c) $\beta = 45°$, $\gamma = 99°$, $c = 120$
   (d) $\beta = 95°$, $a = 4$, $b = 7$
   (e) $\alpha = 109°$, $a = 11$, $b = 17$
   (f) $\gamma = 65°$, $b = 32$, $c = 30$
   (g) $a = 20$, $b = 30$, $c = 40$
   (h) $a = 8$, $b = 12$, $c = 9$
   (i) $a = 145$, $b = 145$, $c = 200$

2. The radius of a circle is 3 inches. Find the angle subtended at the center by a chord 2 inches long.

3. Two angles of a triangle are 70° and 65° and the radius of the inscribed circle is 5 inches. Find the lengths of the sides of the triangle.

4. The hands of a clock are 2.2 inches and 1.7 inches long, respectively. How far apart are their tips when the time is 2:25 P.M.?

5. Two chords from a point P on a circle have lengths 2 feet and 3 feet respectively, and the angle between them is 96°. Find the radius of the circle.

III.6 RELATIONSHIPS BETWEEN THE TRIGONOMETRIC FUNCTIONS

We list below the most frequently used relationships between the trigonometric functions. The derivation and application of these formulas is given in Chapter 5 and will not be duplicated here.

Each equation is true for all angles A and B for which each side is meaningful.

BASIC FORMULAS

$\sin A \csc A = 1$

$\cos A \sec A = 1$

$\tan A \cot A = 1$

$\tan A = \sin A / \cos A$

$\cot A = \cos A / \sin A$

$\sin^2 A + \cos^2 A = 1$

$1 + \tan^2 A = \sec^2 A$

$\cot^2 A + 1 = \csc^2 A$

REDUCTION FORMULAS

$\sin (90° - A) = \cos A$

$\cos (90° - A) = \sin A$

$\tan (90° - A) = \cot A$

$\sin (180° - A) = \sin A$

$\cos (180° - A) = -\cos A$

$\tan (180° - A) = -\tan A$

$\sin (-A) = -\sin A$

$\cos (-A) = \cos A$

$\tan (-A) = -\tan A$

$\sin (90° + A) = \cos A$

$\cos (90° + A) = -\sin A$

$\tan (90° + A) = -\cot A$

$\sin (180° + A) = -\sin A$

$\cos (180° + A) = -\cos A$

$\tan (180° + A) = \tan A$

$\sin (360° + A) = \sin A$

$\cos (360° + A) = \cos A$

$\tan (360° + A) = \tan A$

ADDITION FORMULAS

$\sin (A + B) = \sin A \cos B + \cos A \sin B$

$\sin (A - B) = \sin A \cos B - \cos A \sin B$

$\cos (A + B) = \cos A \cos B - \sin A \sin B$

$\cos (A - B) = \cos A \cos B + \sin A \sin B$

$$\tan (A + B) = \frac{\tan A + \tan B}{1 - \tan A \tan B}$$

$$\tan (A - B) = \frac{\tan A - \tan B}{1 + \tan A \tan B}$$

DOUBLE-ANGLE FORMULAS

$\sin 2A = 2 \sin A \cos A$

$\cos 2A = \cos^2 A - \sin^2 A$

$\qquad = 2 \cos^2 A - 1$

$\qquad = 1 - 2 \sin^2 A$

$$\tan 2A = \frac{2 \tan A}{1 - \tan^2 A}$$

HALF-ANGLE FORMULAS

$$\sin^2 A/2 = \frac{1 - \cos A}{2}$$

$$\cos^2 A/2 = \frac{1 + \cos A}{2}$$

$$\tan A/2 = \frac{1 - \cos A}{\sin A}$$

$$\qquad = \frac{\sin A}{1 + \cos A}$$

TABLE OF APPROXIMATE VALUES OF TRIGONOMETRIC FUNCTIONS*

Deg.	Sin	Tan	Sec	Csc	Cot	Cos	Deg.
0°	.000	.000	1.000	——	——	1.000	90°
1°	.017	.017	1.000	57.30	57.29	1.000	89°
2°	.035	.035	1.001	28.65	28.64	0.999	88°
3°	.052	.052	1.001	19.11	19.08	.999	87°
4°	.070	.070	1.002	14.34	14.30	.998	86°
5°	.087	.087	1.004	11.47	11.43	.996	85°
6°	.105	.105	1.006	9.567	9.514	.995	84°
7°	.122	.123	1.008	8.206	8.144	.993	83°
8°	.139	.141	1.010	7.185	7.115	.990	82°
9°	.156	.158	1.012	6.392	6.314	.988	81°
10°	.174	.176	1.015	5.759	5.671	.985	80°
11°	.191	.194	1.019	5.241	5.145	.982	79°
12°	.208	.213	1.022	4.810	4.705	.978	78°
13°	.225	.231	1.026	4.445	4.331	.974	77°
14°	.242	.249	1.031	4.134	4.011	.970	76°
15°	.259	.268	1.035	3.864	3.732	.966	75°
16°	.276	.287	1.040	3.628	3.487	.961	74°
17°	.292	.306	1.046	3.420	3.271	.956	73°
18°	.309	.325	1.051	3.236	3.078	.951	72°
19°	.326	.344	1.058	3.072	2.904	.946	71°
20°	.342	.364	1.064	2.924	2.747	.940	70°
21°	.358	.384	1.071	2.790	2.605	.934	69°
22°	.375	.404	1.079	2.669	2.475	.927	68°
23°	.391	.424	1.086	2.559	2.356	.921	67°
24°	.407	.445	1.095	2.459	2.246	.914	66°
25°	.423	.466	1.103	2.366	2.145	.906	65°
26°	.438	.488	1.113	2.281	2.050	.899	64°
27°	.454	.510	1.122	2.203	1.963	.891	63°
28°	.469	.532	1.133	2.130	1.881	.883	62°
29°	.485	.554	1.143	2.063	1.804	.875	61°
30°	.500	.577	1.155	2.000	1.732	.866	60°
31°	.515	.601	1.167	1.942	1.664	.857	59°
32°	.530	.625	1.179	1.887	1.600	.848	58°
33°	.545	.649	1.192	1.836	1.540	.839	57°
34°	.559	.675	1.206	1.788	1.483	.829	56°
35°	.574	.700	1.221	1.743	1.428	.819	55°
36°	.588	.727	1.236	1.701	1.376	.809	54°
37°	.602	.754	1.252	1.662	1.327	.799	53°
38°	.616	.781	1.269	1.624	1.280	.788	52°
39°	.629	.810	1.287	1.589	1.235	.777	51°
40°	.643	.839	1.305	1.556	1.192	.766	50°
41°	.656	.869	1.325	1.524	1.150	.755	49°
42°	.669	.900	1.346	1.494	1.111	.743	48°
43°	.682	.933	1.367	1.466	1.072	.731	47°
44°	.695	0.966	1.390	1.440	1.036	.719	46°
45°	.707	1.000	1.414	1.414	1.000	.707	45°
Deg.	Cos	Cot	Csc	Sec	Tan	Sin	Deg.

*Use left-hand column and top headings for angles between 0° and 45°. Use right-hand column and bottom headings for angles between 45° and 90°.

FROM: William L. Hart, *Contemporary College Algebra and Trigonometry*. Boston, D. C. Heath and Company, © 1967.

ANSWERS TO SELECTED
TEXT EXERCISES

Section 1.1

2. (a) $\{x : x \text{ is a real number and } x^3 = -3\}$ $\{y : y \text{ is a real number and } y^3 + 3 = 0\}$

(c) $\{x : x \text{ is an integral multiple of } 3\}$ $\{a : \text{For some integer } n, a = 3n\}$

(e) $\{x : x \text{ is a real number and } x^2 - 1 = 0\}$ $\{y : y = 1 \text{ or } y = -1\}$

(g) $\left\{z : z = 1 \text{ or } z = 3 \text{ or } z = -\dfrac{5}{2}\right\}$

$\{y : y \text{ is a real number and } (y-1)(y-3)(2y+5) = 0\}$

3. (a) (i), (ii), (v), (vi), (vii), and (ix) belong to A. All belong to B. (ii), (vi), and (ix) belong to C.

(c) $r \in B$ means r is a real number.

4. (a) $A \subset B$; **(c)** $A \subset B$; **(e)** none; **(g)** $A \subset B$ and $B \subset A$ and $A = B$.

5. (a) $\left\{-\dfrac{1}{6}\right\}$; **(c)** $\left\{-\dfrac{13}{18}\right\}$; **(e)** $\left\{\dfrac{1}{2}, -\dfrac{4}{5}\right\}$; **(g)** $\left\{-\dfrac{1}{3}, 2\right\}$; **(i)** $\{-3\}$

6. (a) $A \subset B$; **(c)** $A \subset B$.

7. (a) $\left\{x : \dfrac{x^4 - 1}{x - 1} = 0\right\} = \{-1\}$

(c) $\left\{p : \dfrac{5}{p-3} + \dfrac{4}{(p-3)^2} = 6\right\} = \left\{\dfrac{13}{3}, \dfrac{5}{2}\right\}$

(e) $\left\{a : \dfrac{1}{1 + \dfrac{1}{a}} = \dfrac{a}{a+1}\right\} = \{a : a \neq 0 \text{ and } a \neq -1\}$

(g) $\left\{t : \dfrac{3}{t} - \dfrac{4}{t^2} = -1\right\} = \{1, -4\}$

(i) $\{c : 1 - c + 2(1-c)^2 = 3\} = \left\{0, \dfrac{5}{2}\right\}$

(k) $\left\{y : \dfrac{y-1}{y-2} \div \left(1 - \dfrac{1}{y^2}\right) = 1\right\} = \{-2\}$

8. No.

9. Yes. $\{t : t \text{ is real and } \sqrt{t^2} = -t\} = \{t : t \text{ is real and } t \leq 0\}$

11. 0 and -1.

12. 0.

14. (a) $x = 0$ and $y = 1$, or $x = \dfrac{1}{2}$ and $y = 0$.

    (c) $x = 4$ and $y = -2$, or $x = -4$ and $y = 2$.

Section 1.2

2. (a) $x - y < 0$; (c) $c + d - (a - p) \geq 0$; (g) $x + \sqrt{2} + d > 0$ and $x + \sqrt{2} - d < 0$.

3. (a) $x - y > 0$; (d) $r + (-s) \geq 0$; (f) If $b - a > 0$, then $\dfrac{a + 2b}{3} - \dfrac{2a + b}{3} > 0$.

4. (b) $1 - (-6) = 7$ and $7 \geq 0$.

    (d) $\dfrac{22}{7} - 3.14 = \dfrac{22 - 21.98}{7} = \dfrac{.02}{7} > 0$.

5. (a) True, since $\dfrac{10}{3} - 3 = \dfrac{10 - 9}{3} = \dfrac{1}{3} > 0$.

    (d) True, since $\dfrac{1}{3} - .333 = \dfrac{1 - .999}{3} = \dfrac{.001}{3} > 0$.

    (f) False, since $\dfrac{1{,}709}{183} - \dfrac{28}{3} = \dfrac{5{,}127 - 5{,}124}{549} = \dfrac{3}{549} > 0$.

6. If $a \in R$, $b \in R$, and $b > 0$, then, $(a + b) - a = b > 0$, so $a < a + b$.

8. The converse of this statement is "if $z > -1$, then $z + 1 > 0$," and it is true.

11. Suppose $a > 0$ and $b < 0$. Then also $-b > 0$, so $-ab = a(-b) > 0$, by Property 02. Hence, $ab < 0$.

13. The corresponding statements for quotients are

    (a) If c/d is positive, then either c and d are both positive or both negative.

    (b) If c/d is negative, then either c is positive and d is negative, or c is negative and d is positive.

15. Statement is false. Let $a = -3$, $b = -2$. Then $a < b$, but $a \not< 2b$.

18. No, because if x is any number greater than 2, then also $\dfrac{x + 2}{2} > 2$, but $\dfrac{x + 2}{2} < x$.

Section 1.3

2. (a) $\{x : x < 4\}$; (c) $\{s : s > 10\}$; (e) $\{x : x < 1\}$; (g) $\{x : 0 < x < 2\}$.

3. (a) $\{x : x < -3 \text{ or } x > -2\}$; (d) $\{x : x < 2\}$; (g) $\{x : x = 1\}$; (i) $\{x : x \leq 1\}$;

    (j) $\{x : 1 < x < 2 \text{ or } x > 3\}$.

7. (b) $-17 < -5x - 2 < -7$; (d) $-3 < x^2 - 4 < 5$; (e) $-11 < 3x^2 + 2x - 16 < 17$.

8. (b) $-1.46 < -6x^2 + 2x + 4 < 1.34$; (c) $-\dfrac{1}{11} < \dfrac{1}{x} - 1 < \dfrac{1}{9}$; (d) $-\dfrac{21}{121} < \dfrac{1}{x^2} - 1 < \dfrac{19}{81}$.

11. (a) $x < 0$ or $x > \dfrac{1}{100}$; (e) $x < -\sqrt{1{,}001}$, or $-1 < x < 1$, or $x > \sqrt{1{,}001}$.

12. All are true, except Exercise 9 and the "if" part of parts (iii) and (iv) of Theorem 1.3.1.

13. $A = 10.20$ sq. in. with an error of at most $.032725$ sq. in.

Section 1.4

2. (a) 5; (c) 12; (e) $\left| \dfrac{1}{x(x + 1)} \right|$; (g) $\dfrac{1}{221}$.

3. (a) $\{-4, 2\}$; (c) $\{5, 7\}$; (e) $\left\{ -\dfrac{8}{3}, \dfrac{16}{3} \right\}$.

4. (b) $\{-1, 0\}$; **(d)** $\varnothing$; **(e)** $\{2, 4\}$.

5. (a) $\{x: x \geq 3\}$; **(c)** $\{a: a \leq 2\}$; **(e)** $\left\{b: b \leq -\dfrac{3}{4}\right\}$; **(g)** R.

10. $|x^2| = x^2$; $|(-x)^2| = |x^2| = x^2$; $|-x^2| = |x^2| = x^2$.

11. (a) No. Take $x = -2$, $y = -1$. Then $-2 = x < y = -1$, but $2 = |x| \not< |y| = 1$.

(b) No. If $x = 1$, $y = -2$, then $1 = |x| < |y| = 2$, but $1 = x \not< y = -2$.

Section 1.5

2. (c) $\{x: -3 < x < 0 \text{ and } -4 \leq x \leq -2\} = \{x: -3 < x \leq -2\} = (-3, -2]$

(d) $\{x: -3 < x < 0 \text{ or } -4 \leq x \leq -2\} = \{x: -4 \leq x < 0\} = [-4, 0)$

(g) $\{x: x < 1 \text{ or } x \geq 3, \text{ and } -2 \leq x < 0 \text{ or } 2 < x < 5\} = \{x: -2 \leq x < 0 \text{ or } 3 \leq x < 5\}$.

(h) $\{x: 0 \leq x \leq 2 \text{ and } x < 1, \text{ or } x \geq 3 \text{ and } x > 4\} = \{x: 0 \leq x < 1 \text{ or } x > 4\}$.

3. (d) $(-3, 3]$; **(f)** $[2, 3)$; **(g)** $\{a: a \leq 0 \text{ or } a \geq 6\}$

4. R.

8. The set of numbers not belonging to the set is
$\{x: 0 < x < 2 \text{ and } |x + 3| \geq 4\} = [1, 2)$

Section 1.6

2. (a) $\left\{\dfrac{1}{3}\right\}$; **(c)** $\varnothing$; **(e)** $\left\{-\dfrac{3}{4}, \dfrac{1}{2}\right\}$; **(g)** $\{1\}$; **(i)** $\left\{t: -\dfrac{2}{3} \leq t \leq \dfrac{1}{5}\right\}$.

3. (a) $\left\{x: x < \dfrac{1}{2}\right\}$; **(c)** $\left\{x: \dfrac{1}{5} \leq x \leq \dfrac{1}{3}\right\}$; **(e)** $\{c: c \geq 0\}$; **(g)** $\{t: t < -3\}$.

4. $\{x: -3 \leq x \leq 1 \text{ or } x > 2\}$.

5. False. Take $x = -2$, $y = 2$. Then $|x - y| = |-2 - 2| = |-4| = 4$
but $|x + y| = |-2 + 2| = |0| = 0$.

7. All numbers x, y for which $xy \geq 0$.

Section 1.7

2. (a) $2|x - 1| + 5$; **(b)** $|x - 1| + 1$; **(c)** $3|x - 1| + 7$; **(d)** $|x - 1| (3|x - 1| + 7)$.

4. (a) $|x + 2| (3|x + 2| + 11)$; **(c)** $d = \dfrac{1}{200}$, or any smaller positive number.

5. (a) $2\left|x - \dfrac{1}{2}\right| \left(\left|x - \dfrac{1}{2}\right| + \dfrac{7}{2}\right)$.

6. $d = .0003$, or any smaller positive number.

8. $|x^2 - x + 1| \leq |x + 1|^2 + 3|x + 1| + 3$.

Section 2.1

1. (a) $3\sqrt{2}$; **(c)** $\sqrt{\pi^2 - 8\pi + 20}$.

3. (b) $D = (-2, 4)$.

4. (c) (i) $|b|$; **(ii)** $|a|$.

5. (a) (i) $\{(x, y): y = -5\}$; **(ii)** $\{(x, y): x = 2\}$;

(c) (i) $\{(x, y): y = 0\}$; **(ii)** $\{(x, y): x = 7\}$.

6. The point $(0, 37/8)$.

7. The point $(17/2, -11/2)$.

11. (b) 5; **(d)** $U = (1, -3)$, $S = (-2, 6)$; **(e)** The points $(4, 6)$ and $(4, -2)$.

13. (c) The point $(-2/5, -1/5)$.

14. $\{(x, y): x^2 + y^2 = 1\}$

15. (a) $|PF| = \sqrt{(x - 1)^2 + y^2}$; **(b)** $|x + 1|$; **(c)** $\sqrt{(x - 1)^2 + y^2} = |x + 1|$;

(d) $S = \{(x, y): y^2 = 4x\}$.

17. $\mathcal{H} = \{(x, y): x^2 - y^2/3 = 1\}$

Section 2.2

(c)

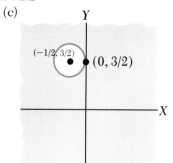

(d)

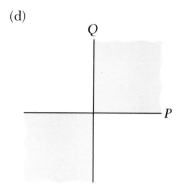

(f)

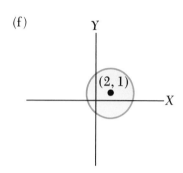

(h)

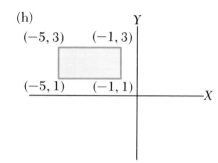

2. (a) $\{(x, y) : |x| < 1 \text{ and } |y| < 1\}$
   (b) $\{(a, b) : (a - 2)^2 + (b - 2)^2 = 4\}$
   (d) $\{(s, t) : \text{if} -1 < s < 0, \text{then } |t| \le 1\}$
3. (a) $|x| < 1$ and $|y| < 1$, in the XY plane.
   (b) $(a - 2)^2 + (b - 2)^2 = 4$, in the AB plane.
   (d) If $-1 < s < 0$, then $|t| \le 1$, in the ST plane.
4. (b) (i) $(x + \frac{1}{2})^2 + (y - \frac{1}{4})^2 = 4$
       (ii) $(s + \frac{1}{2})^2 + (t - \frac{1}{4})^2 = 4$
       (iii) $(z + \frac{1}{2})^2 + (w - \frac{1}{4})^2 = 4$
   (e) (i) $x = 0$; (ii) $s = 0$; (iii) $z = 0$.

6. (a)

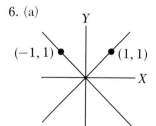

(b)

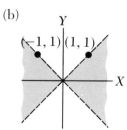

(c)

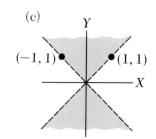

8. (a)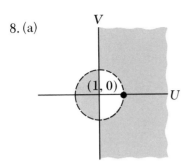

(b)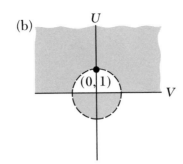

11. (b)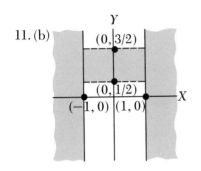

(d)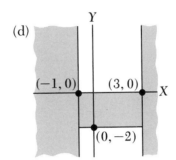

Section 2.3

1. (b) $q = 27(p - 5)$; (c) $s + 5 = \frac{5}{4}(t + 6)$; (f) $y - 11/5 = (\pi/2)(x + 14/5)$.
2. (b) Slope $-\frac{2}{5}$, vertical intercept $\frac{7}{5}$.
    (c) Slope $-\frac{5}{2}$, vertical intercept $\frac{7}{2}$.
    (f) Slope 0, vertical intercept $\frac{13}{4}$.

3. (b)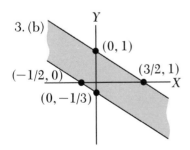

(d)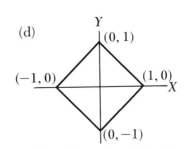

(e)

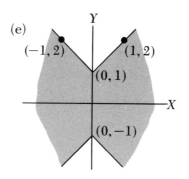

5. $P = (1, -4)$, or $P = (3, -2)$, or $P = (-1, 4)$.

6. (b)

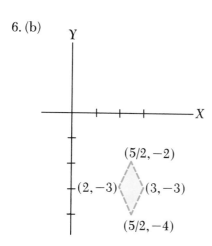

(d)

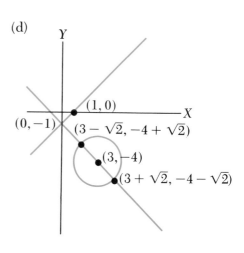

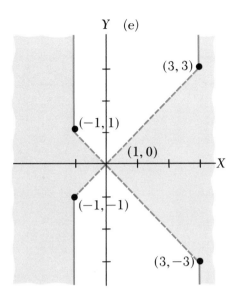

7. (a) $0 \le x \le 1$ and $0 \le y \le -2x + 2$ in the XY plane.
   (c) $y > -3x - 5$ and $y < -\frac{1}{5}x + \frac{3}{5}$ and $y \ge {}_2x - \frac{3}{2}$ in the XY plane.
   (d) $x^2 + (y + 2)^2 \le 10$ and $y \le 3x - 2$ in the XY plane.

8. (b) The point $\left(-\frac{1}{5}, \frac{21}{10}\right)$.
   (c) The point $\left(\dfrac{B^2x_0 - ABy_0 - AC}{A^2 + B^2}, \dfrac{A^2y_0 - ABx_0 - BC}{A^2 + B^2}\right)$.

9. $5(x + 2)^2 + 5(y - 3)^2 = 144$.

10. The lines are $12x + 5y - 65 = 0$, and $12x - 5y + 65 = 0$ in the XY plane.

11. (c) $\{L_r : r \in R\}$ is the set of all lines in the XY plane having slope $-\frac{2}{3}$.

Section 2.4

1. (a) (i) $(-1, -3)$ (ii) $(-1, 3)$ (iii) $(1, -3)$.
   (c) (i) $(0, 4)$ (ii) $(0, -4)$ (iii) $(0, 4)$.

2. (a)

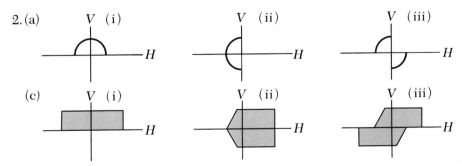

3. (b) Yes.

6. (d) (i) 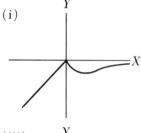   (ii)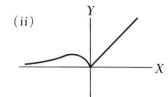

(iii) 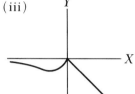   (iv)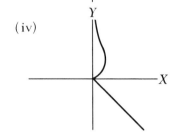

8. (a) (i) $-2x + 3y + 1 = 0$,   **(ii)** $2x - 3y + 1 = 0$,
       (iii) $2x + 3y - 1 = 0$,   **(iv)** $3x + 2y + 1 = 0$.

Section 2.5

1. (b) Horizontal intercept 0; vertical intercept 0; $E_H = \{u : u \geq 0\}$; $E_V = R$; symmetry with respect to horizontal axis.

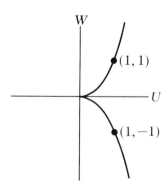

(d) Horizontal intercepts 0, ± 3; vertical intercept 0; $E_H = [-3, 3]$; $E_V \subset [-9, 9]$, since $\sqrt{9 - x^2} \leq 3$ if $|x| \leq 3$ (actually, $E_V = [-\tfrac{9}{2}, \tfrac{9}{2}]$); symmetry with respect to $(0, 0)$.

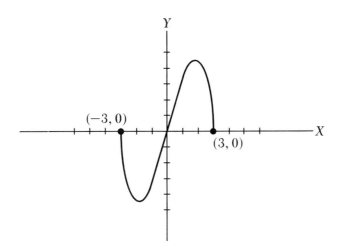

(h) No horizontal intercept; vertical intercepts ± 2; $E_H = R$; $E_V = \{y: |y| > 2\}$; symmetry with respect to both axes and $(0, 0)$:

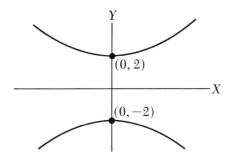

2. (i) $x \in E_H$ means that the equation $(x - 3)^2 + 4(y + 1)^2 = 4$ is satisfied by at least one number y. This equation can be written $4(y + 1)^2 = 4 - (x - 3)^2$, which can be solved for y if, and only if, $4 - (x - 3)^2 \geq 0$, *i.e.*, $|x - 3| \leq 2$.
(ii) $y \in E_V$ means that the equation $(x - 3)^2 + 4(y + 1)^2 = 4$ is satisfied by at least one number x. The equation can be written $(x - 3)^2 = 4 - 4(y + 1)^2$, which can be solved for x if, and only if, $4 - 4(y + 1)^2 \geq 0$, *i.e.*, $|y + 1| \leq 1$.

Section 2.6

1. (a) (i) $(3, 2)_{UV}$; (ii) $(-8, 14)_{XY}$; (vi) $(a + 3, \, a + 2)_{UV}$; (ix) $(d - 3, \, d^3 - 2)_{XY}$.
    (b) (i) $u = 5$; (iii) $u - 3 = v - 2$; (vi) $(u - 3)(v - 2) = 1$;
       (viii) $v - 2 = (u - 3)^2 + (v - 2)(u - 3) + 7$.
    (c) (i) $x = -3$; (ii) $(x + 3)^2 + 5(y + 2)^2 - 6(x + 3) - 20(y + 2) + 28 = 0$.

2. (b)

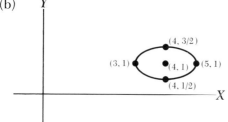

(d)

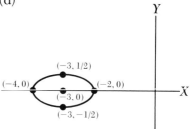

3. (a)

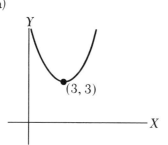

(c)

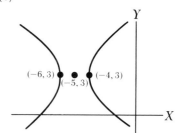

(f)

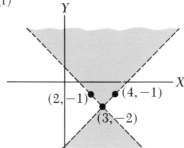

4. (a) The ST plane is a translation of the XY plane with $(0, 0)_{ST} = (3, 3)_{XY}$.

6. (a) First quadrant in the ST plane is the graph of the condition $x - h > 0$ and $y - k > 0$ in the XY plane.

  (b) (i) $x - h > 0$; (iv) $y - k < 0$.

  (c) In XY plane, $E_H = \{x : |x - h| \leq 2\}$, $E_V = \{y : |y - k| \leq 3\}$.

12. From XY to UV: $u = x - h$, $v = y - k$.

  From UV to XY: $x = u + h$, $y = v + k$.

  From ST to UV: $u = cs$, $v = ct$.

From UV to ST: $s = \left(\dfrac{1}{c}\right)u$, $t = \left(\dfrac{1}{c}\right)v$.

From ST to XY: $x = cs + h$, $y = ct + k$.

From XY to ST: $s = \left(\dfrac{1}{c}\right)(x - h)$, $t = \left(\dfrac{1}{c}\right)(y - k)$.

Section 3.1

1. (a) Function. $f: f(x) = \dfrac{2x - 1}{3}$.

(b) Not a function.

(c) Not a function.

(d) Funtion. $f: f(x) = x$.

(e) Function. $f: f(x) = \begin{cases} x + 3 & \text{if } x \le 1 \\ 2 & \text{if } x > 1 \end{cases}$.

(f) Function. $f: f(s) = -s^2$.

(g) Function. $g: g(y) = y^{2/3}$.

(h) Not a function.

(i) Function. $h: h(u) = \sqrt{u^2 - 1}$.

(j) Not a function.

2. (a) Each vertical line intersects G in at most one point.

(b) There is some vertical line that intersects G in more than one point.

4. (a) $\mathscr{D}_f = \{y: |y| \ge 2\}$. Symmetric with respect to the vertical axis.

(c) $\mathscr{D}_h = \{x: |x| \ge 2\}$. Symmetric with respect to the vertical axis.

(e) $\mathscr{D}_g = R$. Symmetric with respect to origin.

5. (a) $\mathscr{D}_f = R$. $f = \{(x, y): y = 3x + 2\}$.

(c) $\mathscr{D}_F = \{t: t \ge 4\}$. $F = \{(t, u): u = \sqrt{t - 4}\}$.

(e) $\mathscr{D}_h = R$. $h = \{(t, u): t > 1 \text{ and } u = t^2, \text{ or } t \le 1 \text{ and } u = 3 - 2t\}$.

(g) $\mathscr{D}_F = R$. $F = \{(x, y): y = x^4\}$.

(i) $\mathscr{D}_f = \{u: u \ne -1\}$. $f = \left\{(u, v): v = \dfrac{u^2 - 1}{u + 1}\right\}$,

or $f = \{(u, v): v = u - 1 \text{ and } u \ne -1\}$.

6. No. $\mathscr{D}_g = \{x: x < -1 \text{ or } x \ge 1\}$ but $\mathscr{D}_f = \{x: x \ge 1\}$.

7. (a) $f(-1) = 1$; **(c)** $f(t) = t^2$; **(e)** $f(2x) = 4x^2$; **(g)** $f(f(x)) = x^4$.

8. (a) $g(2x) = 2mx + b$; **(c)** $g(t + h) = mt + mh + b$; **(e)** $g(g(u)) = m^2u + mb + b$.

9. $\dfrac{f(x + h) - f(x)}{h} = 8x - 3 + h$ provided $h \ne 0$.

11. (a) $A: A(r) = \pi r^2$, $r > 0$.

(c) $A: A(s) = s^2$, $s > 0$.

(e) $d: d(t) = 60t$, $t \ge 0$.

(g) $p: p(h) = \dfrac{2\sqrt{h^4 + 16} + 8}{h}$, $h > 0$.

(i) $A: A(h) = h\sqrt{2rh - h^2}$, $0 < h < 2r$.

Section 3.2

2. "A function f is one-to-one" means that no two distinct ordered pairs in f have the same second coordinate. Equivalently, if (x_1, y_1) and (x_2, y_1) are in f, then $x_1 = x_2$.

4. In Exercise 4, (b) and (d) are one-to-one. In Exercise 5, (a), (c), and (i) are one-to-one.

8. (a) $f(-2) \ge f(-1)$ and $f(1) \le f(2)$.

(c) $f(1) \ge f(2)$ and $f(-1) \le f(1)$.

Section 3.3

1. (a) $(f + 4g)(x) = \dfrac{1}{3x^2 - 2} + 4\sqrt{x + 7}$ for $x \geq -7$ and $x \neq \pm\sqrt{\dfrac{2}{3}}$.

   (c) $\left(\dfrac{f}{g}\right)(u) = \dfrac{1}{(3u^2 - 2)\sqrt{u + 7}}$, for $u > -7$ and $u \neq \pm\sqrt{\dfrac{2}{3}}$.

   (e) $\left(\dfrac{g}{2f}\right)(y) = \dfrac{(3y^2 - 2)\sqrt{y + 7}}{2}$, for $y \geq -7$, $y \neq \pm\sqrt{\dfrac{2}{3}}$.

   (g) $f(g(z)) = \dfrac{1}{3z + 19}$, for $z \geq -7$ and $z \neq -\dfrac{19}{3}$.

   (i) $(g \cdot g)(t) = t + 7$, for $t \geq -7$.

2. (b) $(fg)(x) = \left(\dfrac{x}{2} - \dfrac{1}{3}\right)\sqrt{2 - x^2}$, for $|x| \leq \sqrt{2}$.

   (d) $(f - g)(2t) = t - \dfrac{1}{3} - \sqrt{2 - 4t^2}$, for $|t| \leq \dfrac{\sqrt{2}}{2}$.

   (f) $g(f(x)) = \sqrt{\dfrac{17}{9} - \dfrac{x^2}{4} + \dfrac{x}{3}}$, for $\dfrac{2}{3} - 2\sqrt{2} \leq x \leq \dfrac{2}{3} + \sqrt{2}$.

   (h) $(f \cdot f)(x) = \dfrac{x^2}{4} - \dfrac{x}{3} + \dfrac{1}{9}$, for all $x \in R$.

3. $f(3) = f(t) = f(f(1)) = -2$.

5. $A = 4$, $B = 1$.

7. $A = 3$, $B = -1$, $C = 2$.

9. $A = 1$, $B = 2$, $C = 1$.

13. (a) If x_1 and $x_2 \in \mathcal{D}_{fg}$ with $x_1 < x_2$, then $0 < f(x_1) < f(x_2)$ and $0 < g(x_1) < g(x_2)$. Therefore, $f(x_1)g(x_1) < f(x_2)g(x_2)$ so fg is increasing.

   (b) Not necessarily. Let $f \colon f(x) = x$ and $g \colon g(x) = x$. Then f and g are increasing, but $fg \colon (fg)(x) = x^2$ is not.

   (c) Not necessarily, as in part (b).

Section 3.4

1. (a) $f \circ g \colon (f \circ g)(x) = \dfrac{1}{(x + 1)^2} - 2$; $\mathcal{D}_{f \circ g} = \{x \colon x \neq -1\}$.

   $g \circ f \colon (g \circ f)(x) = \dfrac{1}{x^2 - 1}$; $\mathcal{D}_{g \circ f} = \{x \colon x \neq \pm 1\}$.

   (c) $f \circ g \colon (f \circ g)(x) = 5x - 7 - 2\sqrt{x - 1}$; $\mathcal{D}_{f \circ g} = \{x \colon x \geq 1\}$.

   $g \circ f \colon (g \circ f)(x) = (5x^2 - 2x - 3)^{1/2}$; $\mathcal{D}_{g \circ f} = \{x \colon x \notin (-3/5, 1)\}$.

2. (a) $f \colon f(x) = x^2 - 1$; $g \colon g(x) = x + 4$.

   (c) $f \colon f(x) = x^2 + 1$; $g \colon g(x) = x + 2$.

   (e) $f \colon f(x) = \sqrt{x}$; $g \colon g(x) = x + 3$.

   (g) $f \colon f(x) = 2|x|$; $g \colon g(x) = x - 2$.

5. $k \colon k(d) = \dfrac{d}{2}$, $d > 0$. k gives the radius of a circle in terms of its diameter.

7. $F = f \circ g$ where $f \colon f(s) = s^2$, $s > 0$ and $g \colon g(d) = \dfrac{d}{\sqrt{2}}$, $d > 0$.

9. F assigns to each point (x, y) its reflection in the vertical axis. $F \circ F$ is the identity function, *i.e.*, it associates each point with itself.

13. $A = (x, g(x))$; $B = (g(x), g(x))$; $C = (g(x), f(g(x)))$; $D = (x, f(g(x)))$.

Section 4.1

1. (a) Degree 3, leading coefficient -5, constant term 0.

   (c) No degree, leading coefficient 0, constant term 0.

(**e**) Not a polynomial function.
(**g**) Not a polynomial function.
(**i**) Degree 4, leading coefficient 1, constant term 45.

3.

(a)

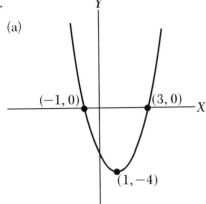

(c)

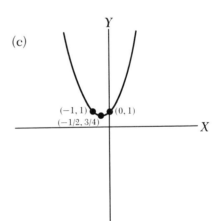

(e)

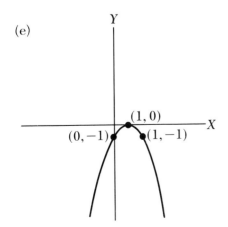

7.
(a)

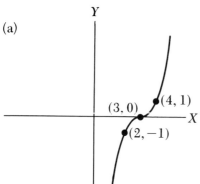

(c)

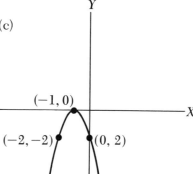

(e)

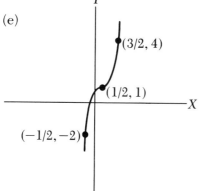

8. Symmetric with respect to line $x = -\dfrac{b}{2a}$ in the XY plane.

9. (a) $q: q(x) = -\dfrac{1}{2}x^2 + \dfrac{1}{2}x + 1.$

(c) Not always. There is if no two of the points lie on the same vertical line and the three points are noncollinear.

12. $P + Q$ is a polynomial function with degree less than or equal to the larger of m and n. Same is true of $P - Q$. $P \cdot Q$ is a polynomial function of degree $m + n$. $\dfrac{P}{Q}$ is not necessarily a polynomial function. $P \circ Q$ is a polynomial function of degree $m \cdot n$.

13. (a) $A: A(s) = s(4 - s), 0 < s < 4$.
   (b) The maximum area of a rectangle having perimeter 8 in., is 4 in.^{2} and occurs when the rectangle is a square having side length 2 in.

Section 4.2

1. (a) $Q: Q(x) = -2x - 1; \ R: R(x) = -3x$.
   (c) $Q: Q(x) = -(x - 2)^2; \ R: R(x) = 0$.
   (e) $Q: Q(x) = 0; \ R: R(x) = x^2 + 2x - 3$.

2. (a) $\dfrac{3}{2}$; (c) 0; (e) No zeros.

3. (a) -2 and 3; (b) $\left\{ \dfrac{1 \pm \sqrt{33}}{2} \right\}$; (c) $\varnothing$.

5. (a) $p: p(x) = 3(x - 1)\left(x - \dfrac{1}{2} \right)\left(x - \dfrac{1}{3} \right)\left(x - \dfrac{1}{4} \right)$.
   (c) $p: p(x) = x(x - 1)(x^2 - 2x - 16)(x^2 - 4x - 2)$.
   (e) $p: p(x) = -5\left(x + \dfrac{1}{2} \right)\left(x - \dfrac{4}{3} \right)(x - \pi)$.

7. (a) $Q: Q(x) = -2x^2 + 15 - 110; \ R: R(x) = 771$.
   (c) $Q: Q(x) = x^6 + 3x^5 - 3x^4 + 3x^3 - 8x^2 + x - 1; \ R: R(x) = 3$.

8. (a) $\{-1\}$; (c) $\left\{ -\dfrac{1}{7} \right\}$.

Section 4.3

1. (a), (c), (d), (e), (g), and (h) have *IVP* on $[a, b]$; (a), (c), (h), and (i) have *IVP* on $[c, d]$; (a), (c), and (h) have *IVP* on every interval.

2.

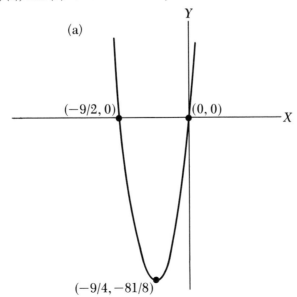

(a)

$(-9/2, 0)$ $(0, 0)$

Y

X

$(-9/4, -81/8)$

(c)

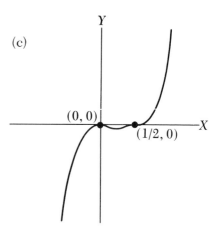

(e)

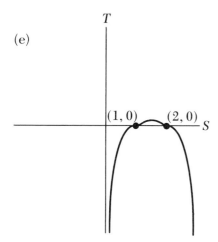

3. (a) $\left\{ x: x \le \dfrac{-1 - \sqrt{5}}{2} \text{ or } -\dfrac{1}{2} \le x \le \dfrac{-1 + \sqrt{5}}{2} \right\}$

    (c) $\{ x: x \le -3 - \sqrt{6} \text{ or } x \ge 3 + \sqrt{6} \}$

    (e) $\{ t: 0 < t < 3 \}$

    (g) $\{ x: -1 < x < -\dfrac{1}{2} \text{ or } x > 0 \}$

4. (a), (b), and (d)

5. (a) $p: p(x) = x(x + 3)^2$

    (c) $p: p(x) = (x + 3)^2 x^2 \left(x - \dfrac{7}{3} \right)$

    (e) $p: p(x) = \dfrac{1}{48} (x + 3)(x + 2)^2 (x + 1)(x - 2)^3$

7. -1.5

9. $S(x) = \dfrac{x^2 - c^2}{x - c} = x + c, \, x \ne c$

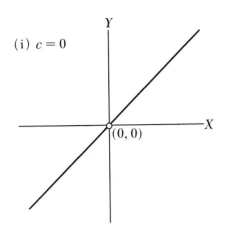

(i) $c = 0$

(0, 0)

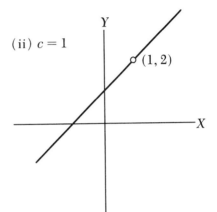

(ii) $c = 1$

(1, 2)

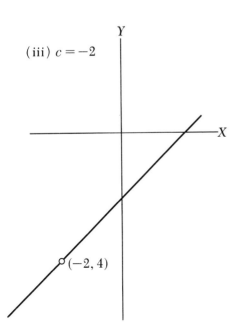

(iii) $c = -2$

(−2, 4)

Section 4.4

1. (a) $f = \dfrac{P}{Q}$ with $P: P(x) = 3x^2 - 2x + 1$,

$$Q: Q(x) = x^2 - 4; \ \mathscr{D}_f = \{x: x \neq \pm 2\}.$$

(c) $h = \dfrac{P}{Q}$ with $P: P(x) = x^3 - 2x^2 + x$,

$$Q: Q(x) = (x-1)^2; \ \mathscr{D}_h = \{x: x \neq 1\}.$$

(e) $G = \dfrac{P}{Q}$ with $P: P(x) = x + 1$,

$$Q: Q(x) = 2x - 2; \ \mathscr{D}_G = \{x: x \neq 1\}.$$

(g) $f = \dfrac{P}{Q}$ with $P: P(t) = t$,

$$Q: Q(t) = t(3t^2 + 1); \ \mathscr{D}_f = \{t: t \neq 0\}.$$

2. $f + g: \ (f+g)(x) = \dfrac{x^3 + 3x - 4}{x(2x - 4)}; \ \mathscr{D}_{f+g} = \{x: x \neq 0 \text{ and } x \neq 2\}.$

$f \cdot g: \ (fg)(x) = \dfrac{x^2 + 1}{2x^2 - 4x}; \ \mathscr{D}_{f \cdot g} = \{x: x \neq 0 \text{ and } x \neq 2\}.$

$f \circ g: \ (f \circ g)(x) = \dfrac{x^2 + 1}{x(2 - 4x)}; \ \mathscr{D}_{f \circ g} = \left\{x: x \neq 0 \text{ and } x \neq \dfrac{1}{2}\right\}.$

Section 4.5

1.

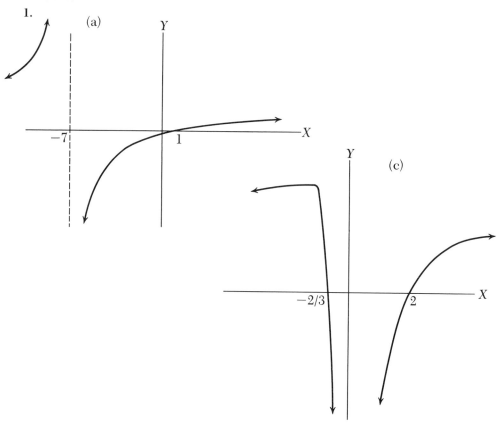

(e)

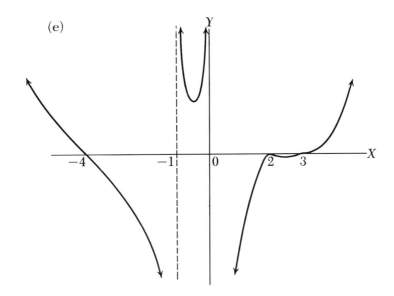

2. (a) $f: f(x) = \dfrac{-x}{(x+2)(x-2)}$

   (c) $f: f(x) = \dfrac{x^2}{\left(x+\dfrac{3}{2}\right)\left(x-\dfrac{3}{2}\right)^2}$

3. (a) $\left\{x: -3 < x \le \dfrac{1}{2}\right\}$

   (c) $\{x: x < -3 \text{ or } x > -2\}$

   (e) $\left\{x: x > \dfrac{3}{2}\right\}$

6. (b) $f: f(x) = \dfrac{x}{(x+1)(x-1)^2}$

   (d) $f: f(x) = \dfrac{(x+1)(2x-1)}{2x^2}$

Section 5.1

1. (a) $z = \pi$, $k = 1$; (c) $z = \pi/2$, $k = -2$; (e) $z = \pi$, $k = -41$; (g) $z = 7\pi/6$, $k = 1$.
2. (b) $w(7\pi/2) = (0, -1)$; (d) $w(\pi/6) = (\sqrt{3}/2, 1/2)$; (f) $w(-65\pi/3) = (1/2, \sqrt{3}/2)$;
   (h) $w(2\pi) = (1, 0)$.
3. $w(2\pi/3) = (-1/2, \sqrt{3}/2)$; $w(5\pi/3) = (1/2, -\sqrt{3}/2)$; $w(-5\pi/3) = (1/2, \sqrt{3}/2)$;
   $w(5\pi/2) = (0, 1)$; $w(-7\pi/4) = (1/\sqrt{2}, 1/\sqrt{2})$; $w(-15\pi/6) = (0, -1)$;
   $w(3\pi/2) = (0, -1)$.
5. (a) Part (i): each of $w(x + \pi)$ and $w(x - \pi)$ is the reflection of $w(x)$ in the
   origin; Part (ii): $w(\pi - x)$ is the reflection of $w(x)$ in the vertical axis;
   Part (iii): no obvious symmetry; Part (iv): $w(\pi/2 - x)$ is the reflection of
   $w(x)$ in the bisector of quadrants I and III.
6. (a) $|w(0)w(\pi/3)| = |w(\pi/3)w(2\pi/3)| = 1$; (c) The arc from $w(0)$ to $w(4\pi/3)$
   has length $4\pi/3$, as does the arc from $w(\pi/3)$ to $w(5\pi/3)$, so the chords subtended by these arcs have equal length.

12. (a) $((\sqrt{3}+1)/2\sqrt{2}, (\sqrt{3}-1)/2\sqrt{2})$; (d) $(\sqrt{2+\sqrt{2}}/2, \sqrt{2-\sqrt{2}}/2)$.
13. (a) If $T > 0$, then for all $x \in R$, $g(x + T) = c = g(x)$; (b) If n is a positive integer, then for each $x \in \mathscr{D}_h$, $x + n \in \mathscr{D}_h$ also, since $x + n$ is not an integer if x is not. But also $h(x + n) = 2 = h(x)$, so n is a period of h. The number $1/2$ is not a period of h, since if $x = -3/2$, for example, then $x \in \mathscr{D}_h$ but $x + \frac{1}{2} \notin \mathscr{D}_h$.

Section 5.2

2. $w(0) = (1,0)$, $\cos 0 = 1$, $\sin 0 = 0$; $w(\pi/6) = (\sqrt{3}/2, 1/2)$,
   $\cos \pi/6 = \sqrt{3}/2$, $\sin \pi/6 = 1/2$; $w(\pi/4) = (1/\sqrt{2}, 1/\sqrt{2})$,
   $\cos \pi/4 = 1/\sqrt{2}$, $\sin \pi/4 = 1/\sqrt{2}$; $w(\pi/3) = (1/2, \sqrt{3}/2)$,
   $\cos \pi/3 = 1/2$, $\sin \pi/3 = \sqrt{3}/2$; $w(\pi/2) = (0, 1)$, $\cos \pi/2 = 0$, $\sin \pi/2 = 1$.
3. $\cos \pi/12 = (\sqrt{3}+1)/2\sqrt{2}$, $\sin \pi/12 = (\sqrt{3}-1)/2\sqrt{2}$;
   $\cos 82\pi/3 = -1/2$, $\sin 82\pi/3 = -\sqrt{3}/2$; $\cos(-61\pi/12) = -(\sqrt{3}+1)/2\sqrt{2}$,
   $\sin(-61\pi/12) = (\sqrt{3}-1)/2\sqrt{2}$; $\cos 15\pi/4 = \sqrt{2}/2$, $\sin 15\pi/4 = -\sqrt{2}/2$.
4. $Z_1 = \{x : x = n\pi$ for some integer $n\}$.
   $P_1 = \{x : 2k\pi < x < (2k + 1)\pi$ for some integer $k\}$.
   $N_1 = \{x : (2n - 1)\pi < x < 2n\pi$ for some integer $n\}$.
7. (a) $\cos x = -2\sqrt{2}/3$; (c) $\sin x = \sqrt{2/3}$; (d) $\cos x = 4/5$.
9. $\cos \pi/8 = \sqrt{2+\sqrt{2}}/2$, $\sin \pi/8 = \sqrt{2-\sqrt{2}}/2$.
11. In all parts, consider the problem of determining where the line $t = d$ in the ST plane intersects $C = \{(s, t) : s^2 + t^2 = 1\}$.
12. (b) $\mathscr{D}_f = [-1, 1]$, $\mathscr{R}_f = [-\pi/2, \pi/2]$; (e) d; (f) $f(\sin \pi/4) = \pi/4$, $f(\sin \pi/2) = \pi/2$,
    $f(\sin 3\pi/4) = \pi/4$, $f(\sin 7\pi/6) = -\pi/6$; (h) $f(\cos x) = \pi/2 - x$ if $0 \le x \le \pi/2$.
13. (b) $\mathscr{D}_g = [-1, 1]$, $\mathscr{R}_g = [0, \pi]$; (d) $g(1) = 0$, $g(-1) = \pi$, $g(\sqrt{3}/2) = \pi/6$.
    $g(1/\sqrt{2}) = \pi/4$, $g(0) = \pi/2$; (g) $g(\cos x) = -x$ if $-\pi \le x \le 0$.
14. (a) $\{x :$ For some integer n, $x = \pi/6 + 2n\pi$ or $x = -\pi/6 + 2n\pi\}$.
    (d) $\{x :$ For some integer n, $x = (2n + 1)\pi\}$.
    (e) $\{x :$ For some integer n, $x = 2\pi/3 + 4n\pi$ or $x = -2\pi/3 + 4n\pi\}$.
15. (a) $\{x :$ For some integer k, $x = -\pi/6 + 2k\pi$ or $x = 7\pi/6 + 2k\pi\}$.
    (c) $\{x :$ For some integer n, $x = n\pi\}$.
    (f) $\{x :$ For some integer n, $x = \pi/8 + n\pi$ or $x = 3\pi/8 + n\pi\}$.

Section 5.3

3. (b) $\{x :$ For no integer n is $x = n\pi/2\}$; (c) This would automatically exclude the odd multiples of $\pi/2$ from $\mathscr{D}_{\cot}$.
4. (b) $\{x :$ For no integer n is $x = n\pi\}$.
7. (a) Given any real number a, the argument in Example 3 shows that for some number x_a between $-\pi/2$ and $\pi/2$, $a = \tan x_a$, so $a \in \mathscr{R}_{\tan}$. This shows $R \subset \mathscr{R}_{\tan}$. But tan is a real function, so $\mathscr{R}_{\tan} \subset R$. Hence, $\mathscr{R}_{\tan} = R$.
9. (a) $\{x :$ For some integer n, $x = \pi/4 + n\pi\}$.
   (c) $\{x :$ For some integer n, $x = \pi/6 + 2n\pi$ or $x = -\pi/6 + 2n\pi\}$.
   (f) $\{x :$ For some integer n, $x = \pi/2 + n\pi\}$.
10. (a) $\{x :$ For some integer n, $x = n\pi\}$.
    (c) $\{x :$ For some integer n, $x = \pi/12 + n\pi/2\}$.
    (e) $\{x :$ For some integer n, $x = 1/2 + (6n + 1)5\pi/12\}$.
11. (a) $\{x :$ For some integer n, $n\pi < x < n\pi + \pi/2\{$.
    (c) $\{x :$ For some integer n, $(4n - 1)\pi/2 < x < (4n + 1)\pi/2\}$.
12. (a) $\{x :$ For some integer n, $(4n + 1)\pi/4 < x < (4n + 2)\pi/4$
                  or $(4n - 1)\pi/4 < x < n\pi\}$.
    (c) $\{x :$ For some integer n, $x = 2n\pi$ or $(4n + 1)\pi/2 < x < (4n + 3)\pi/2\}$.
    (e) $\{x :$ For some integer n, $n\pi < x < \pi/6 + n\pi\}$.

13. (b) $\mathcal{D}_h = R$, $\mathcal{R}_h = (-\pi/2, \pi/2)$; **(d)** $h(1) = \pi/4$, $h(-1) = -\pi/4$, $h(-\sqrt{3}) = -\pi/3$, $h(-1/\sqrt{3}) = -\pi/6$, $h(0) = 0$; **(f)** $h(\tan \pi/4) = \pi/4$, $h(\tan(-\pi/5)) = -\pi/5$, $h(\tan \pi) = 0$; **(h)** $x/\sqrt{1+x^2}$.

Section 5.4

8. (a) Graph of g is the reflection of the graph of sin in the horizontal axis; **(c)** Same as (a); **(d)** H and cos are the same.

11.

(b)

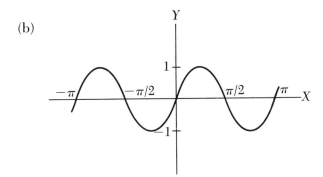

(c)

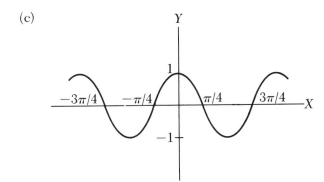

(a)

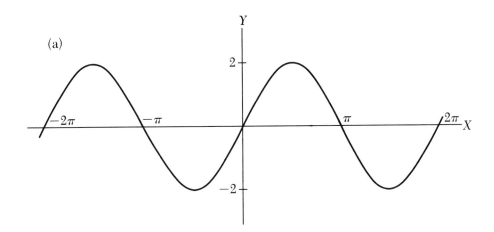

(d)

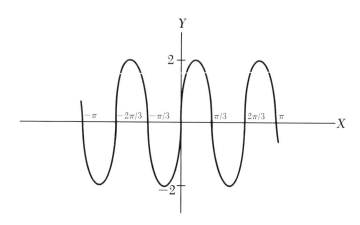

Section 5.5

1. **(a)** $\sin x/\cos x + 1/\cos x$; $\{x\colon$ For no integer n is $x = (2n + 1)\pi/2\}$.
   (b) $\sin x + 1/\cos x$; $\{x\colon$ For no integer n is $x = (2n + 1)\pi/2\}$.
   (c) $1/\cos^2 x + \cos^2 x/\sin^2 x$; $\{x\colon$ For no integer k is $x = k\pi/2\}$.
   (d) $\cos^2 x/\sin^2 x - \sin^2 x/\cos x$; $\{x\colon x \neq k\pi/2,\ k$ an integer$\}$.
   (e) $1/(1 + \cos x)$; $\{x\colon$ For no integer k is $x = k\pi\}$.
   (f) $\sin^2 x/\cos^2 x + \cos^2 x$; $\{x\colon x \neq (2n + 1)\pi/2,\ n$ an integer$\}$.
   (g) $1/(\sin x \cos x)$; $\{x\colon$ For no integer k is $x = k\pi/2\}$.
   (h) $(1 - \cos x)^2/\sin^2 x$; $\{x\colon$ For no integer k is $x = k\pi\}$.
   (i) $4 \sin x \cos^2 x - \sin x$; $\{x\colon x \in R\}$.
   (j) $\cos x - 4 \sin^2 x \cos x$; $\{x\colon x \in R\}$.
2. **(a):** **(i)** and **(iv)**, $(\sin x + 1)/\sqrt{1 - \sin^2 x}$.
   (ii) and **(iii)**, $-(\sin x + 1)/\sqrt{1 - \sin^2 x}$.
   (c): **(i)**–**(iv)**, $1/(1 - \sin^2 x) + (1 - \sin^2 x)/\sin^2 x$.
   (i): $3 \sin x - 4 \sin^3 x$.
   (j): (i) and (iv), $\sqrt{1 - \sin^2 x}(1 - 4 \sin^2 x)$.
   (ii) and (iii), $\sqrt{1 - \sin^2 x}(4 \sin^2 x - 1)$.
4. **(a)** $\cos 5\pi/12 = (\sqrt{3} - 1)/2\sqrt{2}$, $\sin 5\pi/12 = (\sqrt{3} + 1)/2\sqrt{2}$.
   $\tan 5\pi/12 = 2 + \sqrt{3}$, $\cot 5\pi/12 = 2 - \sqrt{3}$.
   $\sec 5\pi/12 = \sqrt{6} + \sqrt{2}$, $\csc 5\pi/12 = \sqrt{6} - \sqrt{2}$.
   (d) $\cos \pi/16 = \frac{1}{2}\sqrt{2 + \sqrt{2 + \sqrt{2}}}$, $\sin \pi/16 = \frac{1}{2}\sqrt{2 - \sqrt{2 + \sqrt{2}}}$, etc.
5. **(a)** $\tan (x_1 - x_2) = (\tan x_1 - \tan x_2)/(1 + \tan x_1 \tan x_2)$
   $\{(x_1, x_2)\colon$ For no integer n is $x_1 = (2n + 1)\pi/2$ nor is $x_2 = (2n + 1)\pi/2$,
   and for no integer k is $x_1 - x_2 = (2k + 1)\pi/2\}$.

Section 5.6

1. **(b)** Ampl. $3/4$, per. $4\pi/3$, phase displ. $-2\pi/9$.

(b)

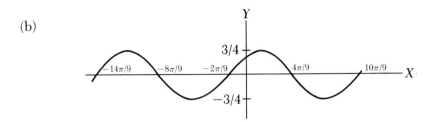

(**d**) Ampl. π, per. 2π, phase displ. π.

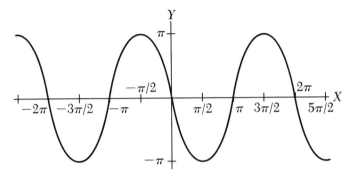

(**f**) Ampl. $\sqrt{2}$, per. 1, phase displ. 0.

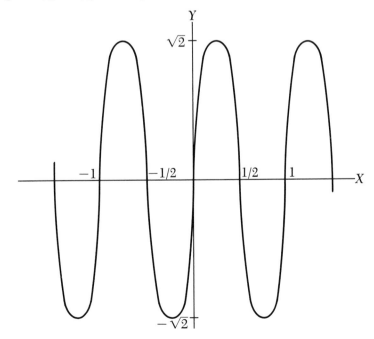

2. (a) $f: f(x) = \sin(2x + \pi/3)$; ampl. 1, per. π, phase displ. $\pi/6$.
   (c) $h: h(x) = \sin(x + \pi/4)$; ampl. 1, per. 2π, phase displ. $\pi/4$.
   (d) $F: F(x) = 2\sqrt{3}\sin(4x + 5\pi/6)$; ampl. $2\sqrt{3}$, per. $\pi/2$, phase displ. $5\pi/24$.
   (f) $H: H(x) = \sin(2x + \pi)$; ampl. 1, per. π, phase displ. $\pi/2$.
   (g) $q: q(x) = 3\sin(2x + \pi - 1)$; ampl. 3, per. π, phase displ. $(\pi - 1)/2$.
3. Case 1: For $A > 0$, $k < 0$, write $f: f(x) = A\sin(-kx - B + \pi)$.
   Case 2: For $A < 0$, $k > 0$, write $f: f(x) = -A\sin(kx + B + \pi)$.
   Case 3: For $A < 0$, $k < 0$, write $f: f(x) = -A\sin(-kx - B)$.
4. (b) $h: h(x) = 2\sin(2x + \pi/6)$; ampl. 2, per. π, phase displ. $\pi/12$.

Section 6.1

1. (a) $f^{-1}: f^{-1}(y) = 2(y - 10)$; (b) $g^{-1}: g^{-1}(y) = (1/m)(y - b)$.
   (c) $f^{-1}: f^{-1}(s) = s/(2 - 3s)$; (d) $h^{-1}: h^{-1}(v) = v^2/(v^2 - 1)$, $v \geq 0$, $v \neq 1$.
   (g) $G^{-1}: G^{-1}(u) = (du - b)/(a - cu)$.
   (h) $H^{-1}: H^{-1}(y) = (1/2)(y + \sqrt{y^2 + 4y})$, $y \geq 0$.
4. If x_1 and x_2 are in A, and $f(x_1) = f(x_2)$, then $x_1 = (g \circ f)(x_1) = g(f(x_1)) = g(f(x_2)) = (g \circ f)(x_2) = x_2$, so f is one-to-one. However, if $f: f(x) = \sqrt{x}$ and $g: g(x) = x^2$, then $g \neq f^{-1}$.

Section 6.2

1.   (b)   (d)

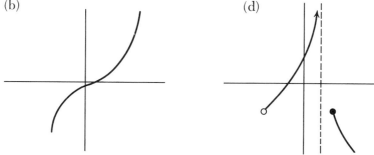

2. (a) $f^{-1}: f^{-1}(x) = 3x - 6$

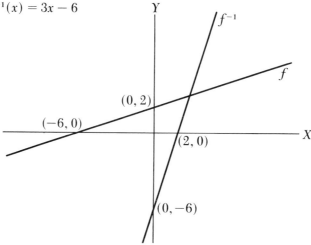

(c) h^{-1}: $h^{-1}(u) = \sqrt{u}$

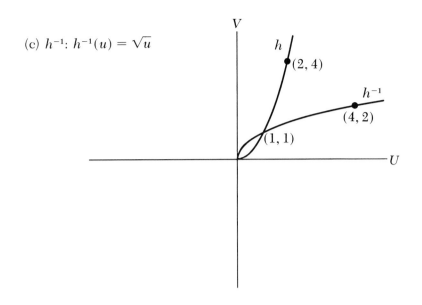

(e) F^{-1}: $F^{-1}(t) = (3t + 1)/(t - 2)$

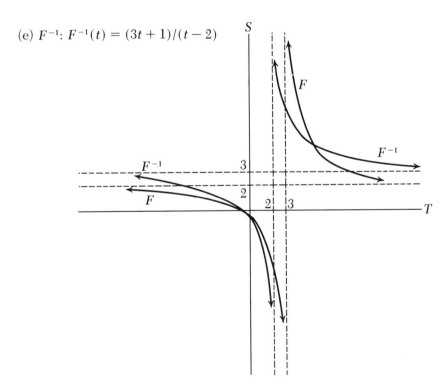

4. The graphs are identical.

Section 6.3

1. (a) $-\pi/4$; (c) $\pi/3$; (e) 0; (g) $2\pi/3$; (i) π.

3. All real numbers a; $0 < b < \pi$.

4. (a) $\cos \circ \mathrm{Sin}^{-1}$: $(\cos \circ \mathrm{Sin}^{-1})(x) = \sqrt{1 - x^2}$,
$\tan \circ \mathrm{Sin}^{-1}$: $(\tan \circ \mathrm{Sin}^{-1})(x) = x/\sqrt{1 - x^2}$.
(b) $\sin \circ \mathrm{Cos}^{-1}$: $(\sin \circ \mathrm{Cos}^{-1})(x) = \sqrt{1 - x^2}$,
$\cot \circ \mathrm{Cos}^{-1}$: $(\cot \circ \mathrm{Cos}^{-1})(x) = x/\sqrt{1 - x^2}$.
(c) $\sin \circ \mathrm{Tan}^{-1}$: $(\sin \circ \mathrm{Tan}^{-1})(x) = x/\sqrt{1 + x^2}$.
$\cos \circ \mathrm{Tan}^{-1}$: $(\cos \circ \mathrm{Tan}^{-1})(x) = 1/\sqrt{1 + x^2}$.

5. (a) $\mathrm{Cos} \circ \mathrm{Sin}^{-1}$: $(\mathrm{Cos} \circ \mathrm{Sin}^{-1})(x) = \sqrt{1 - x^2}$, $0 \le x \le 1$
(b) $\mathrm{Sin} \circ \mathrm{Cos}^{-1}$: $(\mathrm{Sin} \circ \mathrm{Cos}^{-1})(x) = \sqrt{1 - x^2}$, $0 \le x \le 1$
(e) $\mathrm{Tan} \circ \mathrm{Sin}^{-1}$: $(\mathrm{Tan} \circ \mathrm{Sin}^{-1})(x) = x/\sqrt{1 - x^2}$, $0 \le x < 1$
(f) $\mathrm{Tan} \circ \mathrm{Cos}^{-1}$: $(\mathrm{Tan} \circ \mathrm{Cos}^{-1})(x) = \sqrt{1 - x^2}x$, $0 < x \le 1$

7. (a) $\{x : x = \frac{1}{6}(1 + \mathrm{Sin}^{-1} 3/4 + 2k\pi)$ or
$x = \frac{1}{6}(1 - \mathrm{Sin}^{-1} 3/4 + (2k + 1)\pi)$, k an integer$\}$
(b) $\{x : x = \frac{1}{2}(-\theta + \mathrm{Sin}^{-1}(1/2\sqrt{10}) + 2k\pi)$ or
$x = \frac{1}{2}(-\theta - \mathrm{Sin}^{-1}(1/2\sqrt{10}) + (2k + 1)\pi$, k an integer$\}$,
where $\theta = \mathrm{Tan}^{-1} 1/3$.
(d) $\varnothing$

8.

(a)
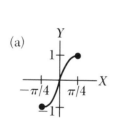

(c)
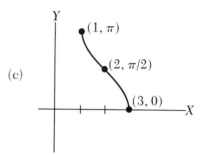

(e)
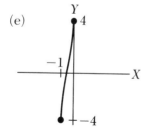

(f)
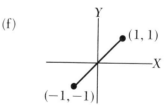

10. If $\left[\dfrac{2x + \pi}{2\pi}\right] = 2n$, then $\mathrm{Sin}^{-1} \sin x = x - 2n\pi$;
if $\left[\dfrac{2x + \pi}{2\pi}\right] = 2n + 1$, then $\mathrm{Sin}^{-1} \sin x = (2n + 1)\pi - x$.

12. $\mathrm{Cot}^{-1} u = \pi/2 - \mathrm{Tan}^{-1} u$, $u \in R$.

Section 7.1

1. (a) 1/2; (c) 1/8; (e) 64/27; (g) 1/16; (i) 1/3125.
2. (a) $x^5 y^{-9}$; (c) $x - y$; (e) $x^{-1/2}/(1 - x^{5/2})$; (g) $x(2x + 1)^{-1/2}(x + 1)$; (h) 4.
5. (a) R; (b) R; (c) $\{b : b \geq 0\}$; (d) R; (e) $\{y : y \geq 0\}$; (f) $\{a : a \neq 0\}$;
   (g) $\{(x, y) : xy \geq 0\}$; (h) $\{(a, b) : a \geq 0 \text{ and } b \geq 0\}$.
6. (b) The graph of $f_{1/b}$ is the reflection in the vertical axis of the graph of f_b.

Section 7.2

1. The graph of s is symmetric with respect to $(0, 0)$; the graph of c is symmetric with respect to the vertical axis.

4.

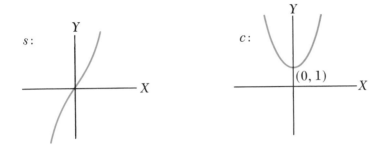

5.

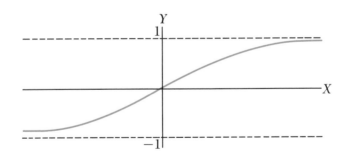

7. If there were such a number d, then
   $1 = d^0 = H(0) = a^{b^0} = a$, which contradicts $a \neq 1$.
8. (a) Theorem 7.2.1(ii); (b) $H = F_a \circ F_b$.
10. (a) *LUB* is 3, *GLB* is -2; (c) *LUB* is π, *GLB* is 0;
    (e) *GLB* is 3, not bounded above; (h) *GLB* is 0, *LUB* is 1.

Section 7.3

2. Let $x = \log_b y$, so $y = b^x$. Then $\log_a y = \log_a b^x = x \log_a b$,
   so $\log_b y = x = \log_a y / \log_a b$.
3. (b) 2; (d) 2; (e) z; (f) -2; (h) 1/2.
4. (a) $-7/4$; (c) 2; (e) no solution; (f) 6; (g) 6 and -6; (i) $\{t : t > 21/8\}$;
   (j) $\{x : -999/6 < x < 1001/6 \text{ and } x \neq 1/6\}$.

5.

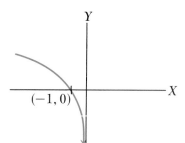 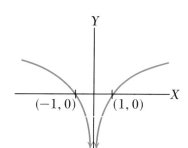

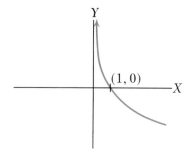 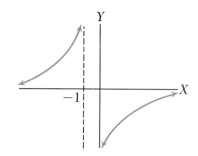

6. $H^{-1}: H^{-1}(y) = \log_b (\log_a y)$. Notice that the domain of H^{-1} is $\{y: y > 1\}$
if $a > 1$, and is $\{y: 0 < y < 1\}$ if $0 < a < 1$.

7. $D = \{x: x \geq 1\}$.

8. (a) $10^{\sin x \log_{10} x}$, $\{x: x > 0\}$; (c) $10^{\cos x \log_{10} \sin x}$, $\{x: 2k\pi < x < (2k + 1)\pi$ for some
integer $k\}$; (d) $10^{x \log_{10} (\log_2 x)}$, $\{x: x > 1\}$; (f) $10^{\log_{10} x \cdot 10^{x \log_{10} x}}$, $\{x: x > 0\}$;
(h) $10^{x \log_{10} 2}$, $\{x: x \in R\}$.

9. (b) $t_0 = (\log_{10} 2)/k$.

ANSWERS TO APPENDIX EXERCISES

APPENDIX I

Section I.1

1. Sum: (a) 1; (b) -7; (c) 4; (d) -5; (e) 11; (f) 3.
   Difference: (a) -3; (b) 1; (c) 8; (d) 5; (e) -3; (f) -7.
2. (a) 4; (b) 11; (c) -50. 3. (a) 7; (b) -11; (c) 5.
4. (a) $x - y + z - u + w$; (b) $-a + b - c - d$; (c) $x + y - z + w - v$.
5. (a) by; (b) $2zw - uv$; (c) $-2xyz$.

Section I.2

1. (a) -24; (b) 2,560; (c) $-2,520$; (d) 1. 2. (a) xyz; (b) $xy + xz$; (c) $-6ab$;
   (d) $-20abc$; (e) $-18a^3$; (f) $-cdx^2$; (g) $-abx^2 + acx^2$.

Section I.3

1. Sum: (a) 5/6; (b) $-2/3$; (c) $-4/3$; (d) $-1/3$; (e) 17/6; (f) $-9/4$.
   Difference: (a) 1/6; (b) $-5/6$; (c) -2; (d) $-1/15$; (e) 19/6; (f) $-7/4$.
2. (a) 3/2; (b) -9; (c) -5; (d) 3/2; (e) -18; (f) 8. 3. (a) $-1/9$; (b) 3/32; (c) 6/5;
   (d) 2/5; (e) 6. 4. (a) $-63/20$; (b) $-9/50$; (c) 9/8. 5. (a) $-(ad + bc)/bd$;
   (b) $-ad/bc$; (c) $(x - z)/y$; (d) uw/v; (e) u/vw.

Section I.4

1. (a) $-2x - y + 3z$; (b) $7xy - z + 3x$; (c) $(7/6)a - (7/2)b + (5/4)c$;
   (d) $2x^2 + (a + 2)x + (3 - b)y^3 - 1$. 2. (a) $-5x + 3y - 7z$; (b) $3a + 7b$;
   (c) $5x^2 + 2y + 4$; (d) $-3a^2 + 2ab + 6b^2$. 3. (a) $6y - 4z + 4x$; (b) $5uv - 6w$;
   (c) $11a^2 - ab - 4b^2$; (d) $8x + 2y - 7z - 1$; (e) $6x - 2y - 2z$;
   (f) $-abc - 6xy + x - 2y$; (g) $11x^2y - 18y^3 + 24xy + 30x$.

Section I.5

1. (a) $-2x^3y$; (b) $-12a^2bc^3$; (c) $27uvwxy$; (d) $-40a^2bc^2$. 2. (a) $6x^2 - 8xy$;
   (b) $5a^2b^2c - 2abc^2$; (c) $-12u^2v + 24uv^2 - 18uvw$; (d) $26x^3 - 39x^3y + 52x^2y^2$.

347

3. (a) $x^2 + 2xy + y^2$; (b) $9v^2 + 6v + 1$; (c) $64y^2 - 48y + 9$; (d) $4 - 12t + 9t^2$;
(e) $36z^2 + 48uz + 16u^2$; (f) $a^2b^2 - 2abcd + c^2d^2$. 4. (a) $27u^3 + 27u^2 + 9u + 1$;
(b) $8 - 60x + 150x^2 - 125x^3$; (c) $a^6 - 3a^4b + 3a^2b^2 - b^3$; (d) $x^3 - 3x^2 + 3x - 1$;
(e) $8y^3 + 36y^2z + 54yz^2 + 27z^3$; (f) $a^3x^3 + 3a^2bx^2y + 3ab^2xy^2 + b^3y^3$.

5. (a) $25a^2 - 16b^2$; (b) $3x^2 + x - 2$; (c) $4a^2 - (17/6)a + 1/2$; (d) $36a^2x^4 - y^4$;
(e) $-4z^2 - 3z + 10$; (f) $3x^2 - (5/6)x - 2/9$.

6. (a) $2x^3 - x^2y - 8xy^2 + 4y^3$; (b) $a^3 - 2ba^2 - 4ab^2 + 8b^3$;
(c) $125x^4 + 25x^3y - 90x^2y^2 - 52xy^3 - 8y^4$; (d) $x^2 - 2xy + y^2 - z^2$;
(e) $16a^2 - 8ab + b^2 + 8ac - 2bc + c^2$;
(f) $8a^6 + 12a^4 + 6a^2 - 12a^4b - 12a^2b + 6a^2b^2 + 1 - 3b + 3b^2 - b^3$.

Section I.6

1. (a) $(5a - 2b)x$; (b) $(3x + 4y)x$; (c) $(a - 3)(x - 2)$; (d) $x(2z)$; (e) $x(6x - a + bx^2)$
(f) $(c - d)(c - d + 4)$; (g) $(b - 1)(3b^2 + 1)$ (h) $x^2(7y - 4z)$; (i) $2(-x + 3y)$;
(j) $ab^2(a - 3b + 2b^2)$.

2. (a) $(y + 4)^2$; (b) $(a - 5)^2$; (c) $(3 - x)^2$ (d) $4(3 + b)(3 - b)$;
(e) $(4x + 3y)(4x - 3y)$; (f) $(5a + 6)(5a - 6)$; (g) $(2x - y)(4x^2 + 2xy + y^2)$;
(h) $(a - 1)(a^2 + a + 1)$; (i) $(z + 1)(z^2 - z + 1)$; (j) $(3b + 1)(9b^2 - 3b + 1)$;
(k) $(5 - 4x)(25 + 20x + 16x^2)$; (l) $8(5a + b)(25a^2 - 5ab + b^2)$;
(m) $(x - 4)(x - 1)$; (n) $(y - 11)(y - 5)$; (o) $(7 - z)(4 + z)$; (p) $(x + 10)(x + 2)$;
(q) $(2b - 5)(2b - 9)$; (r) $(2a + 3)(a + 3)$; (s) $(5y - 3)(3y + 2)$;
(t) $(3x - 2)(2x + 1)$.

3. (a) $2axy^2(x + 2y)(x - 2y)$; (b) $(x + 2)(y - 3)$; (c) $(a - 5)(b - 1)$;
(d) $(x - y + 2)^2$; (e) $(2c - d + 3)(2c - d - 1)$;
(f) $(3y^2 + y + x + 4)(3y^2 + y - x - 4)$; (g) $(6x + y - 3)(2x + y + 3)$;
(h) $b^4(a^2 + 3)(a + \sqrt{3})(a - \sqrt{3})$; (i) $(5x + 2)(3x + 2)(3x - 2)$;
(j) $(3b + 2)(\sqrt{7}b + \sqrt{8})(\sqrt{7}b - \sqrt{8})$; (k) $(a + x)(a - x)(b + y)((b^2 - by + y^2)$;
(l) $(2y)(x + 2y)(3x + 2y)$; (m) $4b(a - 2b)(a + b)$; (n) $(y^2 + 9)(y + 3)(y - 3)$;
(o) $(3x + 1)^4$; (p) $(x^2 + y^2)(x + y)^2(x - y)^2$; (q) $(2y - 3)(4y + 3)(2y + 1)$;
(r) $(2b - 3)^4$; (s) $(x + 1)(x^2 + x + 1)$; (t) $(a - 7)(a - 2)(a - 10)(a + 1)$.

Section I.7

2. (a) $11/6(x - 1)$; (b) $(x - 8)/(x - 4)(x + 4)$; (c) $3y(2y + 3)/(y - 1)(2y - 1)$;
(d) $(b + 3)/(b + 5)(b + 9)$; (e) $x/(x - y)(x - 7y)$; (f) $(a + 2)(a + 1)/(a^2 + 2)$;
(g) $2y(2y - \sqrt{5})(2y + \sqrt{5})/(4y + 9)$; (h) $2/(x - y)(x - z)$; (i) $4/(c - 4)$;
(j) $(x^2 + 1)/x(x + 1)$; (k) 2; (l) $x(x + y + z)/z(x - y + z)$;
(m) $x(x^2 + 1)/(x - 1)^2(x^2 + x + 1)$; (n) $(y + z)(x + y + z)/(y - z)(x + y - z)$.

Section I.8

1. (a) $-5/3$; (b) $-6/5$; (c) -3; (d) $3/4$; (e) $26/295$; (f) $15/14$.
2. (a) -6; (b) $5/6$; (c) $-66/5$; (d) -2; (e) -2; (f) 4.
3. (a) $5, 5/2$; (b) $-7/5, -1/3$; (c) $3/8, 3$; (d) $-6/7, -2$; (e) $9/2, -5/2$; (f) $3/2, -1/5$;
(g) $-3, 1/6$; (h) $-1/15, -1/2$; (i) $4/3, 2/3$; (j) $5/6, -3/8$.
4. (a) ± 1; (b) $\pm \sqrt{5/2}$; (c) $1, 2$; (d) $\pm \sqrt{3}$; (e) $\pm \sqrt[4]{3}, \pm \sqrt[4]{2}$; (f) $\pm 2, \pm 5$.
5. (a) $10, 4a$; (b) $0, -(b + 2)$; (c) $2a, 2a/(a - 1)$; (d) $-2a/3, 5b/2$; (e) $-a, b$;
(f) $(y \pm \sqrt{y + 2})$; (g) $a - b, (a + b)^2/(a - b)$.

Section I.9

1. (a) No solution; (b) 3; (c) No solution; (d) $(5 + \sqrt{21})/2$; (e) No solution;

(f) 3/4; (g) No solution; (h) No solution; (i) 8/3; (j) 11/7; (k) 6; (l) 1.
2. (a) 11/8; (b) No solution; (c) No solution; (d) No solution; (e) $-7/9$;
   (f) $-6, -9/4$; (g) $ab/(a + b - c)$ (h) $-(a^2 + ab + b^2)/(a + b)$.
3. (a) 3, 3/10; (b) 9/4 (c) No solution; (d) $-4/9$; (e) 16; (f) No solution.

Section I.10

1. (a) $x = 3$, $y = 4$; (b) $x = -2/5$, $y = 3/4$; (c) $s = -4$, $t = 5$;
   (d) $u = 423/118$, $v = 42/59$; (e) $x = -7$, $y = -3$; (f) $h = 39/115$, $k = -141/46$;
   (g) $x = -8/5$, $y = 6/5$; (h) $w = -1/11$, $z = 9/11$; (i) Inconsistent;
   (j) $a = -228/37$, $b = -239/37$ (k) $x = 7/16$, $y = -7/5$; (l) $x = \pm\sqrt{3}/2$, $y = 1/4$.
2. His speed is 10 miles per hour, that of the current is 2 miles per hour.
3. The number is 59.
4. Six gallons of the 5/6 mixture, 18 gallons of the 8/9 mixture.

Section I.11

1. (a) 64; (b) 9; (c) 16; (d) 1/16; (e) 1/16; (f) 2; (g) -243.
2. (a) $b^2/a^{5/3}$; (b) $c^{1/6}/a^2 b^{1/4}$; (c) $6x^2/y^{2/5} z^{3/7}$; (d) $z^3 w^{2/3}/4x^4 y^{5/4}$; (e) $2d^5/3a^{3/2} b^{1/4} c^{4/5}$.
3. (a) $a^{1/9}$; (b) $x^{1/10}$; (c) $6b^{-11/8}$; (d) $x^{1/6} y^{-3/10}$; (e) $a^{5/8} b^{-4/3}$; (f) $x^{1/6} y$.
4. (a) 0; (b) $(a^{1/3} + b^{1/3})/(a^{2/3} + a^{1/3} b^{1/3} + b^{2/3})$; (c) $x - (xy)^{1/2} + y$; (d) $x^{2/(n+1)}$; (e) $a^{1/m}$.
5. (a) $a^{-2} b^{-1} (b^4 + a^6)$; (b) $y^{-1/2} (x^2 + 2y^3)$; (c) $u^{-3} v^{-1/3} (v - u)(v + u)$;
   (d) $a^{-1} b^{-11/4} (b - a)(b^2 + ab + a^2)$; (e) $(x^{1/3} - y^{1/3})^2$; (f) $(4b^{1/5} + 1)(b^{1/5} - 2)$;
   (g) $2(8 - x)^{-1/2} (2 - x)(2 + x)$; (h) $x(1 - x)^{-1/3} (3 - 4x)$; (i) $2x^3 (4x - x^2)^{-3/2} (5 - x)$;
   (j) $7x^{-2} (28 - x^3)^{1/2} (x + 2)(x^2 + 2x + 4)$.

Section I.12

1. (a) 3; (b) -2; (c) 3; (d) -2; (e) -2; (f) 0; (g) 1.
2. (a) 1/25; (b) 10; (c) 1/2; (d) 1/2; (e) 25/4.
3. (a) 1.0791; (b) 3.7781; (c) -2.1249; (d) $.4771/.3010 = 1.5850$; (e) -0.4306;
   (f) 1.5473.
4. (a) $10^{x \log_{10} 3}$; (b) $10^{2 \log_{10} a}$; (c) $10^{x \log_{10} x}$; (d) $10^{(2x+1)\log_{10} 4x}$; (e) $10^{(1/x)\log_{10}(1+x)}$.
5. (a) x; (b) $\log_{10}(x + 2)$; (c) $\log_3 (a^2 - b^2)$; (d) 2; (e) $3x$.

APPENDIX III

Section III.1

1. (a) $180°$, π rad; (b) $-\pi/12$ rad, $-1/24$ rev.
   (c) $(360/\pi)°$, $1/\pi$ rev; (d) $36°$, $\pi/5$ rad.
   (e) $47\pi/180$ rad, $47/360$ rev; (f) $-540°$, $-3/2$ rev.
   (g) $7\pi/4$ rad, $7/8$ rev; (h) $90°$, $1/4$ rev.
   (i) $\pi/4$ rad, $1/8$ rev; (j) $\pi/6$ rad, $1/12$ rev.
   (k) $60°$, $1/6$ rev; (l) $270°$, $3/4$ rev.
2. (i) $540,000°$ per min; (ii) $3,000\pi$ rad per min; (iii) 25 rev per sec;
   (iv) $180,000\pi$ rad per hr.
3. 225π cm in 1 sec; $13,500\pi$ cm in 1 min; $810,000\pi$ cm in 1 hr.
   Speed is $8,100\pi$ m per hr.

Section III.2

1.

	Angle	sin	cos	tan	cot	sec	csc
(a)	$0°$	0	1	0	undef.	1	undef.
(b)	$30°$	$1/2$	$\sqrt{3}/2$	$1/\sqrt{3}$	$\sqrt{3}$	$2/\sqrt{3}$	2
(c)	$45°$	$1/\sqrt{2}$	$1/\sqrt{2}$	1	1	$\sqrt{2}$	$\sqrt{2}$
(d)	$60°$	$\sqrt{3}/2$	$1/2$	$\sqrt{3}$	$1/\sqrt{3}$	2	$2/\sqrt{3}$
(e)	$90°$	1	0	undef.	0	undef.	1
(f)	$120°$	$\sqrt{3}/2$	$-1/2$	$-\sqrt{3}$	$-1/\sqrt{3}$	-2	$2/\sqrt{3}$
(g)	$135°$	$1/\sqrt{2}$	$-1/\sqrt{2}$	-1	-1	$-\sqrt{2}$	$\sqrt{2}$
(h)	$150°$	$1/2$	$-\sqrt{3}/2$	$-1/\sqrt{3}$	$-\sqrt{3}$	$-2/\sqrt{3}$	2
(i)	π rad	0	-1	0	undef.	-1	undef.
(j)	$-\dfrac{\pi}{4}$ rad	$-1/\sqrt{2}$	$1/\sqrt{2}$	-1	-1	$\sqrt{2}$	$-\sqrt{2}$
(k)	1 rev	0	1	0	undef.	1	undef.
(l)	$\dfrac{3\pi}{2}$ rad	-1	0	undef.	0	undef.	-1
(m)	$-\dfrac{\pi}{2}$ rad	-1	0	undef.	0	undef.	-1
(n)	$-\pi$ rad	0	-1	0	undef.	-1	undef.
(o)	$1110°$	$1/2$	$\sqrt{3}/2$	$1/\sqrt{3}$	$\sqrt{3}$	$2/\sqrt{3}$	2
(p)	$-270°$	1	0	undef.	0	undef.	1

2. (a) $\alpha = 90 + 180 \cdot n$, n an integer.
   (b) $\alpha = 180 \cdot n$, n an integer.
   (c) $\alpha = 90 + 180 \cdot n$, n an integer.
   (d) $\alpha = 180 \cdot n$, n an integer.
3. (a) $-\sqrt{3}/2$; (b) $\sqrt{15}/4$; (c) 10; (d) $-\sqrt{95}/7$; (e) $-\sqrt{145}$; (f) $2/\sqrt{3}$.
4. (a) This follows from equation (vi) on page 305 and the fact that $\sin A$ is positive in the first quadrant.
   (b) Follows from (vi) and the fact that the cosine function is negative in the second quadrant.
   (c) Each side is meaningful if A is an angle with initial or terminal side not on a coordinate axis, and $\sec^2 A + \csc^2 A = 1/\cos^2 A + 1/\sin^2 A$
   $$= (\sin^2 A + \cos^2 A)/(\sin^2 A \cos^2 A)$$
   $$= 1/(\cos^2 A \sin^2 A) = \sec^2 A \csc^2 A$$
   (d) If $\csc A$ exists, so does $\cot A$.
   $\csc^4 A \cot^3 A = \cot^3 A \csc^2 A \csc^2 A = \cot^3 A (1 + \cot^2 A)\csc^2 A$
   $$= (\cot^3 A + \cot^5 A) \csc^2 A.$$
   (e) $\sin^2 x \cos^3 x = \sin^2 x \cos^2 x \cos x = \sin^2 x(1 - \sin^2 x) \cos x$
   $$= (\sin^2 x - \sin^4 x) \cos x$$
5. (a) True if A is in the first or second quadrant.
   (b) True if A is in the third or fourth quadrant.
   (c) True if A is in the first or third quadrant.
   (d) True for all A except integral multiples of $\pi/2$.

Section III.3

1. (a) $\beta = 60°$, $c = 24$, $b = 20.8$
   (b) $\beta = 43°$, $a = 4.4$, $b = 4.1$.
   (c) $\alpha = 10°$, $b = 567$, $c = 576$.

(d) $\alpha = 65°$, $a = 36.2$, $b = 16.9$.
(e) $\beta = 70°$, $a = 3.3$, $c = 9.6$.
(f) $\alpha = 15°$, $a = 1.1$, $c = 4.1$
2. (a) From the triangle:

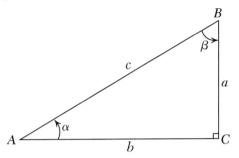

$\sin \alpha = a/c$, so $a = c \sin \alpha$.
$\cos \beta = a/c$, so $a = c \cos \beta$.
$\cot \beta = a/b$, so $a = b \cot \beta$.
$\tan \alpha = a/b$, so $a = b \tan \alpha$.
(b) This follows by noting that $\sin \beta = b/c = \cos \alpha$ and $\cot \alpha = b/a = \tan \beta$.
(c) $\csc \alpha = c/a = \sec \beta$ and $\csc \beta = c/b = \sec \alpha$.

Section III.4

1, 2, and 3.

	θ	$r(\theta)$	Quad	$\sin \theta$	$\cos \theta$	$\tan \theta$	$\cot \theta$	$\sec \theta$	$\csc \theta$
(a)	$30°$	$30°$	I	$1/2$	$\sqrt{3}/2$	$1/\sqrt{3}$	$\sqrt{3}$	$2/\sqrt{3}$	2
(b)	$-225°$	$45°$	II	$1/\sqrt{2}$	$-1/\sqrt{2}$	-1	-1	$-\sqrt{2}$	$\sqrt{2}$
(c)	$-150°$	$30°$	III	$-1/2$	$-\sqrt{3}/2$	$1/\sqrt{3}$	$\sqrt{3}$	$-2/\sqrt{3}$	-2
(d)	$240°$	$60°$	III	$-\sqrt{3}/2$	$-1/2$	$\sqrt{3}$	$1/\sqrt{3}$	-2	$-2/\sqrt{3}$
(e)	$120°$	$60°$	II	$\sqrt{3}/2$	$-1/2$	$-\sqrt{3}$	$-1/\sqrt{3}$	-2	$2/\sqrt{3}$
(f)	$300°$	$60°$	IV	$-\sqrt{3}/2$	$1/2$	$-\sqrt{3}$	$-1/\sqrt{3}$	2	$-2/\sqrt{3}$
(g)	$360°$	$0°$	—	0	1	0	undef.	1	undef.
(h)	$-315°$	$45°$	I	$1/\sqrt{2}$	$1/\sqrt{2}$	1	1	$\sqrt{2}$	$\sqrt{2}$
(i)	$\dfrac{7\pi}{4}$ rad	$\dfrac{\pi}{4}$ rad	IV	$-1/\sqrt{2}$	$1/\sqrt{2}$	-1	-1	$\sqrt{2}$	$-\sqrt{2}$
(j)	$\dfrac{16\pi}{3}$ rad	$\dfrac{\pi}{3}$ rad	III	$-\sqrt{3}/2$	$-1/2$	$\sqrt{3}$	$1/\sqrt{3}$	-2	$-2/\sqrt{3}$
(k)	$\dfrac{3\pi}{2}$ rad	$\dfrac{\pi}{2}$ rad	—	-1	0	undef.	0	undef.	-1
(l)	$\dfrac{683\pi}{6}$ rad	$\dfrac{\pi}{6}$ rad	IV	$-1/2$	$\sqrt{3}/2$	$-1/\sqrt{3}$	$-\sqrt{3}$	$2/\sqrt{3}$	-2
(m)	$216°$	$36°$	III	$-.588$	$-.809$	$.727$	1.376	-1.236	-1.701
(n)	-5 rad	$(2\pi - 5)$ rad	I	$.956$	$.292$	3.271	$.306$	3.420	1.046
(o)	$461°$	$79°$	II	$.982$	$-.191$	-5.145	$-.194$	-5.241	1.019
(p)	$152°$	$28°$	II	$.469$	$-.883$	$-.532$	-1.881	-1.133	2.130
(q)	$-78°$	$78°$	IV	$-.978$	$.208$	-4.705	$-.213$	4.810	-1.022
(r)	$\dfrac{13\pi}{18}$ rad	$\dfrac{5\pi}{18}$ rad	II	$.766$	$-.643$	-1.192	$-.839$	-1.556	1.305

Section III.5

1. (a) $\gamma = 79°$, $b = 33.9$, $c = 34.6$.
   (b) $\alpha = 76°$, $b = 21.8$, $c = 16.6$.
   (c) $\alpha = 36°$, $a = 71.4$, $b = 85.8$.
   (d) $\alpha = 35°$, $\gamma = 50°$, $c = 5.4$.
   (e) No solution.
   (f) $\beta = 75°$, $\alpha = 40°$, $a = 21.3$.
   (g) $\alpha = 29°$, $\beta = 47°$, $\gamma = 104°$.
   (h) $\alpha = 42°$, $\beta = 89°$, $\gamma = 49°$.
   (i) $\alpha = \beta = 46°$, $\gamma = 88°$.
2. 39°
3. 15 in., 19.22 in., and 19.93 in.
4. 2.47 in.
5. 1.9 ft.

INDEX

Numbers in parentheses refer to exercises